OILFIELD METALLURGY
AND CORROSION
THIRD EDITION

By Bruce D. Craig

OILFIELD METALLURGY AND CORROSION

Copyright© 2004 by
MetCorr
4600 South Ulster Street, Suite 700
Denver, Colorado 80237

Craig Bruce D.
       Oilfield metallurgy and corrosion/by Bruce D. Craig.
         —3rd ed. p. cm.
       Rev. ed. of: Practical oilfield metallurgy. 1993.
       Includes bibliographical references and index.
       ISBN 0-9760400-0-X
       1. Oil field — Equipment and supplies. 2. Metallurgy. 3. Corrosion
and anti-corrosivess. I. Craig, Bruce D. Practical oil-field metallurgy. II. Title.
TN871.5.C7 1992
622'.3382—dc20   92-33961
                                              CIP

Printed in the United States of America

TO
My Wife

OILFIELD METALLURGY AND CORROSION

CONTENTS

PREFACE

This book continues to be the only book written specifically on the subject of metallurgy in petroleum drilling and production. It is by no means comprehensive in its approach either to metallurgy or to petroleum drilling and production. In fact, a reader well versed in certain specialty areas of the industry will notice gaps that are unavoidable because of either the author's ignorance in the area or a lack of available information in the literature. The latter is quite frequent because many tools and processes are proprietary and therefore information is not readily available.

The purpose for continuing to update this book is threefold. First, there are many nonmetallurgists in the petroleum industry who are responsible for materials selection and failure analysis, yet no single source is available for reference on the subject. Second, for the practicing metallurgist in the petroleum industry, no reference book contains many of the often-used tables, charts, graphs, etc., that are helpful in day-to-day decision making on materials. Third, the few knowledgeable people in this field continue to dwindle and it is hoped that this book will preserve some of the knowledge that has been gained over 50 years in the petroleum industry as it relates to materials.

Oilfield jargon for equipment and operations is used as often as possible to acquaint the reader with the proper nomenclature and to provide the experienced oilfield engineer with a familiar reference point. Where possible, actual examples from oilfield materials and failures are used to further assist the reader in understanding this discipline.

In the past, knowledge of oilfield metallurgy has been acquired by a combination of learning from experienced individuals in the field and by trial and error. This method of education, while effective, is quite time consuming and costly. The author hopes this book will reduce some of the front-end time of acquainting oneself with the fundamentals prior to becoming an effective materials engineer. This is particularly important at this stage in the history of the petroleum industry because the capabilities of alloys are being challenged in severe environments, and mistakes in application can be of tremendous economical consequence—not to mention the potential for loss of life.

Chapter One of this book is designed to give the reader a basic understanding of metallurgy and to aid in the discussion of metallurgy in subsequent chapters. Chapter Two introduces some of the major aspects of corrosion as they relate to the petroleum industry. Corrosion is an inseparable part of oilfield metallurgy, and the two will be linked throughout the book. While in some ways this may appear to be a corrosion book, it is not. Only metallurgical alternatives to problems are described, whereas other alternatives such as inhibitors, coatings, etc., exist that are not discussed but do enter in corrosion-control planning. Chapters Three, Four, Five, and Six describe the applications and behavior of alloys in various functions in the industry. Finally, Chapter Seven is a brief introduction to failure analysis, which is a very important part of oilfield metallurgy.

As in the first edition, the author would like to acknowledge those whose work is referenced in this book and the many friends in the industry who are not named but who have generously contributed to his education and understanding, not only of metallurgy but also of the field of petroleum engineering. Special thanks go to Liane Smith first for her friendship and second for her input on mercury corrosion of alloys and other contributions to this book and to Manuel Maligas for his help on subsea fasteners. As always thanks to Russ Lewis for his friendship over all these years. Without a doubt one of the most important friends and contributors to this book is Joe Davis of Metallurgical Consultants, Inc., without whom the numerous high quality photographs and micrographs in this book would not have been possible.

1

BASIC METALLURGY

All metals except mercury are solids at room temperature. These solids consist of atoms that form a regular array, or pattern, called crystal lattice. The nuclei of these atoms describe the lattice pins and the tightly bound electrons remain close to these atom centers. Valence electrons, or the outermost, loosely bound electrons, move easily throughout the lattice. These valence electrons are the primary reason for some of the superior properties of metals as compared to non-metallic solids. Electrical and thermal conductivity, magnetism, and luster are the results of the behavior of these valence electrons.

Structure of Metals

Energy considerations as well as the nature of metal bonding produce several different types of lattice structures, three of which are most frequently observed in metals. These three structures, or unit cells as they are most commonly referred to, are face-centered cubic (fcc), body-centered cubic (bcc), and hexagonal close packed (hcp). The first structure (Fig. 1-1) is portrayed as a group of spheres packed closely together. Each sphere represents an atom, which is an idealized but simple way to describe atom packing. The unit cell is the smallest increment to which the periodic structure of metal can be reduced. Examples of metals with

1

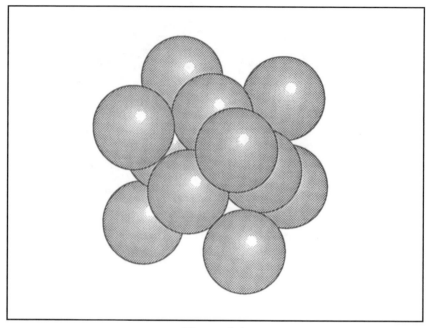

Figure 1-1
Hard sphere model of face-centered
cubic atom packing.

fcc structures are copper, nickel, aluminum, gold, and silver. Figure 1-2 shows the stacking arrangement of a bcc unit cell. Note the greater amount of space present in this structure versus the bcc. Examples of metals with this type of unit cell are: iron, molybdenum, chromium, and vanadium. Figure 1-3 depicts the third unit cell, hcp. Magnesium, zinc, cobalt, and titanium are hcp metals. Some metals display different crystal structures as a function of temperature. For example, the high-temperature crystal structure of titanium is bcc while the room-temperature structure is hcp. These different crystal structures in one metal are called allotropes.

Mechanical properties such as strength, ductility, and toughness of metals and alloys are strongly dependent on their crystal structure. Hexagonal close packed metals commonly have less strength than the fcc and bcc metals. Because of the packing arrangement, their ductility is more dependent on direction than fcc and bcc metals. This often precludes their use as structural alloys in many applications, especially in the oilfield.

Metals do not consist of one large crystal with uninterrupted periodicity of unit cells. Rather, as metals cool from the liquid state, nuclei of solid particles form in the liquid. These nuclei continue to grow during cooling until the solid crystals

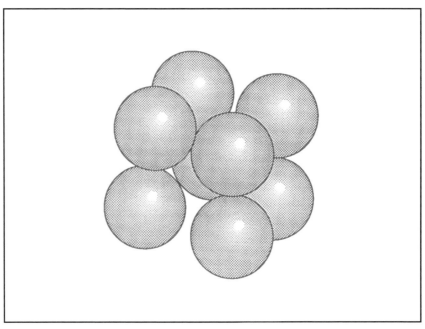

Figure 1-2
Hard sphere model of body-centered cubic atom packing.

begin to impinge on each other. Two grains having planes of random orientation to each other will not match at this interface, therefore, some atomic accommodation must result. This accommodation or transition at the junction of two or more grains produces an interface, or grain boundary. Since atoms are not in their proper place in this boundary and the periodic nature of the grain has been disrupted, the grain boundary has a higher energy than the surrounding matrix. Because of this different atomic structure and boundary energy, grain boundaries have properties that differ from the grains.

A polycrystalline metal has more strength than a single crystal because of grain boundaries. In fact, as grain size is reduced (which increases the total number of grain boundaries), the strength and ductility of a metal is increased, as shown in Figure 1-4. The yield strength of two common low alloy steels, 8650 and 4340, is a function of the grain size. Fine grain size improves not only strength but also toughness. Toughness is the ability of a material to resist fracture.

Many other ramifications of grain boundaries are not appropriate to elucidate here, but one of significance is chemical resistance. Since grain boundaries have higher energy than the grains, they are attacked more rapidly in a corrosive environment. This behavior allows the study of metal structure by optical microscopy

3

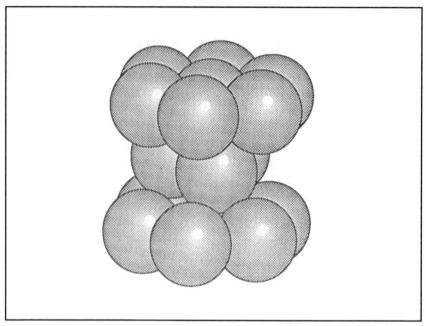

Figure 1-3
Hard sphere model of hexagonal close-packed structure.

and is called metallography. Figure 1-5 shows an example of steel that has been attacked (etched) by a solution of nitric acid and methanol to resolve the grains and grain boundaries. The etching solution is commonly known as Nital.

Pure metals, even in polycrystalline form, do not possess the strength necessary for modern engineering applications. Introducing other elements into a pure metal can provide necessary additional strength. However, the addition of other elements is not restricted solely to the attainment of higher strength. Other elements can provide greater corrosion resistance, increased ductility, enhanced toughness at low temperature, stabilization of the structure against deformation at high temperatures, and a multitude of other properties.

This combination of two or more elements, when at least one is a metal, is called an alloy. The mixture of these elements, defined as a solid solution, can occur in two ways. In one way (Fig. 1-6), the elements substitute themselves on the atom sites of the parent metal. In the other (Fig. 1-7), the elements fit in the interstitial holes between the parent metal atoms. The first situation is referred to as substitutional solid solution while the second is interstitial solid solution. The preference for one type of solid solution versus the other is a function of the sizes of the intervening solute atoms compared to the size of the solvent atoms. The

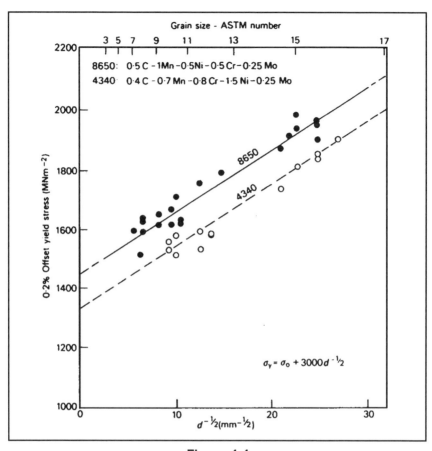

Figure 1-4

Relationship between grain size and yield strength for two low alloy steels (courtesy ASM International).

base metal is referred to as the solvent and the addition of another element is the solute. If the solute atom is small, such as carbon, nitrogen, or hydrogen, circumstances will be energetically more favorable for the atom to sit in an interstitial site than in a substitutional one. The opposite is true for large atoms such as chromium, nickel, and manganese. Thus alloys such as steel that contain carbon in iron represent an interstitial solid solution, while Monel which is copper in nickel is an example of a substitutional solid solution.

The concentration of alloying elements and the type of solid solution contribute to the properties of an alloy much as described for atom packing and grain size. Interstitial solid solutions such as carbon in iron provide a higher degree of strengthening than substitutional solid solutions.

5

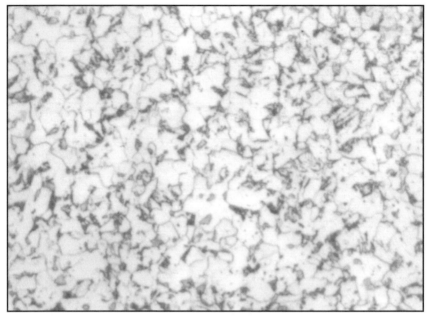

Figure 1-5
Low-carbon (0.12 wt%) steel etched with Nital. Magnified 425 times showing grains and grain boundaries.

Considering all of these methods for increasing the strength of metals, how can their effects be measured? The next section discusses various test methods employed to determine the mechanical properties of an alloy.

Mechanical Properties of Metal

The most common test for quantitative information on the mechanical properties of a metal is the tensile test. In simple terms, for this test a metal is pulled apart at a constant rate. While this test has many sample geometries, one of the standard samples is a round bar of unspecified length that has a reduced section greater than 2 in. in length and is 0.500 in. in diameter. An example of such a bar is shown in Figure 1-8. As the sample is pulled in a tensile machine, the applied load divided by the original cross-sectional area at the center of the sample gives the stress. At the same time, a 2-in. length called the gauge length, which is marked on the reduced section of the bar, is used to measure the change in length of the sample in comparison to its original length—the strain.

Figure 1-9 shows a common engineering stress-strain curve that results when the stress is calculated at each point by dividing the load applied by the original cross-sectional area:

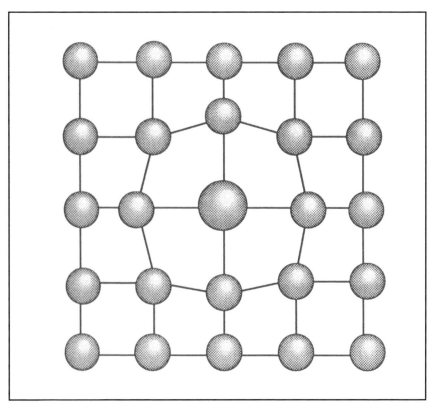

Figure 1-6
Substitutional solid solution of a larger atom substituted on a lattice site of smaller atom base metal.

$$\sigma = \frac{P}{A}$$

Where:

σ = stress, psi

P = applied load, pounds

A = original cross-sectional area, in^2

This is defined as the engineering stress. The engineering strain (ε) is likewise defined as the total elongation minus the original gauge length divided by the original gauge length:

$$\varepsilon = \frac{\Delta l}{l}$$

7

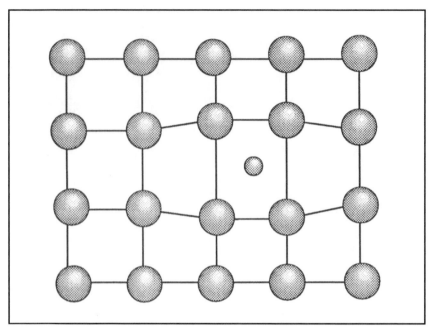

Figure 1-7

Interstitial solid solution of small atom between larger atoms of the base metal.

Where:

Δl = change in length, in.

l = original length, in.

In many tests, the standard gauge length is 2 in.

Two important points on the curve are denoted in Figure 1-9. The first, point A, represents the termination of a linear relationship between stress and strain. This point is referred to as the proportional limit and represents the limit of elastic behavior of the metal. Stresses or strains applied below this limit, when relaxed, will not cause a permanent set or deformation in the metal. From Hooke's law, the relationship between stress and strain is given by:

$$\sigma = E\varepsilon$$

Where:

σ = stress

E= elastic constant (Young's Modulus)

ε = strain

The units of stress are expressed in pounds per square inch (psi) and strain is unitless since it is length divided by length. Strain is commonly given in percent.

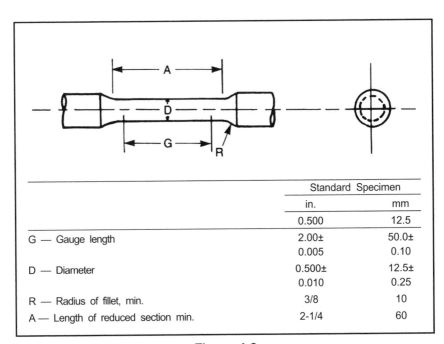

	Standard Specimen	
	in.	mm
	0.500	12.5
G — Gauge length	2.00± 0.005	50.0± 0.10
D — Diameter	0.500± 0.010	12.5± 0.25
R — Radius of fillet, min.	3/8	10
A — Length of reduced section min.	2-1/4	60

Figure 1-8

Standard tensile specimen for determining mechanical properties of a metal
(© ASTM, A 370, reprinted with permission).

The elastic constant, termed the modulus of elasticity or Young's Modulus, is also expressed in psi. For steels the Young's Modulus is typically 30×10^6 psi.

Once point A is exceeded, the strain becomes plastic and a permanent deformation is produced in the metal. Continuing up the curve, at point B the sample cannot support the increased stress so the cross section begins to reduce itself or neck down. Once necking begins, complete fracture occurs quickly as shown by the change in slope of the curve. The maximum stress attained prior to necking divided by the cross-sectional area is defined as the ultimate tensile strength. The amount of necking is directly related to the ductility of a metal. The more necking that occurs, the more ductile it is. A measure of this ductility is the percent reduction in area (%RA). This value is measured from the original cross-sectional area of the tensile specimen and the final cross-sectional area after fracture.

One other measure of ductility is the elongation or stretching of the tensile specimen. If there is significant elongation during the tensile test, the material is quite ductile. Therefore, the change in length of the specimen after testing compared to its original length (most often 2 in. or 50 mm) is reported as a percent elongation.

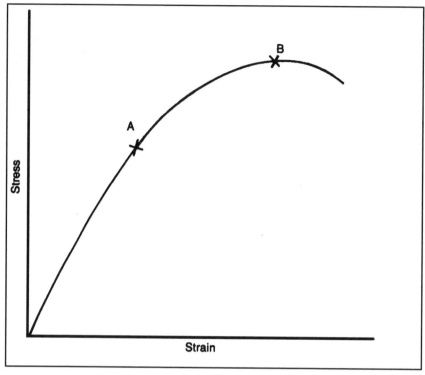

Figure 1-9
Stress-strain curve for a pure metal showing the yield strength (A)
and tensile strength (B).

Since the cross section begins to reduce during necking, it is apparent that dividing the stress by the original cross-sectional area will induce a degree of error. In fact, the same holds true for the strain since its length is continuously changing. Therefore, a more accurate means of describing stress and strain, particularly in the plastic region, uses the instantaneous area and length, respectively. This type of calculation gives the true stress and true strain but can also become difficult to measure; thus most design data are presented as engineering stress and strain.

It is apparent from Figure 1-9 that determining the specific point at which the strain moves from elastic to plastic is quite difficult. Therefore, another aid to engineering is the 0.2% offset yield point. This commonly used technique requires drawing a line tangent to the elastic portion of the curve then drawing a similar line parallel to the tangent at a strain of 0.2%. The intersection of this line with the stress-strain curve designates the yield strength. The yield strength is an important property of a metal or alloy and is used as a reference for calculating allowable or design stresses of a component or structure.

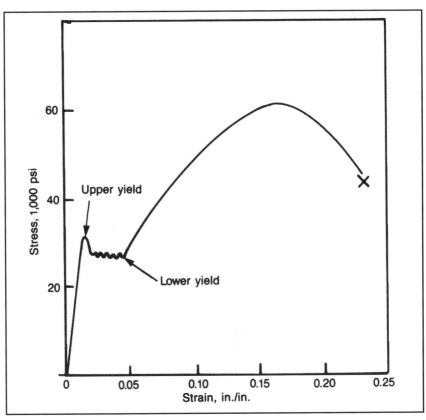

Figure 1-10
Stress-strain curve for AISI 1030 steel showing an upper
and lower yield strength.

Of course, the complexity in defining yield point increases in some alloy systems. Figure 1-10 shows a typical curve for a carbon steel with an upper and lower yield point, neither of which corresponds with the 0.2% offset yield point. Steels used in the petroleum industry usually are not complicated by an upper and lower yield; however, the 0.2% offset yield is not the only method of defining the yield strength. Rather, various API tubular specifications require a yield point defined by a 0.5 to 0.7% extension of the gauge length. For most cases, this does not produce a significantly different yield from that designated by the 0.2% offset method, at least for carbon steels. However, for cold-worked nickel alloys the difference can be significant because of the higher strain hardening rate of these alloys compared to steel. Figure 1-11 presents an example of an API J-55 casing steel stress-strain curve showing the minor difference in yield strength obtained by the two methods.

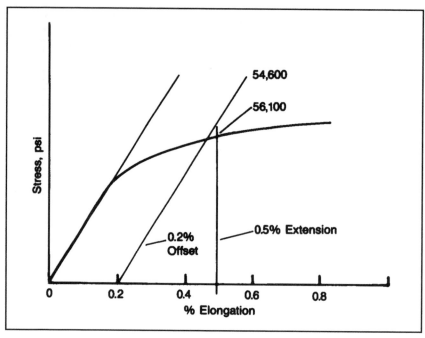

Figure 1-11
Yield strength of J-55 casing determined by 0.2% offset method
and 0.5% extension method.

Tensile testing is quite useful in determining the properties of a metal, but it is also a destructive test. In many instances, a nondestructive method of estimating these properties is necessary. The hardness test allows an alloy to be tested without destruction and on a smaller scale. Hardness testing requires applying a known load to an indentor and subsequently determining the resistance to this indentation. The higher the strength of the metal, the less deformation will occur under the indentor and the shallower the resulting indentation will be.

Although there are a multitude of hardness tests, only a few are frequently used with metals. These are shown in Figure 1-12. The Brinell test is used for field testing large structures or for rapid testing of redundant items (e.g., casing, tool joints, etc.). The impression of the indentor using a 3,000-kg load is 2.25 mm-5.60 mm in diameter for steel.

The Rockwell hardness test is used both in field testing and in the shop or laboratory. The various scales are interrelated and have certain advantages and disadvantages over each other. However, the B and C scales are the most common in the oilfield and are overlapping scales. The B scale is used for soft materials with approximate tensile strengths ranging 57,000-115,000 psi, while the C scale ranges from 110,000-over 330,000 psi. These approximate tensile strengths are used only

Common Hardness Tests

Test	Indentor	Typical Load	Shape of Indentation
Brinell	10 mm sphere (steel or tungsten carbide)	3,000 kg	 ◯
Rockwell A ⎱ C ⎰	Diamond cone	60 kg 150 kg	 ◉
B	1/16-in. diameter ball	100 kg	 ◯
Vickers	Diamond pyramid	1 kg, 10 kg	 ◻
Knoop	Diamond pyramid	1 kg, 10 kg	 ◇

Figure 1-12

Various indentors and types of hardness measurements commonly used in the oil industry.

for steel because other alloys have different relationships between hardness and tensile strength.

The approximate ultimate tensile strengths derived from the hardness tests are quite useful, especially in failure analysis when, because of limitations in sample size, obtaining complete tensile data is impossible. From hardness measurements, an approximate ultimate tensile strength can be determined. By using the rule of thumb that for carbon and low-alloy steel the yield strength is approximately 75-90% of the ultimate tensile strength, a yield strength can be approximated.

The two remaining hardness tests are usually referred to as microhardness tests since the size of their indentations is on the order of several microns (micrometers), although the ASTM defines microhardness based on loads less than 1 kg. These tests are also most frequently used in the laboratory for analyzing microstructures. The loads shown in Figure 1-12 represent only the more common ones used although a wide range of loads is available for microhardness testing depending on the application. Table 1-1 presents the correspondence between hardness scales and approximate tensile strength.

The decision as to which hardness test to use for a particular application depends on factors such as the number of tests to perform, the sensitivity and accuracy required, and the size and geometry of the sample to be tested.

Table 1-1.

Relationship between Common Hardness Scales and Approximate Tensile Strength for Steel.

| Rockwell Scale | | DPH | KHN 500g | BHN | Tensile Strength 1,000 psi |
B	C	10 kg	and Over	3 000 kg	approx.
	70	1,076	972		
	69	1,004	946		
	68	942	920		
	67	894	875		
	66	854	870		
	65	820	846		
	64	789	822		
	63	763	799		
	62	739	776		
	61	716	754		
	60	695	732	614	
	59	675	710	600	
	58	655	690	587	
	57	636	670	573	
	56	617	650	560	
	55	598	630	547	301
	54	580	612	534	291
	53	562	594	522	282
	52	545	576	509	273
	51	528	558	496	264
	50	513	542	484	255
	49	498	526	472	246
	48	485	510	460	237
	47	471	495	448	229
	46	458	480	437	221
	45	446	466	426	214
	44	435	452	415	207
	43	424	438	404	200
	42	413	426	393	194
	41	403	414	382	188
	40	393	402	372	182
	39	383	391	362	177
	38	373	380	352	171
	37	363	370	342	166
	36	353	360	332	162
	35	343	351	322	157
	34	334	342	313	153
	33	325	334	305	148
	32	317	326	297	144
	31	309	318	290	140
	30	301	311	283	136
	29	293	304	276	132
	28	285	297	270	129
	27	278	290	265	126
	26	271	284	260	123
	25	264	278	255	120

| Rockwell Scale | | DPH | KHN 500g | BHN | Tensile Strength 1,000 psi |
B	C	10 kg	and Over	3 000 kg	approx.
	24	257	272	250	117
100.0	23	251	266	245	115
99.0	22	248	261	240	112
98.5	21	241	256	235	110
97.8	20	240	251	227	108
96.7	(18)	230	236	219	106
95.5	(16)	220	231	210	102
93.9	(14)	213	221	205	98
92.3	(12)	206	211	195	94
90.7	(10)	196	205	187	90
89.0		188	196	179	87
86.8		178	188	179	83
85.0		171	178	163	79
82.9		163	170	156	76
80.8		156	163	149	73
78.7		150	157	143	71
76.4		143	150	137	67
74.0		137	144	131	65
72.0		132	140	126	63
69.8		127	135	121	60
67.6		122	129	116	58
65.7		117	124	111	56

Values In parenthesis are not valid but are given for Information only.
(After Metal Progress and ASM Metals Handbook)

Two other properties of metals of consequence in the oilfield are impact and fatigue. The first property deals with the transition in fracture behavior with temperature from ductile to brittle. The second property is the fracture of metals as a result of cyclic loading.

Most body-centered cubic metals and their alloys show a temperature dependence on resistance to crack propagation, whereas fcc and hcp metals do not. Figure 1-13 shows this behavior. Notice that the fcc metals are very resistant to fracture at all temperature while the hcp metals have poor fracture resistance (toughness) at all temperatures. The better resistance of fcc metals to low temperature fracture is the reason for their wide use in cryogenic service. For bcc metals at room temperature and above, the energy necessary to cause rapid unstable crack propagation is quite high as shown by the shelf at the right. At very low temperatures, little energy is required to induce crack propagation. In the middle of these two extremes, a transition region exists in which the fracture changes from a ductile, energy-absorbing fracture to a brittle, low-energy fracture with decreasing temperature.

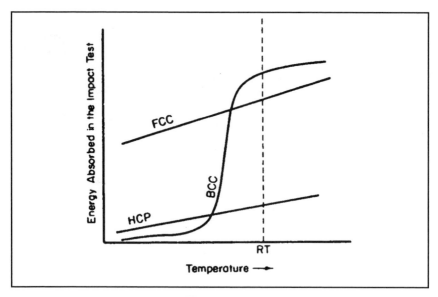

Figure 1-13
Fracture transition behavior as a function of temperature and crystal structure.

The actual temperature at which this transition occurs is difficult to ascertain and open to individual interpretation. Thus, there are many methods to define a transition temperature. Two of the most common are the energy absorbed criterion, frequently 15 ft-lb, and the fracture-appearance transition temperature (FATT). Both of these will be explained, but first an explanation of the impact test will elucidate the meaning of these two transition temperature criteria. Figure 1-14 represents a typical ductile-to-brittle transition curve that has been derived by means of Charpy impact testing. The method is described in detail in ASTM Standard E23, and the specimen geometry is shown in Figure 1-15. This test is the most common method for evaluating the resistance to brittle fracture of a metal and for determining its transition temperature. With the advance of fracture mechanics in the last 40 years, more sophisticated tests have been devised that give an accurate and quantitative picture of the fracture process. However, the Charpy test remains the fastest and least expensive technique for transition temperature determination.

Returning to the two-transition temperature criteria, energy-absorbed value is easily determined by finding the intersection of this desired value with the curve. The resulting temperature is considered the absorbed-energy transition temperature. For example, if 15 ft-lbs is used then the transition temperature for normalized A 515 Grade 70 (Fig. 1-14) is approximately 0°F. The FATT is found by plotting the percent of shear observed on the fracture surface versus the temperature. The temperature at which there is 50% shear fracture is often considered the FATT.

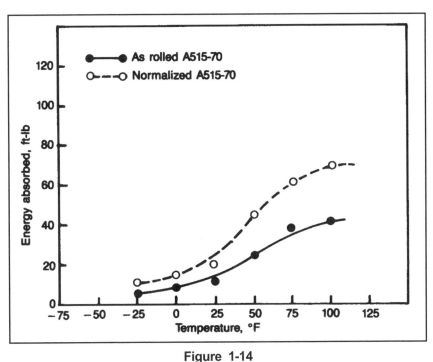

Figure 1-14

Charpy impact curve for ASTM A 515 steel showing the temperature
dependence of fracture (After Bravenec).

Although many parameters affect the transition temperature of an alloy, grain size is probably one of the most important because it can be controlled to provide both higher strength and better toughness. Everything else being equal, the smaller the grain size, the lower the transition temperature and the higher the yield strength. Alloying elements and heat treatment also affect the transition temperature. In steels, a decreased carbon content and a quenched and tempered microstructure generally offer better fracture resistance than a normalized structure. Toughness as a function of carbon content and grain size is shown in Figures 1-16 and 1-17, respectively.

Fatigue is the application of a fluctuating stress, either tensile or compressive. The magnitude of the alternating stress determines the service life of a component. Figure 1-18 shows an idealized fatigue or S-N (stress versus number of cycles) curve. The S-N curve depicts a flat region at the right that represents a threshold or endurance limit. Below this threshold, any applied fluctuating stress theoretically will never produce a fatigue failure. As the cyclic stress is increased, the time to failure is dramatically reduced because of the log function of time to fracture.

17

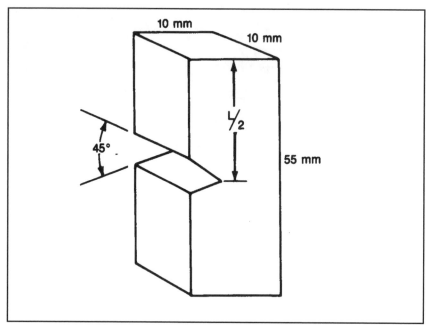

Figure 1-15
Standard Charpy bar geometry according to ASTM Standard E23.

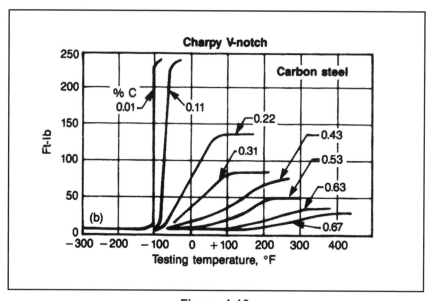

Figure 1-16
Effect of carbon content on notch toughness of mild steel
(After ASM Metals Handbook).

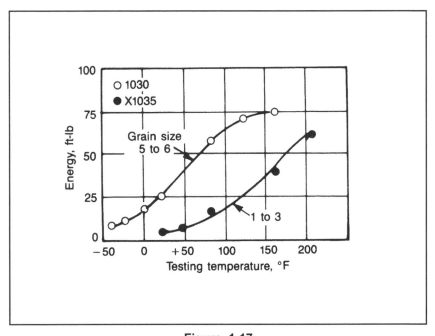

Figure 1-17

Effect of grain size on notch toughness of AISI 1030 and 1035 steel. Larger numbers indicate smaller grain size (After Metals Handbook).

This curve is considered idealized because it is achieved only in vacuum. Once structures are placed in a service environment—even under atmospheric conditions—the S-N curve is described more often by curves like Figure 1-19, in which no true threshold exists and the application of a cyclic stress will ultimately induce failure. This AWS-X-modified curve is used in API RP2A for designing welded joints that are necessary for offshore platforms.

An example of fatigue life can be demonstrated using a frequency of 10 cpm, which produces the resulting scale of time at the top. Thus, at a stress range of 2,000 psi, a component would have a service life of 100 years, while doubling the stress range to 4,000 psi would reduce the life to approximately 50 years.

The fracture surface resulting from fatigue is quite distinctive and easily distinguishable from other forms of fracture. An example of a fatigue fracture is shown in Figure 1-20. The large semi-circular rings are referred to as beach marks and are characteristic of fatigue crack growth.

The threshold stress or fatigue limit for steels is approximately one-half of their tensile strength. This rule of thumb is useful for easy comparison of steels when no other data exists but should never be used for fatigue design.

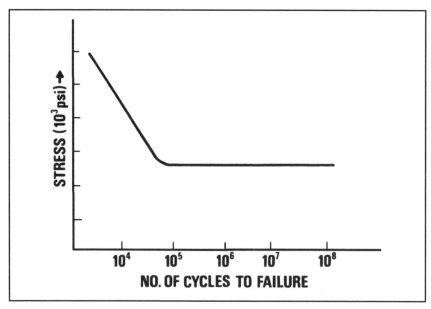

Figure 1-18
Typical S-N curve for fatigue of steel.

Fatigue can be caused by thermal fluctuations, ocean waves, wind, mechanical vibrations such as caused by operating machinery, and numerous other influences. This failure mechanism is quite common in the oilfield but is often misinterpreted. As in brittle fracture, the fracture surface may show bright fracture facets where the crack has propagated across the grains. This cracking has for many years been erroneously referred to as crystallization. This term is incorrect in this context since the metal is always crystalline below its melting point. The crystals are just more readily apparent because of the nature of the fracture and not the sudden formation of a crystalline structure.

Carbon and Alloy Steels

Steel is the most common alloy in the oilfield and as such deserves more attention to its specific behavior than other alloys. Steel is an alloy of carbon in iron with iron as the principal element. Carbon forms an interstitial solid solution in iron. Alloys with greater than 2.5% carbon are referred to as cast irons and will be dealt with in a later section.

Pure iron when cooled slowly from the liquid state goes through three changes in unit cell configuration. These allotropic transformations are liquid to bcc, bcc

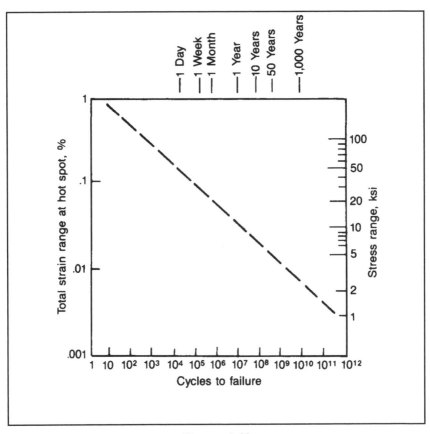

Figure 1-19
Typical fatigue behavior of steel, welded or notched and immersed in seawater
(After API RP 2A).

to fcc, and fcc to bcc in order of decreasing temperature. Thus, at room temperature the structure of pure iron is bcc. When carbon is added to iron in small quantities, there is no change in these transformations when the steel is slowly cooled. At this point, the discussion becomes more complex and is aided by the use of a phase diagram (Fig. 1-21).

The phase diagram is a plot of the equilibrium phases present at a given temperature and composition. While these diagrams are literally packed with information, only their salient points will be presented for clarifying further topics. The diagram in Figure 1-21 consists of several single-phase regions (e.g., liquid, γ) and two-phase regions (e.g., $\alpha + Fe_3C$, $\gamma + $ liquid, etc.). The two phase regions represent equilibrium between the two adjoining single phases. It is apparent from the figure that when cooling from the liquid state along the 1.0% carbon compo-

21

Figure 1-20
Fatigue fracture surface showing fatigue beach marks. Arrows indicate fracture origins.

sition line a region exists over a specific range of several hundred degrees, in which the two phases, liquid and delta iron (δ), are in equilibrium. The amount of each phase present at any temperature can be determined from the Lever law (an explanation of which can be found in any basic metallurgy book).

What is important to understand here is that a variety of phases or combinations of phases can be generated under equilibrium or near-equilibrium conditions. Since the steels commonly used in the oilfield contain less than 0.8% carbon (called hypoeutectoid), the remainder of this section will be devoted to that portion of the phase diagram to the left of the 0.3% carbon concentration line.

To demonstrate one of the uses of this diagram, consider a weld made in ASTM A 106 pipe that is nominally 0.30% carbon with a similar electrode. Since this diagram represents equilibrium conditions, the cooling rate must be quite slow; therefore, assume the weld is wrapped with insulation immediately after completion. Although this example is not close to equilibrium, it approximates the necessary conditions.

As welding begins, the interface between the pipe wall and the welding rod becomes liquid. As cooling begins, the metal follows the 0.30% carbon line into a two-phase region of solid δ (delta iron) and liquid in which the first solid that

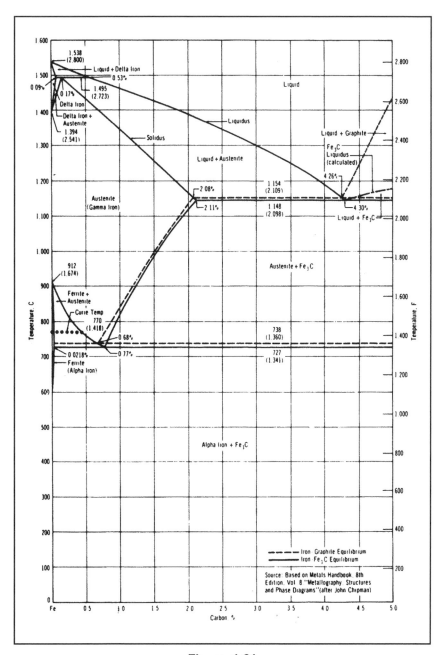

Figure 1-21
Iron-iron carbide equilibrium phase diagram (from Metal Progress).

Figure 1-22

Example of pearlite microstructure from J-55 tubing. Carbon content of this tubing was 0.52%. Etched in 2% Nital and magnified 168 times

forms is of the bcc structure because δ has a solubility for only up to 0.10% carbon and thus cannot absorb all of the carbon in the liquid and form a single phase of δ. Cooling below 2,723°F, the δ phase transforms to γ, or austenite as it is commonly called. Austenite and liquid now are in equilibrium until the temperature drops to approximately 2,690°F. At this point, all remaining liquid solidifies directly to austenite. Cooling through the austenite, which is now a solid single phase, produces no changes until a temperature of about 1,500°F is attained. At this time, the γ wants to transform to α (ferrite), but because of the excess carbon, since α has a solubility of only 0.02%, it must transform only partially, so γ and α are in equilibrium with each other. At 1,360°F, the remaining γ transforms to a two-phase constituent of ferrite plus cementite. The latter is of composition Fe3C that contains 6.67 wt% carbon. This two-phase mixture, in which the cementite is present as alternating plates in a ferrite matrix, is termed pearlite. An example of pearlite from J-55 tubing, is shown in Figure 1-22 and, at a higher magnification, in Figure 1-23, reveals the separate cementite plates in the ferrite matrix.

To this point, the phases formed under near-equilibrium conditions have been discussed, but if cooling is faster, what phases appear under nonequilibrium cooling? Consider the A 106 tube, but this time, instead of being wrapped with an

Figure 1-23

Same as Figure 1-22 but magnified 1,250 times to reveal the cementite (black lines) and ferrite (white areas).

insulating blanket, it is allowed to cool in air. No significant changes occur above the austenite region so only those below are considered. Again, the ferrite forms, but the faster cooling or quench produces a much finer pearlite in which the spacing of the cementite plates is closer. If the cooling is increased, another mixture of ferrite and carbide is produced, but with an entirely different appearance, and is called bainite. Figure 1-24 is an example of bainite. Increasing the cooling rate by using a water or oil quench produces martensite, a single-phase, highly strained matrix (Fig. 1-25).

These various microstructures, which produce a variety of properties, are the basis for the heat treatment of steels. However, it is evident from Figure 1-21 that most of them cannot be predicted from the equilibrium phase diagram. Therefore, a different method must be adopted to describe and predict these microstructures. This method will be dealt with in the next section on heat treatment.

Thus far, only the iron-carbon system has been discussed, but steels typically contain many other elements added on purpose or inherited from the steel making process. Oxygen, sulfur, phosphorous, nitrogen, tin, antimony, and arsenic are the principal impurities. These elements and others are responsible for the diminished resistance of steels to impact loading, high-temperature service, fatigue, etc.

25

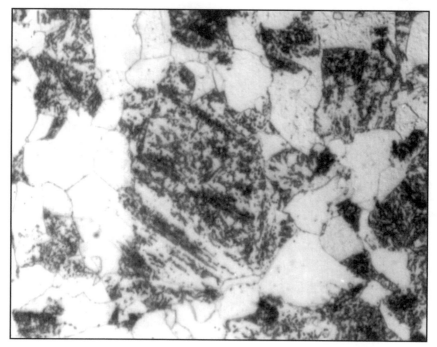

Figure 1-24
Example of bainite in low-alloy steel. Magnified 1000 times.

To overcome these detrimental aspects or enhance certain properties, alloying elements are added.

Silicon and aluminum are excellent deoxidizers, tying up oxygen as inclusions that may further improve the mechanical properties of a steel since these inclusions tend to pin grain boundaries and inhibit grain growth. Silicon also increases strength in quenched and tempered steels and moderately improves hardenability, which will be discussed later in this chapter. Titanium is another deoxidizer but is primarily added because of its ability to strengthen the matrix by precipitating titanium carbides and nitrides.

Molybdenum significantly improves hardenability and high-temperature strength and increases steel's resistance to softening when tempered. When added to austenitic stainless steels, it increases resistance to pitting attack. Nickel is beneficial for improving toughness of a steel and hardenability. When Ni is added to high-chromium steels it stabilizes the austenite phase below room temperature. Manganese also promotes austenite stabilization but is primarily added for increasing hardenability at low cost and tying up sulfur to prevent free sulfur or iron sulfides from being present since they are detrimental to steel.

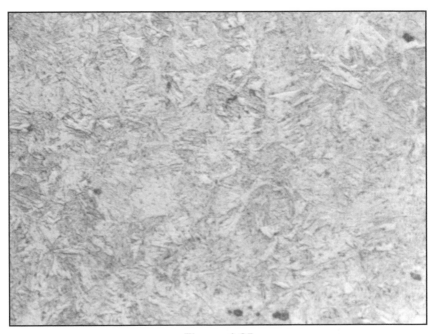

Figure 1-25

AISI 4130 low-alloy steel water-quenched from 1,600°F. Etched to show the fine martensite laths.

Chromium is added to improve corrosion and oxidation resistance and for its hardenability contribution. At higher concentrations, it improves high-temperature strength and abrasion resistance.

Tungsten provides increased strength as a carbide former and resistance to temper softening much as molybdenum does. It also contributes strongly to hardenability and improves the high-temperature strength of steels.

Columbium and vanadium are strong carbide formers and, because of their fine dispersion as carbides help pin grain boundaries thereby producing a fine grain size. They also contribute significantly to hardenability and resistance to softening during tempering.

The addition of alloying elements (up to 5 wt%) categorizes the steel as low alloy, whereas above this value, the steel is called an alloy steel.

With such a variety of elements and different possible combinations, organized numerical codes for often-used alloys were devised. While there are numerous alloy designation systems, only a few are commonly used in the petroleum industry. These are the designation systems of the American Society of Testing and Materials (ASTM), the American Iron and Steel Institute (AISI), and the Society of Automotive Engineers (SAE). The last two, AISI and SAE, are almost identical and will be referred to as AISI for ease of discussion. In addition, although it does not have an alloy system, the American Petroleum Institute (API) has a series of specifications covering products of nominal chemistry that are widely used in the industry. The American Society of Mechanical Engineers (ASME) also has a much-used system of alloy designations, but since it is almost identical to the ASTM, it will not be discussed further.

To explain the systems briefly, the ASTM designation for A 106 Grade B pipe is properly A-106-92 Grade B. The A prefix indicates a ferrous alloy; a B in the prefix is for nonferrous alloys. The 106 has no particular significance, while the 92 is the year of last revision of the standard. The AISI system has an advantage over the ASTM designation in that the composition is indicated in the designation itself. There is a four-number designation for AISI alloys. The first two numbers describe the major alloying elements and the last two, the nominal weight percent of carbon in 0.01% increments. The series is as follows:

10XX	Plain carbon steel
11XX	Free cutting steel: high sulfur
12XX	Free cutting steel: high sulfur and/or phosphorus
13XX	Manganese steel: Mn 1.75%
15XX	Plain carbon steel: Mn 0.75-1.65%

23XX 25XX	Nickel steels: Ni 3.5-5.0%

31XX 32XX 33XX	Nickel-chromium steels: Ni 1.25-3.5%, Cr 0.65-1.57%

40XX	Molybdenum steels: Mo 0.20-0.30%
41XX	Chromium-molybdenum steels: Cr 0.8-1.1 %, Mo 0.15-0.25%

43XX	Ni 1.65-2.00, Cr 0.40-0.90, Mo 0.20-0.30
47XX	Ni 0.90-1.20, Cr 0.35-0.55, Mo 0.15-0.25
81XX	Ni 0.20-0.40, Cr 0.35-0.55, Mo 0.08-0.15
86XX	Ni 0.40-0.70, Cr 0.40-0.60, Mo 0.15-0.25
87XX	Ni 0.40-0.70, Cr 0.40-0.60, Mo 0.20-0.30
88XX	Ni 0.40-0.70, Cr 0.90-0.60, Mo 0.30-0.40
94XX	Ni 0.30-0.60, Cr 0.30-0.50, Mo 0.08-0.15
98XX	Ni 0.85-1.15, Cr 0.70-0.90, Mo 0.20-0.30

46XX 48XX	Nickel-molybdenum steels: Ni 1.55-3.5%, Mo 0.20-0.30%

50XX 51XX	Chromium steels: Cr 0.25-1.05%
61XX	Chromium-vanadium steels: Cr 0.8-0.95%, V 0.1 -0.15%
72XX	Tungsten-chromium steels: W 1.75%, Cr 0.75%
92XX	Silicon-manganese steels: Si 1.2-2.2%, Mn 0.65-0.87%
XXBXX	Boron steels
XXLXX	Leaded steels

Thus, an often-used oilfield steel such as AISI 4140 would contain nominally 1% chromium, 0.2% molybdenum, and 0.4% carbon. Because the use of AISI numbers allows easy recognition of the basic chemistry of the alloy, people commonly try to correlate API products with an AISI designation. In the lower grades of tubing, casing, drillpipe, and line pipe, this is almost impossible because of the lack of specific chemistry requirements for these API grades. For the special grades, such as restricted-yield tubing and casing and higher strength grades, the chemistry gap is somewhat reduced but never to the point that an actual AISI designation can be assigned. This is one of the major problems of oilfield metallurgy. For example, the chemistry of J-55 tubing can vary significantly from mill to mill and still meet the required mechanical properties. These variations will become more evident in Chapter Four when nominal compositions are discussed.

Recently, the ASTM has established the Unified Numbering System (UNS) to consolidate the various alloy systems into one for ease of application. Table 1-2 shows the organization of the UNS designation system.

TABLE 1-2

ASTM Unified Numbering System

AXXXXX	Aluminum and Aluminum Alloys
CXXXXX	Copper and Copper Alloys
EXXXXX	Rare Earth and Similar Metals and Alloys
FXXXXX	Cast Irons
GXXXXX	AISI and SAE Carbon and Alloy Steels
HXXXXX	AISI and SAE H-Steels
JXXXXX	Cast Steels (Except Tool Steels)
KXXXXX	Miscellaneous Steels and Ferrous Alloys
LXXXXX	Low Melting Metals and Alloys
MXXXXX	Miscellaneous Non-Ferrous Metals and Alloys

NXXXXX   Nickel and Nickel Alloys
PXXXXX   Precious Metals and Alloys
RXXXXX   Reactive and Refractory Metals and Alloys
SXXXXX   Heat and Corrosion Resistant Steels (Including Stainless),
         Valve Steels, and Iron-Base "Superalloys"
TXXXXX   Tool Steels, Wrought and Cast
WXXXXX   Welding Filler Metals
ZXXXXX   Zinc and Zinc Alloys

Heat Treatment of Steel

The heat treatment of steel most often involves heating into the austenite region shown in Figure 1-21 and, depending on the desired properties, cooling at a predetermined rate to room temperature. The faster the quench or cooling rate, the finer the microstructure and the higher the strength. Also, with increasing strength, the ductility decreases dramatically. To regain some of the ductility, a carbon steel is reheated to temperatures below 1,360°F, which is called the lower critical temperature or Ac_1. This form of heat treatment is referred to as tempering. The Ac_1 is not a constant temperature but is different for every alloy system and is highly dependent on the rate of heating. Diagrams that show the transformation characteristics of steel and the phases formed at time-temperature-transformation are called (TTT) diagrams. Figure 1-26 is an example of one of these diagrams. These diagrams are useful from a practical standpoint since they represent those phases or mixtures formed under nonequilibrium conditions. They also describe the kinetics of transformations, which, of course, an equilibrium phase diagram cannot. The basis of the TTT diagram is transformation under isothermal conditions. Thus, steel must be cooled from the critical temperature instantaneously to a temperature of interest and then held constant at that temperature. The various lines represent the start and finish of the transformation to pearlite, ferrite, bainite, or martensite.

To illustrate the concept and use of the diagram, assume steel is instantly cooled to 1,200°F from the austenite region and held at this temperature for 1 min. Lines that are crossed when the temperature is held constant are the austenite plus ferrite, the pearlite start, the dotted line indicating 50% completion of the pearlite transformation, and the last line, the pearlite end. Thus, after 1 min the austenite has completely transformed to pearlite and ferrite. The microstructure will look similar to that shown in Figure 1-22 with ferrite at the prior austenite grain boundaries and pearlite within the grains. Although there are many reactions and combinations that can be described by these diagrams, one of their shortcomings is the instantaneous or idealized quench to the requisite tempera-

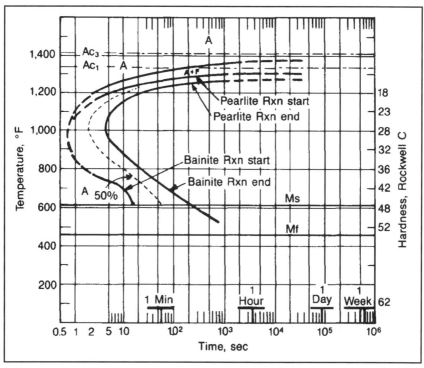

Figure 1-26

Time-temperature-transformation (TTT) diagram for AISI 1040 steel.
Approximate hardness values are shown at the right for isothermal treatment at the respective temperature.

ture. This is especially inconsistent with reality when trying to achieve the lower-temperature transformation products such as martensite.

A more useful diagram to predict the results of heat treatment that compensates for this quench-time inconsistency is a CCT (Continuous Cooling Transformation) diagram. Figure 1-27 shows such a diagram for a medium-carbon steel. There are three regions: ferrite + pearlite, bainite, and martensite. The ferrite + pearlite region is the envelope to the right with the bainite envelope in the middle. The left open sided envelope is for martensite. The one and ninety-nine represent 1% and 99% transformation to the specific product. The values in the small circles at the bottom of the diagram provide hardness information from the resulting microstructure. It is evident by the DPH (diamond pyramid hardness) 620 value that rapid cooling from the austenite at 1,360°F produces almost 100% martensite, whereas very slow cooling produces a structure composed of ferrite and pearlite. The cooling line representing a hardness of DPH 351 shows a partial transformation to bainite while the remaining austenite would transform to martensite.

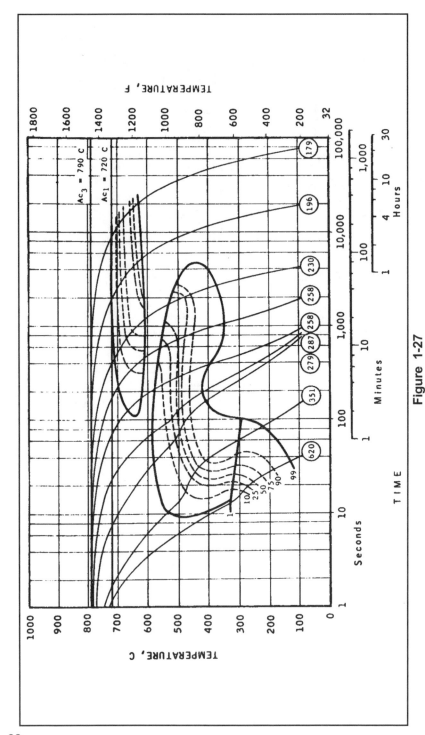

Figure 1-27

Continuous cooling transformation (CCT) diagram for AISI 1040 steel modified with 0.53% molybdenum (After Cias).

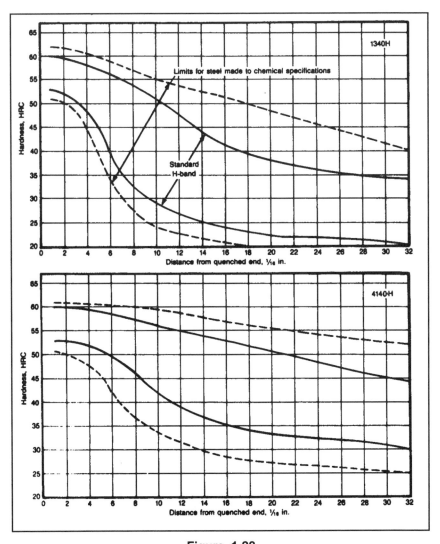

Figure 1-28

Comparison of standard H-bands and wider limits for similar steels made to AISI specifications (After Jatczak, Metals Handbook, 1978).

At this point, it is advantageous to define certain heat-treating terminology. All of these definitions assume the steel is already heated into the austenite region. If cooling occurs in the furnace very slowly, the treatment is referred to as annealing and produces a soft steel with carbides that are spherical in shape or a very coarse pearlite. Normalizing requires removing the steel from the furnace and allowing it to cool in air—usually still air. Quenching is usually achieved with

33

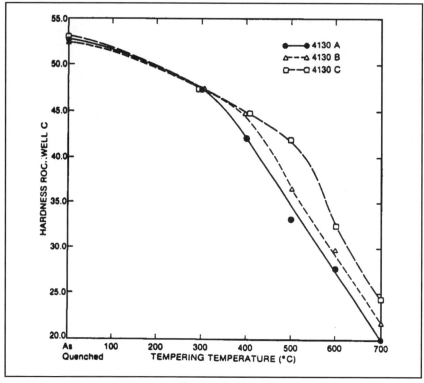

Figure 1-29

Reduction in hardness with increasing tempering temperature for AISI 4130 steel and two modifications with 0.50% molybdenum (4130B) and 0.75% molybdenum (4130C).

anything faster than still air such as forced air, water, brine, or oil and is most often accomplished by immersion.

The major point of both the TTT and CCT diagrams to be gained from this discussion is that transformations are a function of both cooling rate and chemistry. This is important in the manufacture of heavy-wall castings or forgings for valve bodies or heavy-wall pipe for deep wells. To achieve high strength, the alloy must first form martensite. If the necessary cooling rate by quenching cannot be achieved in these heavy-walled products, then alloying elements must be added that will permit slower cooling and still produce a martensitic structure.

The ability to produce martensite either by rapid cooling or by alloying is referred to as hardenability. This term should not be confused with hardness, which is a measure of resistance to indentation. The two are related in that the hardenability of a steel determines the depth and distribution of hardness resulting from quenching from the austenite region. Hardenability is a function of car-

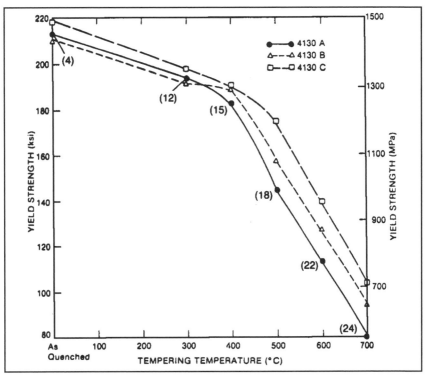

Figure 1-30

Reduction in yield strength with increasing tempering temperature for the same series of alloys shown in Figure 1-29. Values in parenthesis are % elongation in 2 in.

bon content, alloying, austenite grain size, time and temperature during austenizing, and cooling rate. Elements that increase hardenability are manganese, molybdenum, chromium, silicon, nickel, and boron to name the major ones.

In many applications, such as quenched and tempered oilfield tubulars, the ability to produce uniform hardness consistently across the wall thickness requires close controls on the steel chemistry used for manufacturing. This is accomplished by ordering H-steels (e.g., 4140H), which are required to have hardness limits at certain depths that are stricter than for normal carbon and low-alloy steels. This is shown schematically in Figure 1-28. The H-band has a tighter spread on hardness and thus more uniform response to heat treatment and more uniform properties than a standard steel. The 1340H steel is some times used for tool joints in heavy-wall drillpipe, and the 4140H is used in numerous oilfield applications. Notice that both steels display a declining hardness with depth into the steel. This limit to the depth of hardening has serious ramifications on heavy wall equipment, such as well head and Christmas tree components, and their ability to contain high pressures.

35

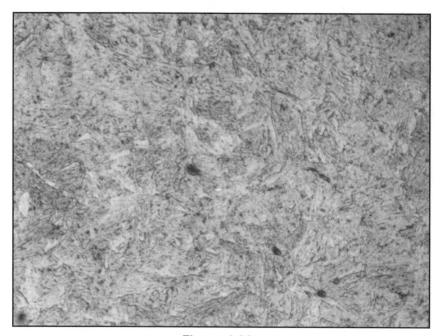

Figure 1-31a

Tempered martensite of 4130 steel, tempered 1 hr at 300°C. Nital etch, magnified 690 times.

Once the martensitic structure is obtained, it is frequently tempered to regain some ductility although there is also an accompanying loss of strength. Figures 1-29 and 1-30 show the loss in hardness and yield strength with temperating temperatures for AISI 4130 steel and its modifications. As can be seen by the longation data (Fig. 1-30), which are a good measure of ductility, from a 300°C temper to a 700°C temper the elongation doubles while the yield strength falls by more than half. The microstructure also changes significantly and is shown in Figure 1-31. Figure 1-31a shows a lightly tempered martensite with a high degree of directionality. The needles, or laths as they are called (Fig. 1-31a) are remnants of the quenched martensite. Figure 1-31b, however, shows little relation to the original martensite and is more uniform and nondirectional in appearance. These differences in microstructure are the major factors underlying the strength and ductility of a steel. It is this relationship between structure and properties of a metal that forms the basis of metallurgy and should be the important concept gained from this chapter.

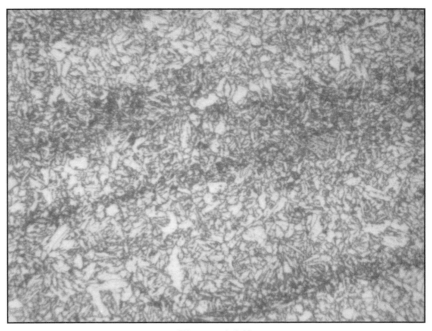

Figure 1-31b

Highly tempered structure of 4130 steel. Tempered 1 hr at 700°C. Nital etch, magnified 368 times.

Cast Irons

Cast irons are alloys of iron and carbon (greater than 2.0%) with silicon. Depending on the properties desired, other elements such as manganese, phosphorus, nickel, cerium, and magnesium are added. The main classes of cast iron are gray, white, malleable, and ductile. As in steels, the variations in structure of these alloys produce a variety of properties.

Gray iron has flakes of graphite in a ferrite matrix (Fig. 1-32), which gives this alloy its characteristic gray appearance when fractured. Ferritic gray cast iron has low strength but is less costly compared to other cast irons. Gray cast irons with carbon contents less than 4.3% are termed hypoeutectic and those greater than 4.3%, hypereutectic. The former are noted for their high strength, while the latter display excellent thermal shock resistance. The presence of graphite in flake form enhances the machinability of these alloys. However, it also significantly reduces the ductility of the gray cast irons because of the strong notch effect it presents.

Gray irons are designated by the ASTM with a two-digit system that corresponds to the minimum tensile strength in 1,000-psi increments. Thus, a Class No. 40 cast iron would have a minimum tensile strength of 40,000 psi.

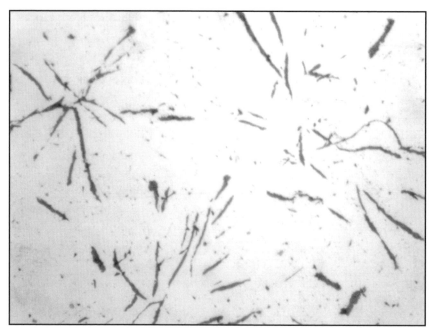

Figure 1-32
Gray cast iron showing graphite flakes. No etch, magnified 175 times.

White cast iron is distinguished from the other cast irons by its lack of graphite (Fig. 1-33). Because of the high concentration of iron carbides, this cast iron is quite hard (BHN 400-450) and brittle, which makes it a good alloy for service in highly abrasive environments. White irons alloyed with nickel and chromium and quenched to martensite can attain hardnesses of 600-725 Brinell.

Malleable cast irons are made from white iron castings that are heated to 1,500-1,750°F, held for a specified length of time depending on thickness and composition, then slowly cooled through a temperature range of 1,400-1,300°F. There are three types of malleable iron: ferritic, pearlitic (martensitic), and alloy. The first has a ferritic microstructure with carbon present in nodule form; the second type has carbon retained both in nodules and in cementite or marten site; and the alloy malleable iron has carbon in the form of graphite nodules as in the ferritic type. Malleable cast irons are used where both high strength and wear resistance are needed. Adding magnesium or cerium to molten gray iron causes the graphite flakes to spheroidize (Fig. 1-34), promoting increased ductility compared to gray east iron. Ductile irons have greater impact resistance than other east irons and, like steel, can be heat-treated to tensile strengths on the order of 180,000 psi. An important property of ductile iron is that it behaves elastically, like steel, when

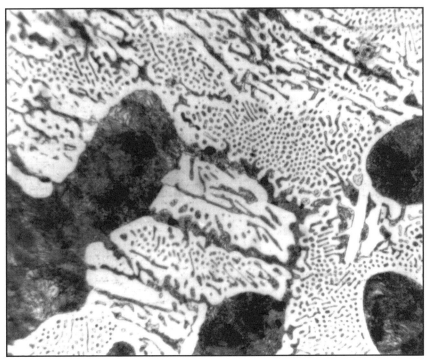

Figure 1-33

Hypoeutectic white cast iron, large dark areas of pearlite and speckled areas of ledeburite. Nital etch, magnified 150 times.

stressed and thus follows Hooke's law. Gray iron, on the other hand, does not. Because of the sharp notch effect of the graphite, it shows only elastic behavior under light loads.

Ductile irons are designated by ASTM A 536 by a series of three numbers: for example, 60-40-18 in which 60 represents a minimum tensile strength of 60,000 psi, 40 a minimum yield strength of 40,000 psi, and 18 a minimum elongation of 18%. Ductile iron is used in applications in which high strength plus good ductility are required.

Tensile strengths of cast irons in the four major categories fall in the following ranges: 20-80 ksi for gray irons, 13-90 ksi for white irons, 50-100 ksi for malleable irons, and 55-175 ksi for ductile irons. Hardness values of cast irons are 140-350 Brinell for gray irons, up to 600 for white irons, 110-270 for malleable irons, and 130-300 for ductile irons. A simple relationship between hardness and tensile strength does not exist for cast irons as it does for steel because of the more heterogeneous microstructure prevalent in the cast irons.

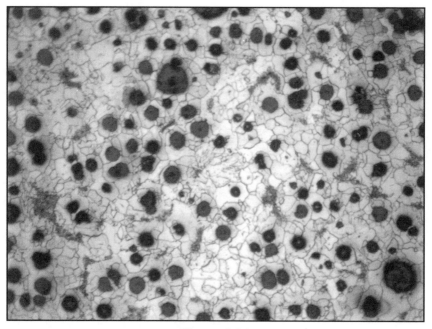

Figure 1-34

Ductile iron showing graphite nodules in a ferrite matrix. Nital etch, magnified 145 times.

In the oilfield, cast irons are used in valves, pumps, packers, bridge plugs, and other assemblies. It should be appreciated that selection of cast irons requires a knowledge of the intended application since, in many ways, cast irons are less forgiving than steels.

Stainless Steels

Stainless steels were not widely used in petroleum production except very specialized applications such as trim on valves or parts in downhole tools until the early 1980's. At that time and since, drilling and production in aggressive environments have led to the need for highly alloyed materials such as stainless steels, nickel-base alloys, cobalt-base alloys, and titanium alloys.

Chromium is the element that gives stainless steel the stainless quality. To be classed as stainless, steels must contain 12% chromium or more. Nickel added in excess of 6% increases corrosion resistance and substantially improves mechanical and fabricating properties. Molybdenum increases pitting resistance and enhances high-temperature strength.

Stainless steels are classified according to their metallurgical structure as shown in Table 1-3. The 200 and 300 series are austenitic while the 400 series is either martensitic or ferritic. Another series is the precipitation hardening stainless steels. These steels have a different designation such as 17-4 PH, indicating that they contain nominally 17% Cr-4% Ni. Lastly, there are a group of alloys referred to as duplex stainless steels that combine the austenite and ferrite phases in one alloy.

The 200 and 300 series are not hardenable by heat treatment, but only by cold work. The mechanical properties of the austenitics are classified according to minimum tensile and yield strength into four categories called tempers.

Tempers	Min. Tensile Strength, psi	Min. Yield Strength, psi
1/4 hard	125,000	75,000
1/2 hard	150,000	110,000
3/4 hard	175,000	135,000
Fully hard	185,000	140,000

The term "temper" as used here is a misnomer since these steels are not tempered at all but must be cold worked to achieve strength. The austenitics in general have superior corrosion resistance compared to the, ferritic and martensitic grades.

The ferritic stainless steels cannot be hardened by heat treatment and are used primarily in the annealed condition or with a minor amount of cold work. The martensitic alloys, on the other hand, have a high degree of hardenability and are widely used where both strength and corrosion resistance are needed. In recent years there has been a significant increase in the use of martensitic and so called super martensitic stainless steels for downhole tubulars and pipelines. Properly heat treated martensitic stainless steels will show a completely martenistic microstructure. Figure 1-35 shows a micrograph of 13 Cr tubing where a large fraction of retained ferrite appears. The precipitation-hardened stainless steels achieve their strength through heat treatment by two means. The first is transformation to martensite while the second, aging, causes the precipitation of a second phase that adds an additional strengthening increment.

The duplex stainless steels are widely used in the oil industry for a variety of components. They are not hardenable by heat treatment but generally are higher strength than the austenitics. The yield strength of annealed duplex stainless steels is generally about 70,000-80,000 psi. Moreover, duplex stainless steels have excellent corrosion resistance that is often better than either the ferrite or the austentite taken alone. The standard duplex stainless steels generally have a composition of 22-25% Cr. 5% Ni and 3% Mo and nitrogen is added for enhanced pitting resistance. The super duplex stainless steels contain higher Ni and Mo. A partial

41

Table 1-3 Compositions of AISI standard grades of stainless steels

UNS designation	AISI type	C	Mn	P	S	Si	Cr	Ni	Mo	Others
						Composition, %(a)				
Austenitic grades										
S20100	201	0.15	5.60-7.50	0.06	0.03	1.00	16.00-18.00	3.50-5.50	—	0.25N
S20200	202	0.15	7.50-10.0	0.06	0.03	1.00	17.00-19.00	4.00-6.00	—	0.25N
S20500	205	0.12-0.25	14.00-15.50	0.03	0.03	0.50	16.50-18.00	1.00-1.75	—	0.32-0.40N
S30100	301	0.15	2.00	0.045	0.03	1.00	16.00-18.00	6.00-8.00	—	—
S30200	302	0.15	2.00	0.045	0.03	1.00	17.00-19.00	8.00-10.00	—	—
	302B	0.15	2.00	0.045	0.03	2.00-3.00	17.00-19.00	8.00-10.00	—	—
S30300	303	0.15	2.00	0.2	0.15	1.00	17.00-19.00	8.00-10.00	0.60	—
	303Se	0.15	2.00	0.2	0.06	1.00	17.00-19.00	8.00-10.00	—	0.15Se min
S30400	304	0.08	2.00	0.045	0.03	1.00	18.00-20.00	8.00-10.00	—	—
S30403	304L	0.03	2.00	0.045	0.03	1.00	18.00-20.00	8.00-10.00	—	—
S30430	304HQ	0.08	2.00	0.045	0.03	1.00	17.00-19.00	8.00-10.00	—	3.00-4.00C
	304N	0.08	2.00	0.045	0.03	1.00	18.00-20.00	8.00-10.00	—	0.10-0.16N
S30500	305	0.12	2.00	0.045	0.03	1.00	17.00-19.00	10.50-13.00	—	—
S30800	308	0.08	2.00	0.045	0.03	1.00	19.00-21.00	10.00-12.00	—	—
S30900	309	0.2	2.00	0.045	0.03	1.00	22.00-24.00	12.00-15.00	—	—
	309S	0.08	2.00	0.045	0.03	1.00	22.00-24.00	12.00-15.00	—	—
S31000	310	0.25	2.00	0.045	0.03	1.50	24.00-26.00	19.00-22.00	—	—
	310S	0.08	2.00	0.045	0.03	1.50	24.00-26.00	19.00-22.00	—	—
S31400	314	0.25	2.00	0.045	0.03	1.50-3.00	23.00-26.00	19.00-22.00	—	—
S31600	316	0.08	2.00	0.045	0.03	1.00	16.00-18.00	10.00-14.00	2.00-3.00	—
	316F	0.08	2.00	0.2	0.10 min	1.00	16.00-18.00	10.00-14.00	1.75-2.50	—
S31603	316L	0.03	2.00	0.045	0.03	1.00	16.00-18.00	10.00-14.00	2.00-3.00	—
	316N	0.08	2.00	0.045	0.03	1.00	16.00-18.00	10.00-14.00	2.00-3.00	0.10-0.16N
S31700	317	0.08	2.00	0.045	0.03	1.00	18.00-20.00	11.00-15.00	3.00-4.00	—
S31703	317L	0.03	2.00	0.045	0.03	1.00	18.00-20.00	11.00-15.00	3.00-4.00	—
S32100	321	0.08	2.00	0.045	0.03	1.00	17.00-19.00	9.00-12.00	—	Ti×5C min
	329	0.10	2.00	0.04	0.03	1.00	25.00-30.00	3.00-6.00	1.00-2.00	—
	330	0.08	2.00	0.04	0.03	0.75-1.50	17.00-20.00	34.00-37.00	—	—
S34700	347	0.08	2.00	0.045	0.03	1.00	17.00-19.00	9.00-13.00	—	0.10Ta.0. Nb:10xC
S34800	348	0.08	2.00	0.045	0.03	1.00	17.00-19.00	9.00-13.00	—	Nb:10xC

Type (UNS ... AISI)	C	Mn	P	S	Si	Cr	Ni	Mo	Other
Ferritic grades									
S40500 ...405	0.08	1.00	0.04	0.03	1.00	11.50–14.50	—	—	0.10–0.30
S40900 ...409	0.08	1.00	0.045	0.045	1.00	10.50–11.75	—	—	Ti:6xC–0.70
S42900 ...429	0.12	1.00	0.04	0.03	1.00	14.00–16.00	—	—	—
S43000 ...430	0.12	1.00	0.04	0.03	1.00	16.00–18.00	—	—	—
430F	0.12	1.25	0.06	0.15	1.00	16.00–18.00	—	0.60	—
430FSe	0.12	1.25	0.06	0.06	1.00	16.00–18.00	—	—	0.15Se min
S43400 ...434	0.12	1.00	0.04	0.03	1.00	16.00–18.00	—	0.75–1.25	—
S43600 ...436	0.12	1.00	0.04	0.03	1.00	16.00–18.00	—	0.75–1.25	Nb:5xC–0.70
S44200 ...442	0.20	1.00	0.04	0.04	1.00	18.00–23.00	—	—	—
S44400 ...444	0.025	1.00	0.04	0.03	1.00	17.50–19.50	—	1.75–2.50	(Ti+Nb) 4(C+N)
S44600 ...446	0.20	1.50	0.04	0.03	1.00	23.00–27.00	—	—	0.25N
Martensitic grades									
S40300 ...403	0.15	1.00	0.04	0.03	0.50	11.50–13.00	—	—	—
S41000 ...410	0.15	1.00	0.04	0.03	1.00	11.50–13.50	—	—	—
S41400 ...414	0.15	1.00	0.04	0.03	1.00	11.50–13.50	1.25–2.50	—	—
S41600 ...416	0.15	1.25	0.06	0.15 min	1.00	12.00–14.00	—	0.60	—
416Se	0.15	1.25	0.06	0.06	1.00	12.00–14.00	—	—	0.15Se min
S42000 ...420	0.15 min	1.00	0.04	0.03	1.00	12.00–14.00	—	—	—
420F	0.15 min	1.25	0.06	0.15 min	1.00	12.00–14.00	—	—	—
S42200 ...422	0.20–0.25	1.00	0.025	0.025	0.75	11.00–13.00	0.50–1.00	0.75–1.25	0.15–0.30; 0.75–1.00
S43100 ...431	0.20	1.00	0.04	0.04	1.00	15.00–17.00	1.25–2.50	—	—
440A	0.60–0.75	1.00	0.04	0.03	1.00	16.00–18.00	—	0.75	—
440B	0.75–0.95	1.00	0.04	0.03	1.00	16.00–18.00	—	0.75	—
440C	0.95–1.20	1.00	0.04	0.03	1.00	16.00–18.00	—	0.75	—
Precipitation-hardening grades									
S13800 ...S13800	0.05	0.20	0.010	0.008	0.10	12.25–13.25	7.50–8.50	2.00–2.50	0.90–1.35Al; 0.01N
S15500 ...S15500	0.07	1.00	0.04	0.03	1.00	14.00–15.50	3.50–5.50	—	2.50–4.50; 0.15–0.45
S17400 ...S17400	0.07	1.00	0.04	0.03	1.00	15.50–17.50	3.00–5.00	—	3.00–5.00cu; 0.15–0.45
S17700 ...S17700	0.09	1.00	0.04	0.04	1.00	16.00–18.00	6.50–7.75	—	0.75–1.50Al

(a) Maximum unless otherwise indicated; all compositions include balance of iron. (courtesy ASM International)

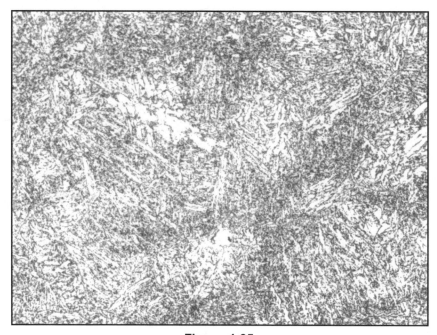

Figure 1-35
Micrograph of 13 Cr tubing showing the needle like appearance of the
tempered martensite and white blocky areas of retained ferrite.
Magnified 400 times.

list of duplex stainless steel alloys is presented in Table 1-4. Figure 1-36 is an example of the duplex stainless steel microstructure.

The duplex stainless steels represent a complex system and as such great care in manufacturing, processing and fabricating must be taken to ensure that this group of alloys lives up to its highest potential. Therefore, it is important to recognize that the duplex stainless steels can, when improperly heat treated or otherwise thermally processed, precipitate a number of detrimental phases. Figure 1-37 shows a typical time-temperature diagram for the regions of precipitation of various carbides, sigma phase (σ), chi (χ) and R phases and a', which is a Cr rich phase responsible for embrittlement of Fe-Cr alloys. Figure 1-38 shows the presence of sigma phase (darkest areas within the islands) in a duplex stainless steel that was aged for 2.5 hours at 1560°F (849°C).

Specific applications of duplex stainless steels in oil and gas production will be presented in Chapter 4.

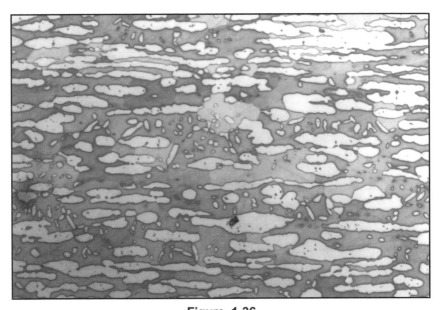

Figure 1-36
Microstructure of duplex stainless steel showing the austenite phase (light) and ferrite phase (dark) Magnified 100 times.

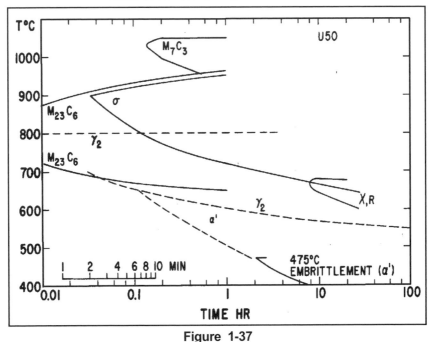

Figure 1-37
Time-temperature-precipitation diagram for various phases in a duplex stainless steel, Uranus 50. (Courtesy of ASM International)

45

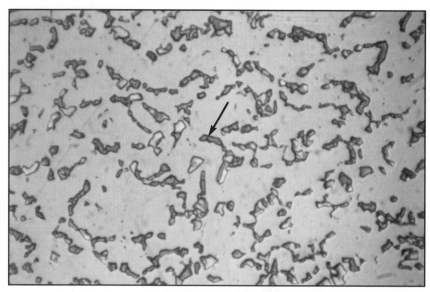

Figure 1-38

Sigma phase precipitation in a 22 Cr duplex stainless steel. The light area is austenite and the islands are ferrite. The very dark part of the ferrite (arrow) is sigma. Magnified 1000 times. Electrolytic KOH etch.

Table 1-4

Nominal Chemical Composition of Some Common Duplex Stainless Steels

Alloy Common Name	UNS Number	C	Cr	Ni	Mo	N	Cu	W
2205	S31803	0.02	22	5	3	0.1		
Ferralium 255	S32550	0.02	25	6	3	0.2	2	
SAF 2507[1]	S32750	0.02	25	7	3.5	0.3		
Zeron 100[2]	S32760	0.02	25	7	3.5	0.2	0.7	0.7
25 Cr (DP3)[3]	S31260	0.02	25	7	3	0.2	0.6	0.3
25CrW (DP3W)[3]	S39274	0.02	25	7	3	0.3	0.6	2

1. Sandvik   2. Weir Materials   3. Sumitomo

Nickel-Base Alloys

The nickel-based alloys represent the next step up in corrosion resistance compared to the stainless steels. Just as in the case of stainless steels, there are a multitude of nickel-base alloys. The most common are the Incoloys, Inconels, Monels and Hastelloys. These alloys, the most common of which are presented in Table 1-5 are primarily composed of nickel, chromium, molybdenum, iron, aluminum, titanium. Monels are nickel-copper alloys, Incoloys are nickel-iron-chromium

Table 1-5 Composition of Common Nickel-Base Alloys

UNS No.	Common Name	Cr	Mo	Ni	Fe	Composition, %(a) Co	Cu	Nb	W	Al	C	Ti	Si	Mn
N08028	Alloy 28	26-28	3.0-4.0	29.5-32.5	bal	—	0.6-1.4	—	—	—	0.03	—	1.00	2.50
N08825	Incoloy 825	19.5-23.5	2.5-3.5	38-46	bal	—	1.5-3.0	—	—	0.2	0.05	0.6-1.2	0.50	1.00
N07725	Incoloy 725	19.0-22.5	7.0-9.5	55-59	bal	—	—	2.75-4.0	—	0.35	0.03	1.0-1.7	0.20	0.35
N09925	Incoloy 925	19.5-23.5	2.5-3.5	38-46	22.0 min.	—	1.5-3.0	—	—	0.1-0.5	0.03	1.9-2.4	0.50	1.00
N07718	Inconel 718	17.0-21.0	2.8-3.3	50-55	bal	1.0	0.30	5.0	—	0.2-0.8	0.08	0.65-1.15	0.35	0.35
N07750	Inconel X-750	14.0-17.0	—	70 min.	5-9	—	0.50	0.7-1.2	—	0.4-1.0	0.08	2.25-2.75	0.50	1.00
N06625	Inconel 625	20-23	8.0-10.0	bal	5.0	—	—	—	—	0.40	0.10	0.40	0.50	0.50
N04400	Monel 400	—	—	63-70	2.5	—	bal	—	—	—	0.30	—	0.50	2.00
N05500	Monel K-500	—	—	63-70	2.0	—	bal	—	—	2.3-3.5	0.25	0.35-0.85	0.50	1.50
N06975	Alloy 2550	23.0-26.0	5.0-7.0	47-52	bal	—	0.7-1.2	—	—	—	0.03	0.7-1.5	1.00	1.00
N06985	Hastelloy G-3	21.0-23.5	6.0-8.0	bal ~41	18-21	5.0	1.5-2.5	0.5*	1.5	—	0.015	—	1.00	1.00
N069	Hastelloy G-30													
N06950	Hastelloy G-50	19.0-21.0	8-10	bal ~48	16-18	2.5	0.5	—	1.0	—	0.02	—	1.00	1.00
N10276	Hastelloy C-276	14.5-16.5	15.0-17.0	bal ~57	4.0-7.0	2.5	—	—	3.0-4.5	—	0.02	—	0.50	1.00
R30035**	MP35N	19.0-21.0	9.0-10.5	33-37	1.0	bal	—	—	—	—	0.025	1.0	0.15	0.15

(a) maximum unless otherwise indicated
* Nb + Ta
** Actually Cobalt-base alloy
bal- balance

Incoloy and Inconel are trade names of Special Metals
Hastelloy is a trade name of Haynes

47

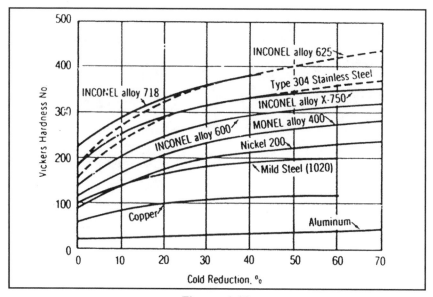

Figure 1-39

Hardness as a function of cold work for various alloys (courtesy Special Metals).

alloys and Inconels are nickel-chromium alloys. The names Incoloy, Inconel,etc are trade names specific to one manufacturer. Other manufacturer's make similar alloys and so it has become common to refer to these alloys as Alloy 825 or Alloy 718, rather than Incoloy 825 or Inconel 718.

Many of the alloys are not heat-treatable and must be strengthened by cold work. Other alloys can be strengthened by aging that produces a precipitate referred to as gamma prime, γ'. Still other alloys such as Alloy 718 rely on the pre-cipitation of gamma double prime, (γ'') for strengthening.

Figure 1-39 shows the response of various alloys to cold work. The higher the degree of cold work, the greater the hardness up to a point after which the hardness is not measurably increased. Figure 1-40 shows the microstructure of annealed Hastelloy G-50 and Figure 1-41 after cold working.

Figure 1-42 is an idealized presentation of aging that demonstrates the time temperature relationship for hardening. As the temperature increases, the time to achieve maximum hardness is reduced. If the optimum time at temperature is exceeded, then overaging occurs and the precipitates enlarge reducing their strengthening effect. The γ' precipitate in a high-nickel alloy is most often com-posed of $Ni_3(Al, Ti)$ although niobium and tantalum may also produce γ'.

The nickel-base alloys are quite complex as a result of the numerous phases that can form. The most common phases are gamma prime (γ') eta (η) gamma double prime (γ''), mu (μ), sigma (σ), Laves and a variety of carbide and carbonitride phas-

48

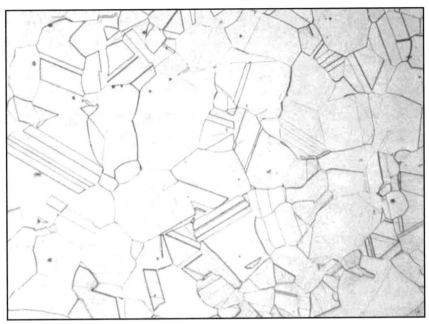

Figure 1-40
Microstructure of annealed Hastelloy G50. Magnified 400 times.

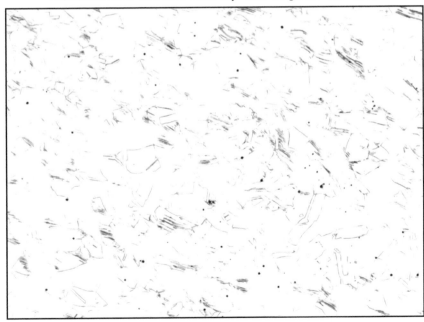

Figure 1-41
Microstructure of the same G50 shown in Figure 1-40 after cold working to produce tubing. Magnified 400 times.

49

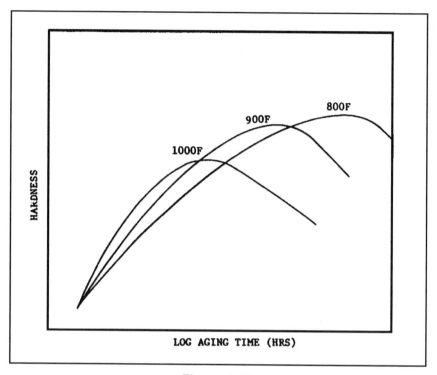

Figure 1-42

Hardness as a function of aging time and temperature for age-hardenable nickel alloys.

es. Some of these phases such as the chromium carbides are reversible and by proper heat treatment can be removed from the alloy. However, other phases such as sigma are practically irreversible and therefore present a serious problem if they are allowed to form.

A good example of potential problems that may be caused by the precipitation of detrimental phases is the failure of an Alloy 718 tubing hanger that occurred in the North Sea and was attributed to, but not confirmed to be, from the presence of delta phase (δ). Alloy 718 is a heat treatable nickel-based alloy that derives its strength by the precipitation of gamma double prime through the aging process. Improper thermomechanical processing can result in the precipitation of the deleterious δ phase along the grain boundaries as globules or acicular (needle-like) precipitates. Figure 1-43 shows the appearance of the acicular δ phase along the grain boundaries in an Alloy 718 sample intentionally air cooled to produce delta phase.

The complexities of the nickel-based alloys requires that they be carefully processed to ensure that the optimum corrosion resistance is achieved while obtaining the necessary strength and toughness to meet the design conditions.

Figure 1-43
Delta phase (needles on the grain boundaries) in an Alloy 718 sample.
Magnified 400 times.

Titanium Alloys

Titanium is a very reactive metal that obtains its superior corrosion resistance from the stable titanium oxide (TiO_2) that forms on the surface.

Titanium has a higher temperature bcc phase referred to as beta and a low temperature (ambient) hcp phase called alpha. Titanium alloys are generally categorized as alpha, near alpha, alpha + beta, near-beta, and beta. Table 1-6 presents some of the more common Ti alloys. The major alloying elements are aluminum, nickel, vanadium, molybdenum, chromium, platinum, and tin. Aluminum and tin promote alpha phase stability while Ni, V, Mo, Cr, and Cu promote the beta phase.

Alpha titanium alloys cannot be strengthened by heat treatment. Likewise, near alpha alloys do not respond to heat treatment. Alpha + beta, near-beta, and beta alloys all display strengthening by heat treatment.

Alpha + beta alloys are generally liquid-quenched for the necessary rapid cooling to provide optimum response to aging. However, beta alloys are typically air-quenched from the solution annealing temperature. Both types of alloys are then aged and strengthening occurs by the decomposition of the supersaturated beta phase. Figure 1-44 shows the mixed alpha and beta phase in Ti-6Al-4V.

One of the advantages of titanium alloys over nickel-base alloys is the high strength that can be achieved by heat treatment. For example, low-alloy steels and titanium alloys can be heat treated to produce useable yield strengths as high as 180,000 psi. However, age-hardenable nickel alloys are limited to about 130,000 psi.

Table 1-6 Some Common Titanium Alloys

UNS No.	Common Designation & Grade	Nominal Composition, wt %					N (max)	C (max)	H (max)	Impurity limits, wt%	
		Al	Sn	Zr	Mo	Others				Fe(max)	O (max)
Unalloyed grades											
R50250	ASTM Grade 1	—	—	—	—	—	0.03	0.10	0.015	0.20	0.18
R50400	ASTM Grade 2	—	—	—	—	—	0.03	0.10	0.015	0.30	0.25
R50550	ASTM Grade 3	—	—	—	—	—	0.05	0.10	0.015	0.30	0.35
R50700	ASTM Grade 4	—	—	—	—	—	0.05	0.10	0.015	0.50	0.40
Alpha and near-alpha alloys											
R52400	ASTM Grade 7	—	—	—	—	0.2Pd	0.03	0.10	0.015	0.30	0.25
R52402	Ti-lean Pd [Grade 16]	—	—	—	—	0.05Pd	0.02	0.10	0.010	0.30	0.20
R52404	[Grade 26]	—	—	—	—	0.10Ru					
R53400	TiCode 12 [Grade 12]	—	—	—	0.3	0.8Ni					
—	Ti-6Al-2Nb-1Ta-0.8Mo	6	—	—	1	2Nb,1Ta					
—	Ti-2.25Al-11Sn-5Zr-1Mo	2.25	11.0	5.0	1.0	0.2Si					
Alpha-beta alloys											
R56400	Ti-6Al-4V [Grade 5]	6.0	—	—	—	4.0V					
R56407	Ti-6Al-4V-ELI [Grade 23]	6.0	—	—	—	4.0V					
R56620	Ti-6Al-6V-2Sn	6.0	2.0	—	—	8.0Mn					
R56403	Ti-6Al-4V [Grade 25]	6.0	—	—	—	0.06Pd,0.6Ni					
—	Ti-7Al-4Mo	7.0	—	—	4.0	—					
R56260	Ti-6Al-2Sn-4Zr-6Mo	6.0	2.0	4.0	6.0	—					
—	Ti-6Al-2Sn-2Zr-4Mo-4Cr	5.0	2.0	2.0	4.0	4.0Cr					
—	Ti-10V-2Fe-3Al	3.0	—	—	—	10.0V					
R56320	Ti-3Al-2.5V [Grade 9]	3.0	—	—	—	2.5V					
R56322	Ti-3Al-2.5V-0.05Pd [Grade 18]	3.0	—	—	—	0.05Pd,2.5V					
Beta alloys											
R58010	Ti-13V-11Cr-3Al	3.0	—	—	—	11.0Cr,13.0V					
—	Ti-8Mo-8V-2Fe-3Al	3.0	—	—	8.0	8.0V					
R58640	Ti-3Al-8V-6Cr-4Mo-4Zr [Grade 19]	3.0	—	4.0	4.0	6.0Cr,8.0V					

Figure 1-44

Microstructure of Ti-6Al-4V magnified 100 times. The white phase is alpha and the dark phase, beta.

In this chapter a large number of alloys and their families have been presented in order to demonstrate the variety of alloys that are available to and used by the petroleum industry to control corrosion. The subsequent chapters in this book will elucidate the specific applications of many of these alloys.

References

American Petroleum Institute. Recommended Practice 2A.

American Society for Metals. "Properties and Selection of Metals." In Metals Handbook. Volume 1. 1961, pp. 227 and 236; 1978, p.494, Volume 13, 1987.

American Society for Testing and Materials. Standards A370 and E23.

Bravenec, E.V. "Analysis of Brittle Fractures During Fabrication and Testing."

ASME Pressure Vessel and Piping Division Meeting. Paper 53. San Francisco, California, May 1981.

Cias, W.W. Phase Transformation Kinetics and Hardenability of Medium-Carbon Alloy Steels. Greenwich, Connecticut: Climax Molybdenum Company.

Dieter, G.E. Jr. Mechanical Metallurgy. New York, New York; McGraw-Hill Book Company, Third Edition, 1986.

Honeycombe, R.W.K., Steels-Microstructure and Properties, ASM International, 1982.

Huntington Alloys Handbook, Fabricating, p. 3, 1981.

Reed-Hill, R.E. and R. Abbaschian, Physical Metallurgy Principles. Third Edition, PWS Publishing Company Inc., 1991.

2

FUNDAMENTALS
OF CORROSION

With few exceptions, metals and alloys are placed in a service environment that in some way alters or degrades the material. This degradation is referred to as corrosion, and no study of metallurgy can be complete without discussing the effect of environments on metals. These effects can manifest themselves in many ways, which will be described in this chapter. Furthermore, corrosion is a frequent downfall of a well-designed alloy system that has been carefully planned based on physical and mechanical properties but whose performance has never been considered in an aggressive environment. Since petroleum production is by its very nature corrosive, the remainder of this book will deal often with the effect of corrosion on metals.

The Corrosion Cell

Corrosion is primarily an electrochemical process, which means that in addition to the chemical reaction there is also the movement of electrons and, as such, a current flow. Since current must flow from one location to another, there are two

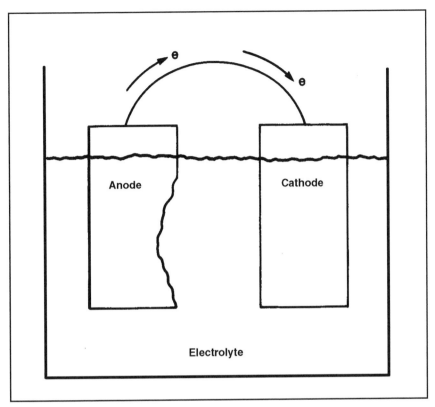

Figure 2-1

Components of an electrochemical cell that produce corrosion.

basic reactions occurring. One involves the discharge of electrons; the surface that supports this reaction is called the anode. The other reaction, which consumes the electrons, is called the cathode. Figure 2-1 represents the basic corrosion cell that includes an anode where metal ions go into solution, and a cathode where electrons are consumed. Electrons move along the path of low resistance.

The anode reaction is called oxidation and is represented as metal (M) going to metal ions (M+):

$$M \rightarrow M^+ + e$$

Likewise, to conserve electrons (e) as required, the following reaction occurs in acid solutions at the cathode and is referred to as reduction:

$$2H^+ + 2e \rightarrow H_2$$

If a voltmeter were introduced into the circuit between the two metal strips, a steady-state potential or voltage would be observed after a short equilibration time. The magnitude of this potential is a function of the type of metal, the solu-

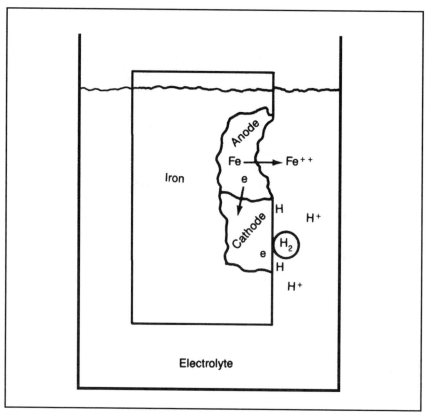

Figure 2-2
Schematic of local anodes and cathodes on steel surface.

tion chemistry, and the temperature. The concept of potential is important since, as will be demonstrated in later examples, the potential of a metal in solution is an indication whether it will corrode or not.

There are a multitude of oxidation/reduction reactions, but the more common ones in the oilfield are:

Oxidation:　$Fe \rightarrow Fe^{+2} + 2e$

　　　　　　$Fe^{+2} \rightarrow Fe^{+3} + e$

Reduction:　$2H^+ + 2e \rightarrow H_2$ (acidic solutions)

　　　　　　$O_2 + 4H^+ + 4e \rightarrow 2H_2O$ (acid solutions)

　　　　　　$O_2 + 2H_2O + 4e \rightarrow 4OH^-$ (neutral or basic solutions)

It is conventional to add the two reactions to describe the complete electro chemical reaction such that iron corroding in hydrochloric acid would be written:

$$Fe + 2HCl \rightarrow FeCl_2 + H_2$$

Anodes and cathodes are not always two separate metals but in fact are commonly spread out over the surface of one metal. This is the result of small variations in composition, surface roughness, cold work, and surface films, to name the primary ones. Figure 2-2 represents the corrosion of steel in an acid solution. Here, the easy electron path is within the metal itself and is not part of an external connection.

Considering the reaction just described for steel in an acid solution, certain characteristics of the environment affect the corrosion reaction. Factors that increase either the anodic or the cathodic reaction increase the corrosion rate since the two are linked. The principal factors are oxygen or oxidizer concentration, temperature, velocity, and concentration of reactants.

None of these parameters has a simple relationship to corrosion rate. For instance, increasing temperature is detrimental up to the boiling point because it increases the reaction rate. A common rule of thumb is, for every $10°C$ increase in temperature, the reaction rate (corrosion rate) doubles. However, above the boiling point, the corrosion rate may actually decrease as the corrosion mechanism changes to a high-temperature attack.

For velocity, the same phenomenon occurs when initially increasing velocity increases the corrosion rate, but at some point the corrosion rate may decrease since reactants do not have sufficient time to initiate corrosion at the metal surface. However, for many applications, increasing velocity, temperature, oxygen, and concentration of corrodents generally can be considered to increase the corrosion rate.

In petroleum production and drilling, the primary agents that cause corrosion are oxygen (O_2), carbon dioxide (CO_2), hydrogen sulfide (H_2S), and chlorides. More recently, elemental sulfur (S) produced from gas and oil wells has been encountered, and it, too, is corrosive. Besides these naturally occurring corrodents, there is the action of hydrochloric (HCl) and hydrofluoric (HF) acids, both of which are used in acid stimulation and the former in wellbore cleanup. Likewise, clear brines for completion and packer fluids can be quite corrosive. The advent of tertiary oil recovery has brought numerous other corrodents into the picture. The specific role of each of these constituents will be discussed in subsequent chapters.

The concept of corrosion rate and the principles behind it have been discussed, but how is it actually measured? One method is to measure the amount of metal loss by weight change. This approach is not satisfactory since sample geometry and lime of exposure can affect the amount of weight lost, making comparison with other methods inaccurate. In fact, the best expressions for corrosion rate use penetration per unit time in units of inches per year (ipy), millimeters per year (mm/y), microns/year (μm/y) or, mils per year (mpy). A conversation table for these common rates is presented in Table 2-1.

TABLE 2-1
Conversions for Corrosion Rate Units

Unit	Factor			
	mpy	ipy	mm/y	μm/y
mils/year (mpy)	1	0.001	0.0254	25.4
inch/year (ipy)	1000	1	25.4	25,400
millimeter/year (mm/y)	39.4	0.0394	1	1000
microns/year (μm/y)	0.0394	0.0000394	0.001	1

* Multiply the unit in this column by the appropriate factor to obtain the new unit in the right columns.

A simple relationship for determining corrosion rate in mils per year from weight-loss data is:

$$mpy = \frac{534\ W}{DAT}$$

Where:
W = weight loss, mg
D = density of specimen, g/cm³
A = area of specimen exposed, sq in.
T = exposure time, hr

Techniques for measuring corrosion rates vary considerably, from the simple immersion of preweighted strips of metal called coupons to the more complex potentiometric methods. While these methods are important, they are not germane to this book. Rather, it is more appropriate here to present the various forms of corrosion as they relate to the oilfield. These forms will be referred to throughout the book to explain the reasons for metallurgical choices in drilling, production, and handling of oil and gas.

Types of Corrosion

Although corrosion has been categorized various ways by many authors, there is no one universal system for classifying the forms of corrosion. However, it is convenient to organize the types as uniform, pitting, crevice, dealloying, intergranular, galvanic, erosion/impingement, and environmentally assisted cracking.

Uniform corrosion represents the ideal case in which the metal is uniformly corroded away at some constant rate. This particular form of attack—while rarely

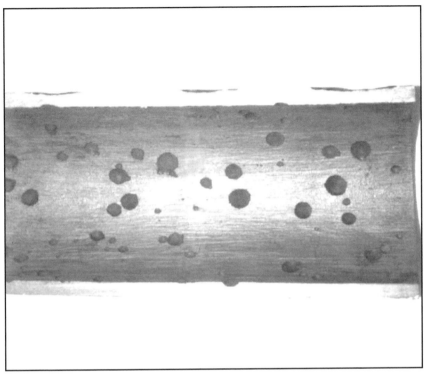

Figure 2-3
Pitting corrosion in J-55 tubing from crude oil containing H_2S.

seen in practice—is the basis for most design. Using a predetermined corrosion rate of so many mils per year, the designer assumes corrosion will progress in a uniform manner. In fact, frequently corrosion is very localized, and failure occurs most often by this means long before failure by general thinning of the metal. Uniform or general corrosion is commonly observed on metal structures exposed to the atmosphere (e.g., offshore platforms, exterior of tanks, etc.).

Pitting attack is one of the most frequent forms of corrosion encountered. It represents a very localized attack and may cause failure in a matter of weeks or months while the remaining area of metal is relatively uncorroded. Figure 2-3 shows an example of pitting attack on a section of tubing that was used in sour (H_2S) oil production. The shape of pits varies with the particular pitting environment. The pits shown in Figure 2-3 are the result of corrosion by hydrogen sulfide and water in the produced fluids.

It is generally accepted that once pitting is initiated, the remaining unpitted surface area becomes cathodic to the pits. As the pits progress, the pH of the solution in the bottom of the pit is reduced, often to a pH of 1. This pH reduction, along with the anodic character of the pit, drives the corrosion process until the metal is perforated or a change in the environment stifles the continuing reaction. At any given time during the pitting of a metal surface, a statistical distribution of pit depths will range from almost nil to a maximum depth. Most pits will have some average depth between these two extremes. During the time it takes to perforate the metal, some pits initiate and then stop growing, while others propagate to various depths and stop or continue to grow until failure. Pitting often begins with a log normal distribution that over time becomes a normal distribution. Currently, there is not a good understanding as to why some pits grow to completion while others may initiate, propagate, and arrest. This explains the difficulty in predicting pitting corrosion and its rate of attack. Moreover, it is dangerous to attempt to estimate the remaining life of a structure based on pit depth measurements. While pitting can be catastrophic and difficult to predict, much is known about which environments induce pitting for many alloy systems.

The chloride ion is a particularly aggressive pitting agent for low-alloy and stainless steels, as shown in Table 2-2. Chloride pitting typically initiates at inclusions (usually sulfide inclusions) in the steel because the local alloy chemistry is significantly different than in the rest of the matrix. Carbon and low-alloy steels also pit in solutions containing hydrogen sulfide, carbon dioxide, and oxygen. Dissolved oxygen enhances pitting corrosion, especially in the presence of hydrogen sulfide, carbon dioxide, and chlorides.

Figure 2-4 shows the corrosion rate of steel as a function of dissolved oxygen content in water. Corrosion of steel from dissolved oxygen is almost always by pitting. Note how little oxygen is necessary, in the parts per million (ppm) range, to cause attack. It has been found that total elimination of oxygen in oilfield

Table 2-2

Minimum Concentration of Cl^- Necessary for Pit Initiation in 1 N H_2SO_4 Solution.

Alloy	Cl^- (Normality)
Fe	0.0003
Fe-5.6 Cr	0.017
Fe-11.6 Cr	0.069
18.6 Cr-9.9 Nl-Fe	0.1
20.0 Cr-Fe	0.1
24.5 Cr-Fe	1.0
29.4 Cr-Fe	1.0

(After Stolica, reprinted with permission from Pergamon Press Ltd.)

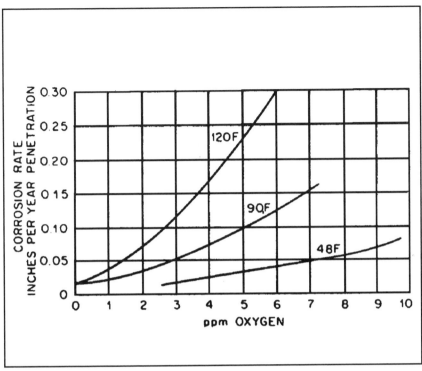

Figure 2-4
Corrosion rate of steel as a function of dissolved oxygen content in water
(courtesy Betz Laboratories).

waters is almost impossible but a reasonable threshold below which attack does not occur is 20 parts per billion (ppb).

Carbon dioxide and hydrogen sulfide also produce pitting and while under some circumstances they may lead to uniform corrosion, it is more common to observe pitting attack. Unlike oxygen, these gases generally cause corrosion when present in concentrations on the order of tenths of a percent or greater.

Oxygen also aids attack of another form of corrosion—crevice corrosion. This type of attack arises from two surfaces in contact with each other. These contacts can be gaskets, metal touching metal, corrosion products, or deposits that have settled on the metal surface.

Deposits can result by the precipitation of mineral scales ($CaSO_4$, $CaCO_3$, or $BaSO_4$) from water, or sand and silt Lying at the bottom of a line. The moisture under the deposit is depleted in oxygen compared to the rest of the solution. This variation in oxygen concentration will affect the potential of the metal as described earlier so that with two different potentials a corrosion cell is set up. The oxygen-rich surfaces of the metal act as cathodes, while the metal under the deposit becomes the anode. Because of the importance of oxygen in this type of attack, it is also referred to as oxygen depletion cell corrosion or concentration cell corrosion.

However, there is a critical size range in which crevice corrosion can occur. If the opening is too narrow, the solution will not easily enter the crevice: and if it is too large, mixing with the bulk solution will not allow the development of a stagnant region in the crevice. In general, a crevice of approximately 0.001 to 0.050 in. is necessary, although the particular situation will affect this size range.

Dealloying or selective leaching is the selective corrosion of one element in an alloy. Dezincification is the classic example of dealloying whereby zinc is selectively attacked and removed from brass alloys, leaving only the copper behind. Gray cast iron also suffers this type of attack in which the iron matrix is selectively corroded, leaving behind a layer of graphite. This attack of cast irons has been called graphitization or graphitic corrosion. Gray cast-iron butterfly valves and water pumps used in the petroleum industry are most susceptible to this type of attack. Table 2-3 gives a brief description of some of the alloys susceptible to selective leaching and the element removed.

Intergranular corrosion occurs most frequently in austenitic stainless steels as a result of heat treatment or welding that promotes a change in chemistry between the grain boundaries and the grains. These treatments leave the regions adjacent to the grain boundaries depleted in chromium compared to the metal matrix leading to a higher degree of susceptibility to corrosion. Corrosion then proceeds along the grain boundary network at a much higher rate than in the matrix. Figure 2-5 shows an example of intergranular corrosion of a CF8M (316) stainless steel pump impeller. The critical temperature change for inducing susceptibility to this form of attack is 950-1,450°F regardless if the alloy is held in this temperature range or slowly cooled through it. Thus, it is common practice to rapidly quench the austenitic stainless steels from above 1,800°F to avoid the problem. Low-carbon or stabilized grades of austenitic stainless steels are used to avoid this problem

Galvanic corrosion is one of the most common yet least-recognized corrosion problems. When two or more dissimilar metals are connected electrically and placed in a solution, current will flow between them because of the potential difference of the metals. The metal with least resistance to corrosion (active metal) in the particular environment will become the anode, while the more corrosion-resistant metal (noble metal) will become the cathode. The two metals do not have to be connected by standard electrical means; intimate contact will suffice. Corrosion of the anode will usually be more severe than corrosion of that metal alone in the same solution, while the cathode will achieve a degree of protection from the environment—sometimes to the extent that corrosion is completely stopped on the cathodic metal. These effects can be measured and have been done

Table 2-3.

Combinations of Alloys and Environments Subject to Selective Leaching, and the Elements Removed by Leaching.

Alloy	Environment	Element Removed
Brasses	Many waters, especially under stagnant conditions	Zinc (dezincification)
Gray Iron	Soils, many waters	Iron (graphitic corrosion)
Aluminum bronzes	Hydrofluoric acid, acids containing chloride ions	Aluminum
Silicon bronzes	Not reported	Silicon
Copper nickels	High heal flux and low water velocity (In refinery condenser Tubes)	Nickel
Monels	Hydrofluoric and other acids	Copper In some acids, nickel in others
Alloys of gold or platinum with nickel, copper, or silver	Nitric, chromic, and sulfuric acids	Nickel, copper, or silver (parting)
High-nickel alloys	Molten salts	Chromium, Iron, molybdenum, and tungsten
Cobalt-tungsten-chromium alloys	Not reported	Cobalt
Medium-carbon and high-carbon steels	Oxidizing atmospheres, hydrogen at high temperatures	Carbon (decarburization)
Iron-chromium alloys	High-temperature oxidizing atmospheres	Chromium, which forms a protective film
Nickel-molybdenum alloys	Oxygen at high temperature	Molybdenum

(After Metals Handbook, Volume 10)

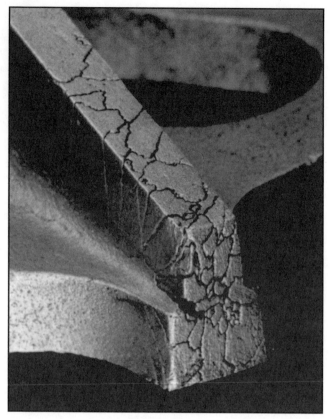

Figure 2-5
Intergranular corrosion of an austenitic stainless steel pump impeller.

for couples of metals in seawater at 25°C (see Table 2-4). Table 2-4 provides a relative ranking of metals and alloys regarding their resistance to corrosion in seawater. The greater the distance between two metals in the table, the greater their potential difference and the higher the probability the active metal will suffer accelerated corrosion.

Note that some alloys and metals are listed twice in the table—once with the word "active" following and once with the word "passive." Some metals and alloys become essentially immune to corrosion in certain environments because of the formation of a surface film so thin that it is impossible to see with the naked eye or even with an optical microscope. The stability of these films is paramount to the enhanced corrosion resistance of these alloys. Moreover, corrosion films represent the controlling factor in almost all corrosion (see Craig). Although little is known about the actual construction of these passive films, considerable knowledge exists concerning the effect of alloying on the formation of these films in different alloy systems. Thus the addition of chromium to iron can produce a passive alloy (18-8 stainless steel) of considerable corrosion resistance compared to the original iron. However, in an environment where the passive film is no~ functional, the active surface becomes far less noble as indicated in Table 2-4.

A more active metal in the series will corrode at the expense of a more noble one. Thus, coupling zinc to steel will cause the zinc to corrode and will protect the steel. This is the reason for galvanizing steel; when pinholes in the galvanizing occur, the steel underneath, once exposed to the environment, will be protected by the zinc. This is also the basis for cathodic protection. Sacrificial anodes are made of metals or alloys that are more active than steel, which allows for the consumption of the anode and the protection of the steel structure. However, if steel is coupled to copper, the distance on the chart is large so steel in this case will be the anode and have a greater tendency to corrode.

The galvanic series is useful for approximating the behavior of coupled alloys; however, care must be used in its application. Several parameters affect galvanic corrosion and as such may affect the actual behavior of a couple in service. Two important factors in galvanic corrosion are the temperature and the relative area of the metals. Increasing temperature in many cases may cause a reversal in the anode/cathode relationship. The galvanic series is applicable to many oilfield waters at ambient temperature; however, the zinc/steel couple has been found to reverse at about 140°F such that zinc becomes the cathode. This reversal has been responsible for failures of galvanized systems or systems protected with zinc sacrificial anodes. It has also been qualitatively determined that as the carbonate concentration of the solution increases, the temperature of potential reversal for the zinc/iron system decreases. These effects point to the need to measure the potential of a couple, especially in cathodic protection, in the actual environment prior to its application. It must always be borne in mind that Table 2-4 relates only to seawater and that extending it to other environments may result in some changes in the position of metals and alloys in the series.

The other factor, area-of-anode-to-area-of-cathode, is of considerable importance. If the anode area is smaller than the cathode area, the corrosion rate may be increased many orders of magnitude as a function of this ratio. However, if the anode area is greater than the cathode area, corrosion of the anode will be less than for a 1:1 anode/cathode ratio.

This behavior is shown in Figure 2-6. In this figure, the steel pipe pump column was coated with an epoxy coating and flanged to an aluminum-bronze seawater pump. Since the coating had several small pinholes (holidays) in it, the area of the steel anodes was small in comparison to the large, bronze pump cathode area. Penetration occurred in a matter of weeks. An important but difficult concept to understand intuitively from this example is that, when a couple such as steel to

Figure 2-6

Galvanic corrosion of seawater pump casing. The steel casing was coated with an epoxy, substantially decreasing the anode area. Worst attack is in the flange area where the casing was flanged to a bronze pump.

bronze must be made, the cathode (bronze) should be coated to reduce its area in relation to the anode.

Galvanic corrosion can also occur when metals of the same composition are coupled. If a section of pipe is removed from a pipeline that has been in service for many years and a new piece is installed, the new section will be anodic to the remaining line since the older sections have had time to form corrosion-product films. Generally, this is not a problem since the new pipe will corrode quickly at first while it also forms a comparable corrosion film. Another type of galvanic corrosion occurs most often in wet-gas systems containing carbon dioxide. Here, the heat-affected zone of a weldment is aggressively corroded while the weld bead is unaffected. This attack is the result of a high residual stress inherent in the heat-affected zone caused by welding in comparison to the lower stress in the weld bead, which experienced a slower cooling rate. It is also attributed to the metallurgical structure of the weld. However, depending on the chemistry of the welding rod, this galvanic cell can reverse and the weld bead can become anodic to the heat-affected zone.

Table 2-4.

Galvanic Series of Some Commercial Metals and Alloys in Seawater

Active or anodic	Magnesium
	Magnesium alloys
	Zinc
	Galvanized steel
	Aluminum 1100
	Aluminum 2024 (4.5 Cu. 1.5 Mg. 0.6 Mn)
	Mild steel
	Wrought Iron
	Cast Iron
	13% Chromium stainless steel
	Type 410 (active)
	1-8 Stainless steel
	Type 304 (active)
	Lead-tin solders
	Lead
	Tin
	Muntz metal
	Manganese bronze
	Naval brass
	Nickel (active)
	76 Ni-16 Cr-7 Fe alloy (active)
	60 Ni-30 Mo-6 Fe-1 Mn
	Yellow brass
	Admiralty brass
	Red brass
	Copper
	Silicon bronze
	70-30 Cupro nickel
	G-bronze
	Silver solder
	Nickel (passive)
	76 Nl-16 Cr-7 Fe (Inconel alloy) (passive)
	13% Chromium stainless steel
	Type 410 (passive)
	Titanium
	18-8 Stainless steel
	Type 304 (passive)
	Silver
Noble or cathodic	Graphite
	Gold
	Platinum

(After NACE)

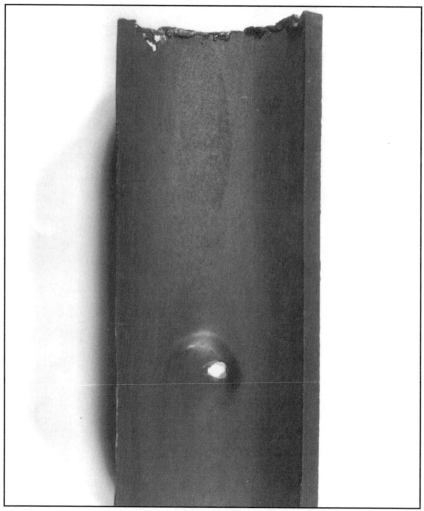

Figure 2-7
Impingement attack of piping caused by high-velocity gas flow.

Erosion-corrosion and impingement represent another form of corrosion. As discussed at the beginning of this chapter, velocity effects are quite complex and it is dangerous to make general statements concerning them; however, for most cases velocity increases corrosion, especially in the presence of fine particles such as sand or silt. Erosion-corrosion involves both the velocity contribution to corrosion as well as the mechanical degradation caused by the abrasion from these fine particles. Impingement is usually considered the more direct blasting of the surface by the fluid. Solids and gas bubbles have a tendency to increase the wastage caused by impingement.

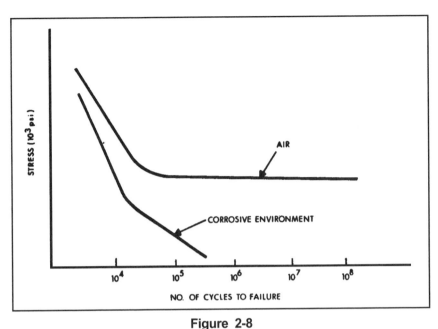

Figure 2-8

The effect of a corrosive environment on fatigue resistance. Note the absence of a definite fatigue limit in the corrosive environment.

Figure 2-7 shows an example of impingement in which a wet gas stream flowing from a pipe entered another pipe at 90°, causing impingement and leaving a highly polished, localized penetration in the wall.

Erosion-corrosion is actually a synergistic effect that is more than the sum of the components. Increasing velocity resulting in erosion causes deterioration by wear; but with the presence of corrodents, the surface is degraded faster than that expected from erosion or corrosion alone. In fact, in many forms of corrosion, there is a synergistic effect between some mechanical action that removes the corrosion product layer and corrosion that attacks the fresh metal.

Probably one of the most catastrophic forms of corrosion is environmentally assisted cracking. There are three basic categories that fall into this type of corrosion cracking: corrosion fatigue, stress-corrosion cracking, and hydrogen damage. The first of these involves a corrosive environment superimposed on the purely mechanical nature of fatigue. Some aspects of fatigue are discussed in the first chapter, and Figure 1-18 shows the fatigue behavior of steel in a noncorrosive environment. Figure 1-19 of the same chapter shows the deleterious effect of a saltwater environment on fatigue resistance, demonstrating the complete loss of a threshold stress or fatigue limit. In many cases, the loss of a threshold is not as abrupt and the corrosion fatigue curve appears more like that shown in Figure 2-8.

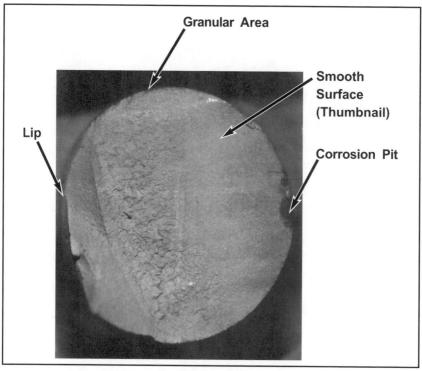

Figure 2-9
Characteristic features of a corrosion-fatigue fracture on a sucker rod.

Fracture most often initiates at the surface of the metal after most of the fatigue life has been spent prior to crack initiation. Once a crack is formed, complete fracture, which is propagation to failure, occurs in about 20% of the remaining life of the part. The fatigue fracture surface is quite distinctive, allowing easy recognition of this type of failure. Figure 2-9 shows the typical corrosion-fatigue failure of an oilfield sucker rod. A pit on the right has initiated the crack that propagated perpendicular to the tensile stress on the rod string. The smooth region represents stable crack growth and has the characteristic thumbnail appearance of a crack advancing from a single initiation point. In many fatigue failures, the faces do not rub each other, and the series of concentric rings (beach marks) are evident as shown in Figure 1-20. Once crack growth has progressed to the point that the remaining cross section cannot sustain the applied load, rapid, unstable fracture occurs, often leaving a bright crystalline appearance and a 45° shear lip. In ferrous metals, the corrosion fatigue fracture is usually transgranular with very little branching present.

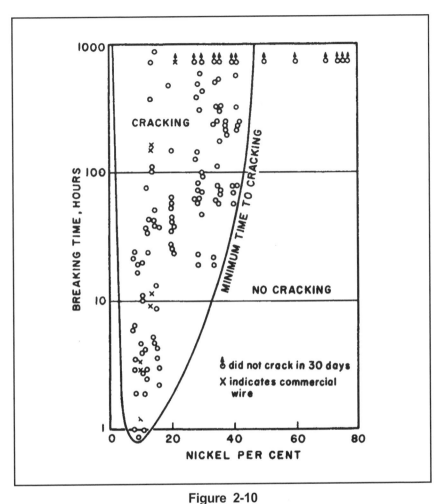

Figure 2-10

The effect of nickel content in iron-chromium-nickel stainless steel on susceptibility to stress-corrosion cracking in boiling Mg$_2$Cl (After Copson).

Unlike purely mechanical fatigue, corrosion fatigue is a strong function of the stress cycle frequency. If cycling is quite rapid, sufficient time is not allowed for contact between the crack lip and the corrosive environment to provide a contri-bution from the corrodents. On the other hand, very slow stress cycling can allow corrosion to blunt the crack tip, arresting or slowing the mechanical action of fatigue. Thus, there is a range of cyclic stress that is particularly conducive to cor-rosion fatigue.

Another form of cracking is stress-corrosion cracking, which is caused by the combined action of corrosion and tensile stress. Stress-corrosion cracking (SCC)

71

Table 2-5. Evaluating Media that causes stress-corrosion cracking.

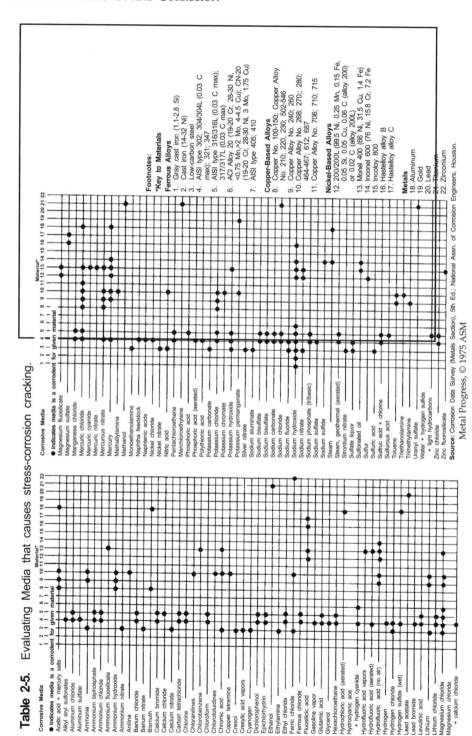

Source: Corrosion Data Survey (Metals Section), 5th Ed.; National Assn. of Corrosion Engineers, Houston.

Metal Progress, © 1975 ASM

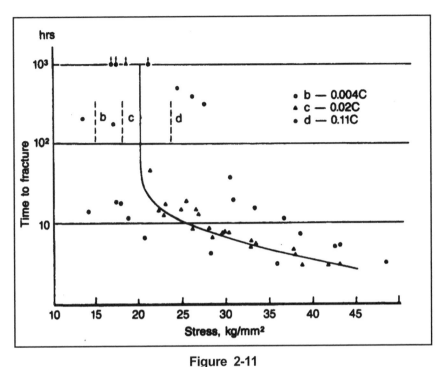

Figure 2-11

Stress dependence of several steels with different carbon content to stress-corrosion cracking in boiling 33% NaOH. Dotted lines b,c, and d represent the lower-yield strength of each steel (After Bohnenkamp).

susceptibility for an alloy is a function of solution chemistry, alloy composition, microstructure, stress, pH, specific ion concentration, and temperature. Not every alloy is susceptible to cracking in every environment; rather, certain chemical species referred to as the specific ion are responsible for cracking each alloy. All metals and alloys are susceptible to SCC in some environment. Table 2-5 gives a description of some of these combinations but is by no means complete.

Changes in alloying content can significantly alter the cracking susceptibility of an alloy system. The classic example of this behavior is the systematic addition of nickel to iron-chromium alloys subjected to boiling 42% $MgCl_2$ (Fig. 2-10). Here, the resistance goes through a minimum at approximately 8% Ni which corresponds to the 18-8 stainless steels. Microstructure is also of great importance. The presence or absence of precipitates and inclusions and the grain size strongly influence cracking resistance. Stress and temperature also influence cracking susceptibility. Increasing stress, temperature, and concentration of the specific ion act to decrease the stress-corrosion cracking life. Time to failure in a particular solution is logarithmically dependent on the applied stress in the same way discussed for fatigue. Figure 2-11 shows this relation for steel in an NaOH solution.

73

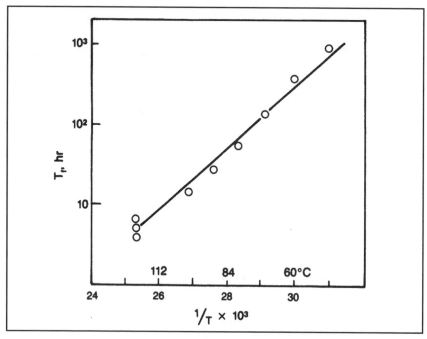

Figure 2-12

Effect of temperature on stress-corrosion cracking of steel in boiling 33% NaOH. Time to fracture (T_f) versus the reciprocal of absolute temperature is shown (After Bohnenkamp).

Similar to the fatigue case, there is often a threshold stress below which fracture will not occur. This same dependence is observed as a function of yield and tensile strength for high-strength steels. Increasing strength reduces the time to failure for stress corrosion cracking. Therefore, very high-strength steels can crack almost instantly when subjected to the right environment.

Increasing temperature also enhances cracking susceptibility (Fig. 2-12). Note in this example that the changes in time to failure with temperature are logarithmic, so increasing the temperature from 72°C-112°C decreases the time to failure one order of magnitude. In many systems, there is a threshold temperature below which cracking does not occur as shown in Figure 2-13, which relates susceptibility to both concentration and temperature. At 100°F and below, no cracking occurs regardless of concentration of NaOH. Increasing concentration at constant temperature also increases cracking tendency as shown in Figure 2-13.

Similarities between stress-corrosion cracking and hydrogen damage have led some to believe that the two are related or that both participate in environmental cracking. Still other investigators adamantly contend that the two are separate, distinct mechanisms and cannot be related to a more general mechanism of environmentally assisted cracking.

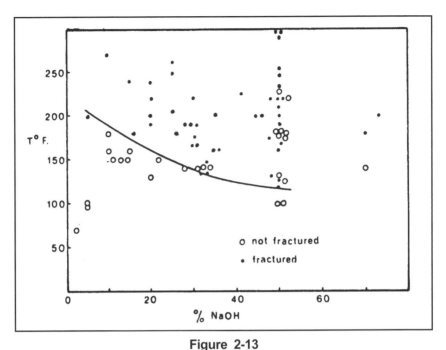

Figure 2-13

Effect of temperature and concentration on cracking of steel in NaOH solutions based on service experience (After Schmidt et al.).

One of the strong cases for the latter viewpoint is the use of applied potentials of either an anodic or cathodic nature during testing. It has been shown that application of a cathodic potential to a specimen cracking by an active path mechanism (stress-corrosion cracking) stops further cracking, while the application tion of an anodic potential accelerates cracking. The reverse was found for those specimens cracking presumably by hydrogen. However, recent work has shown that this method is not always effective and in fact produces rather anomalous results. Therefore, this method is not conclusive in distinguishing stress-corrosion cracking from hydrogen damage mechanisms but illustrates the complexity of these mechanisms.

Another method that has been used for determining which mechanism is operative is examination of the fracture path. A fracture path may be transgranular or intergranular in certain alloy systems in specific environments, and from this, one mechanism can be differentiated from the other; however, more recent work has refuted this method since many factors such as alloy content, microstructure, heat treatment and stress affect the fracture path.

As an example of this and to aid the reader in understanding fracture path, Figures 2-14—2-17 are included. Figure 2-14 is representative of intergranular

Figure 2-14
Intergranular fracture of Type 410 stainless steel bolt subjected to seawater
environment. Magnified 165 times; etched with Villela's reagent.

stress-corrosion cracking as it appears by optical microscopy, displaying a singular crack. Figure 2-15 shows typical branching-type stress corrosion cracking also by optical microscopy. The first example shows 410 stainless steel that cracked in a chloride environment (seawater) while the second shows 304 stainless steel that failed in a zinc bromide completion fluid. Figures 2-16 and 2-17 are included to acquaint the reader with scanning electron micrographs. The first shows an intergranular fracture of 4130 low-alloy steel from hydrogen stress cracking; the second figure shows the same alloy but with a transgranular fracture.

Since there is no consensus on the mechanisms of hydrogen damage and stress-corrosion cracking (SCC) or how to distinguish them readily, hydrogen damage is discussed as a separate environmental cracking mechanism. There is, in fact, good support for this distinction since several phenomena are quite different for the two.

There are many manifestations of hydrogen damage (HD), several of which are common to the oilfield such as sulfide-stress cracking (SSC), hydrogen induced cracking (HIC), blistering, and in special cases, hydriding. More information on the mechanisms involved in these and other forms of hydrogen damage can be found in Volume 13A of the Metals Handbook referenced at the end of this chapter. One of the most common forms of HD in the oilfield is hydrogen-stress crack-

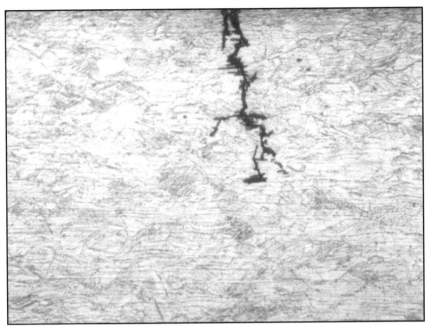

Figure 2-15

Transgranular fracture of a Type 304 stainless steel gravel pack
screen as a result of exposure to $ZnBr_2$ completion fluid.
Etched with oxalic acid; magnified 150 times.

ing (HSC) for which SSC is a special case. HSC is often initiated below the surface
at discontinuities in the metal such as inclusions, grain boundaries, or locations
below a notch that represent a region of high triaxial stress. However, SCC is
always initiated at a surface notch or crevice which is commonly a pit. Thus, susceptibility to SCC is often related to a metal's susceptibility to pitting in an environment, while HSC is a function of the hydrogen absorption characteristics tics
of the metal in the environment. Furthermore, the temperature dependence of
cracking from HSC reaches a maximum around room temperature and is not a
continually escalating function of temperature as is SCC. Figure 2-18 shows this
behavior, which is in stark contrast to that shown in Figure 2-12 for SCC. This figure also demonstrates the effect of how rapidly the specimen is loaded. The minimum in resistance to hydrogen at approximately 25°C (room temperature) has
important ramifications for petroleum production metallurgy (Chapter Four).

Some of the similarities between HSC and SCC are the effects of stress, concentration, alloy composition, and microstructure. The effect of applied stress is
presented in Figure 2-19. This type of curve is commonly referred to as a static
fatigue curve because of its similarity to the fatigue S-N curves; however, in this
case the specimen is subjected to a static load. As in stress-corrosion cracking, the

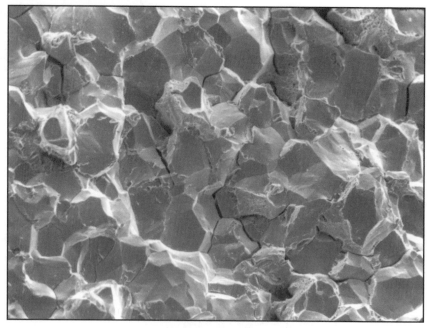

Figure 2-16

Scanning electron micrograph of fracture surface of AISI 4130 low-alloy steel.
Failed in hydrogen, showing intergranular path of fracture magnified 200 times.
Note crystal facets and rock candy appearance.

lower the applied stress, the longer the life to failure; below the threshold stress, failure does not occur.

HSC susceptibility is also a strong function of yield and tensile strength. In general, steels below 80,000 psi yield and 90,000 psi tensile strength are relatively resistant to cracking, although some cases of much lower strength failures have been reported. This threshold is also reported as Rockwell C22, Vickers 248, and Brinell 235. However, this is only a guideline value and not an absolute for design purposes.

As regards HSC, hydrogen ion concentration is the principal component of concern in the environment and when reduced on the surface to hydrogen atoms is absorbed as hydrogen into the metal; thus, pH has a strong influence on HSC. Most corrosion reactions liberate hydrogen at the cathode so that hydrogen is free to either enter the metal or combine to form molecular hydrogen. Some environments such as those containing hydrogen sulfide enhance the ingress of hydrogen by poisoning the hydrogen recombination reaction to molecular hydro gen. The hydrogen molecule is not detrimental to alloys; only the atomic or nascent hydrogen is a problem. Figure 2-20 shows the effect of hydrogen content and tensile strength on the loss in ductility of steel.

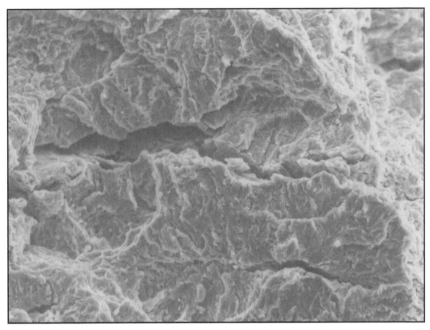

Figure 2-17

Same alloy as Figure 2-16 except showing transgranular fracture.
Magnified 600 times.

Alloy composition is also an important consideration on the behavior of different alloys in the same hydrogen environment. Higher alloying usually imparts greater resistance to hydrogen except when accompanied with increasing strength. For instance, the austenitic stainless steels are typically more resistant than ferrilic steels to HSC except when they are highly cold-worked.

Metallurgical structure also significantly affects the resistance of alloys to HSC. Typically, single-phase structures are more resistant to hydrogen, but there are exceptions such as untempered martensite. In steels at equivalent strength levels, tempered martensite is the most resistant to hydrogen. The bainitic and pearlitic structures have varying degrees of resistance depending on how fine the pearlite is and whether the bainite is upper or lower. Lower bainite is more resistant than upper bainite to HSC. In general, quenched and highly tempered steels are more resistant to HSC than ones that are normalized or normalized and tempered.

Hydrogen-stress cracking and stress-corrosion cracking have become increasingly important considerations with the advent and use of high-strength and high-alloy tubulars for production. These mechanisms will be discussed in greater detail in Chapter Four.

79

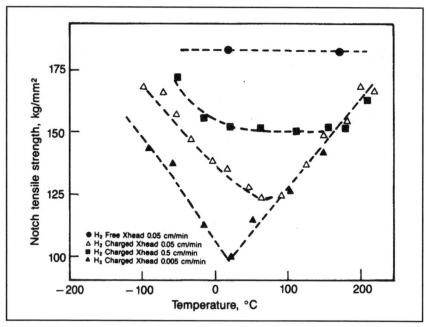

Figure 2-18

Reduction in tensile strength of hydrogen-charged steel as a function of temperature at three different loading rates (After Graville et al.).

Methods of Prevention

The four most common methods of preventing or reducing corrosion in the oilfield are coatings, inhibitors, cathodic protection, and alloying (metallurgy). Since this book is about metallurgy in the oilfield, the first three topics will only briefly be discussed while the fourth will be emphasized in subsequent chapters.

Inorganic, organic or metallic coatings alter the corrosion process by changing the nature of the metal solution interface. Organic and inorganic coatings accomplish this by providing a temporary barrier to the solution/metal reaction interface. It must be remembered that all these coatings are permeable to water, chlorides, hydrogen, and other gases such as carbon dioxide and hydrogen sulfide; thus, coatings represent a temporary although often sufficient solution to corrosion problems.

Metallic coatings are of two basic types: noble and sacrificial. An example of the first is nickel-plated steel. This plate offers a more corrosion-resistant surface in contact with many environments than the steel surface does. However, when the plate is locally removed or damaged by some process such as erosion, a strong galvanic effect may be initiated as a result of the very small anode (steel) and the

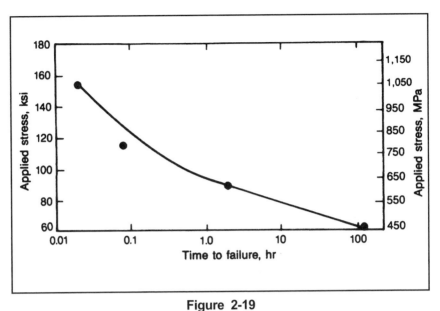

Figure 2-19
Effect of applied stress on hydrogen cracking resistance of 4130 steel.

large cathode (nickel) and may lead to rapid deterioration of the substrate. The second metal coating has already been explained by the example of galvanized steel earlier in this chapter.

Inhibitors represent another method of corrosion control. Inhibitors in this context include any chemical that reduces the tendency for corrosion. Therefore, oxygen scavengers, passivators, biocides, etc., are all included. This method of control is quite complex and discussion of even the fundamentals is not appropriate to this book; however, it represents one of the primary mechanisms for controlling corrosion in the oilfield. Basically, the use of chemicals can alter the corrosion environment by reacting with the corrodents, by forming a transient barrier much as coatings do, or by changing the local potential of the metal surface to a more noble potential, thereby reducing its tendency to corrode in a particular environment.

Cathodic protection involves changing the corrosion cell such that the component that needs protecting becomes the cathode at the expense of another metal, which becomes the anode. The simplest form of cathodic protection involves the direct contact between a metal that must be protected and one that is more active and can be sacrificed. Sacrificial anodes for protecting steel structures are usually alloys of zinc, aluminum, or magnesium. In most water and soil environments, these metals are anodic to steel and, when coupled, will preferentially corrode,

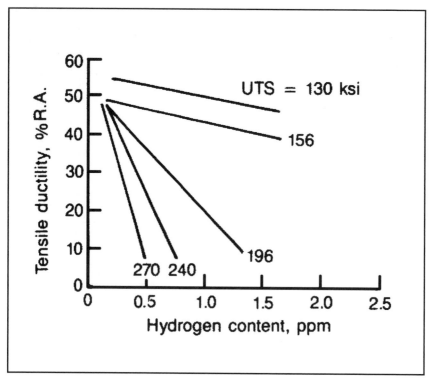

Figure 2-20
Reduction in ductility with increasing hydrogen content and strength
(After Tetelman).

protecting the steel. For environments in which longer protection times are required or more current must be applied than can be supplied by a sacrificial anode such as occurs in soil, an impressed current system may be used. This type of cathodic protection uses a rectifier and anodes that are usually more noble than the steel. The current is driven to the structure from the anode to cause the structure to become cathodic to the anodes.

Cathodic protection systems are widely used for external protection of pipe lines, tanks, well casing, etc. Internal cathodic protection is frequently used in separators and storage tanks.

Materials selection in the form of alloy changes to provide resistance to corrosion is the thrust of this book and will be discussed in detail in remaining chapters. Historically, the drilling and production area of the petroleum industry has not easily adopted metallurgy as a solution to corrosion problems. But with the need to produce oil and gas from more aggressive environments, metallurgical solutions have become more common.

References

ASM International. Metals Handbook, Volume 10, 1975, p. 176.

ASM International, Metals Handbook, Vol 13 A, 2003.

____. "Evaluating Media that Cause Stress-Corrosion Cracking." Metal Progress Data Sheet, Vol. 107 (1975), p. 59.

Betz Handbook of Industrial Water Conditioning, 1976, p. 183.

Bohnenkamp, K. "Caustic Cracking of Mild Steel." Fundamental Aspects of Stress-Corrosion Cracking Houston, Texas: NACE, 1969, p. 374.

Copson, H.R. "Effects of Composition on Stress-Corrosion Cracking of Some Alloys Containing Nickel." Physical Metallurgy of Stress-Corrosion Fracture. New York, New York; Interscience Publishers Inc., 1959.

Craig, B.D., "Fundamental Aspects of Corrosion Films in Corrosion Science," Plenum Press, N.Y. 1991.

Fontana, M.G. Corrosion Engineering New York; McGraw-Hill Book Company, 3rd Edition, 1985.

Graville, B.A.; R.G. Baker; and F. Watkinson. British Welding Journal, 14 (1967), p. 337.

National Association of Corrosion Engineers. Basic Corrosion Course. Eleventh Printing. 1980, pp. 2-7.

Jones, R.H., " Environmental Effects on Engineered Materials" Marcel Dekker, N.Y., 2001

Schmidt, H.W. P.J. Gegner, C. Heinemann, C.F. Pogacar, and E.H. Wyche. Corrosion, 7 (1951), p. 295.

Stolica, N.D. "Pitting Corrosion on Fe-Cr and Fe-Cr-Ni Alloys." Corrosion Science, 9 (1969), p. 455.

Telelman, A.S. "Recent Developments in Classical (Internal) Hydrogen Embrittlement." Hydrogen in Metals. ASM, 1973, p. 17.

Uhlig, H.H. Corrosion and Corrosion Control. New York, New York: John Wiley and Sons Inc.,1967.

3

METALLURGY IN DRILLING

A multitude of special tools and equipment used in drilling oil and gas wells utilize many different alloys. The metallurgy of this equipment has evolved over many years and is often proprietary and therefore not readily available from the literature or the manufacturer. This chapter will present information on the more common equipment used in rotary drilling such as drillpipe, tool joints, drill collars, and blowout preventers (BOP).

Even limiting the discussion to these components presents a broad array of manufacturers' preferences for materials. Therefore, the examples presented do not provide a complete analysis of all of the alloys being used for a specific component; rather, they represent the most common alloy selection and some of the reasons for these choices.

Metallurgy of Drilling Equipment

The emphasis in drilling equipment is on pressure containment and fracture resistance—the latter concerning low-temperature fracture of surface equipment, fatigue of subsurface components, and sulfide-stress cracking (SSC) for both surface and subsurface equipment. Fine grain size and a quenched and tempered martensitic microstructure offer the greatest resistance to fracture and the highest strength for pressure containment. Thus, most equipment metallurgy is selected

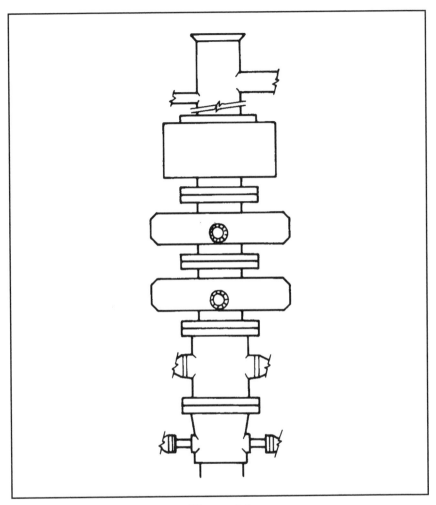

Figure 3-1
Typical BOP stack arrangement for drilling.

with these features in mind. This, of course, requires adequate hardenability for components that are constructed of heavy sections. Some of these are on the order of 6 in. or greater in wall thickness and several tons of mass. Therefore, it is quite common to use 4100 and 4300 series alloys because of their good hardenability, but to keep the carbon content as low as possible from a weldability standpoint since some weld repair is likely on most cast components.

Pressure control at the surface during drilling or workovers is attained using blowout preventers (BOP). A typical BOP stack (see Fig. 3-1) consists of a spherical or annular preventer, ram preventers, a drilling spool, and a casinghead.

85

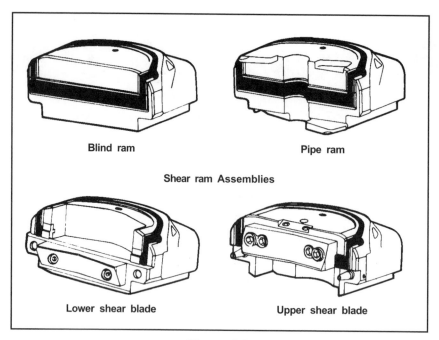

Figure 3-2

Blind, pipe, and shear rams used in ram-type BOP (courtesy Hydril Company).

The spherical preventer seals around the outside of the kelly, tool joint, or drillpipe in the bore or can be closed on an open hole. Sealing is accomplished using elastomeric material. The operating cylinder, which moves the sealing material, typically is made of quenched and tempered 4130 steel. The body of the preventer is usually cast or forged low-alloy steel such as AISI 4130 or 4140.

There are three basic types of ram preventers: shear, blind, and pipe. Since ram bodies are universal, only the rams are changed to comply with the size pipe being run. These bodies are most often made of low-alloy cast or forged steel of the 4130 type. The different types of rams are shown in Figure 3-2. Shear rams are used to shear the pipe completely, sealing off the annulus and the drillpipe. To achieve this shearing quickly and easily, which may entail shearing the high strength tool joint (190,000 psi minimum tensile strength), the shear blades are made of 4340, 4140, or 2 1/4 Cr-1 Mo steel quenched and tempered to a hardness of Rockwell C 45. Blind rams are used to seal off an open hole with no pipe in it, and pipe rams seal around pipe in the hole to isolate the annulus. Since shearing is not necessary on these rams, the hardness levels can be reduced but still may exceed the NACE International requirements for resistance to sulfide stress cracking. Pistons that drive the rams are usually made of quenched and tempered 4140 or 4340 steel.

Table 3-1

API Material Application Pressure Containing Members

Part	2000	3000	5000	10,000	15,000	20,000
			Pressure Ratings (psi)			
			API Material Designation			
Body	36K. 45K. 60K. 75K.	36K. 45K. 60K. 75K.	36K. 45K. 60K. 75K.	36K. 45K. 60K. 75K.	45K. 60K. 75K.	60K. 75K
Integral End Connection	60K	60K	60K	60K	75K	75K
Blind Flange	60K	60K	60K	60K	75K	75K
Blind Hub	60K	60K	60K	60K	75K	75K

(courtesy API)

Materials for different components of these BOPs are specified by the API in API Specification 16A (ISO 13533), "Drill Through Equipment," and Specification 6A: Wellhead Equipment. Table 3-1 shows that the type of material used is dependent on the working pressure of the equipment. The different types of material are shown in Table 3-2. The carbon and low-alloy steel compositions cover common alloys of construction such as 4130, 4140, 8620, 8630, and 2 1/4 Cr-l Mo. The martensitic stainless steels cover AISI 410, F6NM and CA6NM.

Table 3-2

Steel Composition Limits (WT%) Material for Pressure Containing Members

Carbon and Alloying Elements	Martensitic Low Alloy Steels Composition Limits	Stainless Steels Composition Limits
Carbon	0.45 Max	0.15 Max
Manganese	1.80 Max	1.00 Max
Silicon	1.00 Max	1.50 Max
Phosphorus	0.04 Max	0.04 Max
Sulfur	0.04 Max	0.04 Max
Nickel	1.00 Max	4.50 Max
Chromium	2.75 Max	1 00-14.0
Molybdenum	1.50 Max	1.00 Max
Vanadium	0.30 Max	NA

(courtesy API)

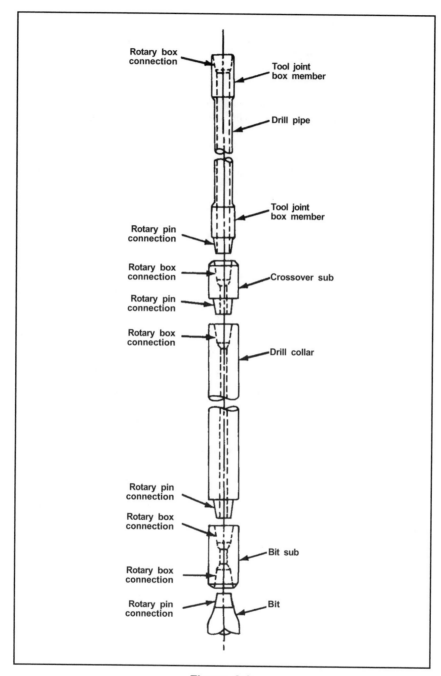

Figure 3-3
Typical drillstem assembly (from API Specification 7).

Bolting on preventers is covered by API "Recommended Practice 53" and, depending on whether the flange type is 6B or 6BX, the nuts are made of ASTM A 194 Grade 1 or 2H, respectively. In both cases, the bolts are made of either ASTM A 193 Grade B and/or A 354 Grade BC.

All material for BOPs must have a minimum average Charpy impact value of 15.0 ft-lb for a set of three full-sized specimens with a minimum of 10.0 ft-lb for any one specimen of the set. It is required for the user to specify a temperature, 0°F, -20°F, or -75°F, at which these values are required to be met.

In cases where an environment containing hydrogen sulfide is anticipated, the maximum hardness for the preventer bodies is HRC 22, and all flange and bonnet bolts should be made of ASTM A 193 Grade B-7M with a hardness of HRC 22 or less and nuts to ASTM A 194 Grade 2M, according to API RP53. API 6A also allows Monel K500 studs in the hot-rolled and age-hardened condition to a maximum hardness of HRC 35 and ASTM A 453 Grade 660 (A 286) solution treated and age-hardened to HRC 35 maximum for both bolts and nuts.

Flanges can be made from ASTM A 105 forgings, A 216-WCB castings, or API Type 2 or Type 4 material.

The drilling spool and casinghead are often made from line pipe specified in API 5L, or from casing specified in API 5CT. The mechanical properties of these items are matched to those of the preventers and casing. Sometimes casingheads are constructed of 4130 or ASTM A 487-9Q steel and are quenched and tempered when special environments such as hydrogen sulfide or low temperature require specific properties. For sulfide-containing environments, controlled hardness to HRC 22 maximum is required. In the case of low-temperature service, notch toughness is enhanced by quenching and tempering.

The drillstem, which is shown in Figure 3-3, is probably the most studied assembly in drilling. Tool joints, drill collars, subs, and drillpipe form the basis of the remaining discussion in this chapter. Drill bits are not discussed because they represent a very specialized component for which little choice in material selection by the user is available.

Tool joints are the end connections of drillpipe and are made by forging. The final heat-treated joint, which is quenched and tempered, is friction-welded, inertia-welded or flash-welded to the pipe body. In friction welding and inertia welding, the pipe is held stationary while the tool joint is rotated onto the pipe body; the resulting contact pressure causes temperature elevation with subsequent welding. For flash welding, both the pipe and the tool joint remain stationary while an electrical current is impressed across the joint. Heat is generated by electric resistance at the interface and welding results. After both processes, postweld heat treatment is applied to the weld zone to improve uniformity of structure and properties. This heat treatment can take the form of a simple high-temperature stress relief, or by induction-heating the weld-heat-affected zone, liquid quench (usually with water), then induction-temper. Historically, these welds have been quite sound with relatively few failures. However, failures of the tool-joint weld have been observed.

Tool-joint material is commonly AISI 4100-series low-alloy steel, usually 4135-4140, although 4145H is also used. For heavy-wall drill pipe, AISI 1340 tool joints are often used. Molybdenum and niobium modified 41XX Steels are often used for their greater resistance to cracking in hydrogen sulfide environments. Tool joints are normally quenched and tempered to a hardness of 30-37 Rockwell C, resulting in yield strengths of 120-150 ksi. Tempering is performed for 2 hr at 1,100-1,200°F. API Specification 7, section 4, requires a minimum yield strength of 120,000 psi, a minimum tensile strength of 140,000 psi, and a minimum elongation of 13% for all new tool joints of all sizes. The yield strength is measured by the 0.2% offset method in comparison to the 0.5% extension method used for tubulars. Small joints that do not provide for easy tensile-specimen removal can be Brinell tested. A minimum Brinell hardness number (HB) of 285 is acceptable on both the box and the pin.

Drill collars are also made of 4135-4140 or 4145H steel quenched and tempered to a hardness range of 285-341 BHN. Drill collars are used to add weight to the string and to keep it in tension so the effects of fatigue are minimized. Minimum tensile requirements for drill collars in API Specification 7 are for OD ranges of 3-1/8 – 6-7/8 in. The yield is 110,000 psi, tensile strength is 140,000 psi and the elongation is 13%; for 7-10 in. OD collars, the yield is 100,000 psi, tensile strength is 135,000 psi, and minimum elongation is 13%. Similar to tool joints, the yield is measured by the 0.2% offset method.

Nonmagnetic drill collars are placed in a string during directional drilling to help determine the actual location of the string and bit. These collars are made from a variety of alloys, the most common of which are Monel K500, 316L austenitic stainless steel, several other austenitic stainless steels and beryllium copper. Austenitic stainless steel collars have failed in drilling environments from chloride stress corrosion cracking reportedly by high residual stresses from manufacturing or sensitization of the collar. Care should be taken when using austenitic stainless steel collars in hot brine drilling fluids.

Drilling jars, stabilizers, subs and, quite often, core barrels are made from 4140 or 414511 steel and heat-treated as described for drill collars and tool joints. Sometimes AISI 4340 or 4340H steel is used for the metallurgy of these items and it too is quenched and tempered, typically to the same or higher hardness level.

Drillpipe is the last part of the drillstem mentioned here but is far from the least. In terms of research and manufacturing, this component represents the most-studied component and often the area of greatest trouble in drilling.

The various grades of drillpipe, according to the API 5D (ISO 11961), are shown in Table 3-3. Steels used for drillpipe are of the C-Mn or Cr-Mo type, the latter being 4100 series steel. Also, to a lesser degree, aluminum drillpipe is used, which is typically Type 2014, an aluminum-copper alloy. The steels are provided in the normalized and tempered or quenched and tempered condition, while the aluminum pipe is heat-treated to the T6 condition.

Table 3-3

API Requirements for Drillpipe*

Grade	Yield Strength, ksi (MPa)		Tensile Strength, ksi (MPa)	Chemistry %		Heat Treatment**
	min.	max.	min.	P (max)	S (max)	
E	75 (517)	105 (724)	100 (689)	0.030	0.030	Heat Treated
X-95	95 (655)	125 (862)	105 (724)	0.030	0.030	O&T/N&T
G-105	105 (724)	135 (931)	115 (793)	0.030	0.030	Q&T/N&T
S-135	135 (931)	165 (1,138)	145 (1,000)	0.030	0.030	Q&T/N&T

* Elongation requirements depend on pipe thickness and therefore are not shown
**Q&T—quenched and tempered
N&T—normalized and tempered
(From API Specification 5D)

Grades X, G and S are required to meet minimum Charpy impact toughness of 40 ft-lbs. (54 Joules) for an average of three specimens and no single value less than 35 ft-lbs. (47 Joules) for full size specimens tested at 70°F (21°C). Subsized specimens are appropriately derated. The reasons for these Charpy requirements are discussed later in this chapter.

Under the requirements of API Specification 5D, drillpipe can only be seamless pipe and must be heat-treated full length, or re-heat-treated if upset. Heat treatment for high-strength series drillpipe is specified as either quenched and tempered or normalized and tempered. The only chemical composition requirements are that the phosphorus and sulfur contents not exceed 0.030% each.

Grade E drillpipe is normalized or normalized and tempered and has a chemistry similar to 1041 or 1045 steel modified with about 1.5%Mn and 0.2% Mo. Grades G, and S are usually quenched and tempered. Grade X is typically normalized and tempered and has a chemistry range of 0.20-0.30%C, 1.20-1.50%Mn, 0.4-0.6%Cr, and 0.2-0.5% Mo. Grade G has a chemistry similar to X, while S-135 is typically 0.27-0.35%C, 1.50-1.60%Mn, 0.1-0.5%Cr, 0.3-0.4% Mo, and 0.012-0.016%V. Heavy-wall drillpipe is made from 4140 and 4145H quenched and tempered steel. Rockwell C hardness of the various grades ranges from 20-28 for Grade E, 27-30 for X-95, 30-34 for Grade G, and 34-37 for S-135.

Aluminum drillpipe as mentioned is frequently made of Type 2014 aluminum, which has the composition 0.5-1.2% si, 1.% Fe max, 3.9-5.0% cu, 0.4-1.2% Mn, 0.2-0.8% Mg, 0.10% Cr max, 0.25% Zn max, and 0.05% Ti max. Typical mechanical properties when heat-treated to the T6 condition are 64 ksi tensile strength, 58 ksi yield strength, 7% elongation, and a HB of 135. Aluminum drillpipe usually comes with steel tool joints that are threaded on to ensure maximum joint strength that cannot be attained with aluminum tool joints.

Titanium drill pipe is available on a limited basis but some manufacturer's use steel tool joints to avoid galling and wear problems. The steel tool joints are threaded on and shrunk fit to the Ti tube. The reason the Ti drill pipe is considered is because of its high strength to weight ratio compared to steel and its low elastic modulus. The low elastic modulus (approximately 1/2 of steel) means the Ti drill pipe is significantly more flexible than steel and thus more suitable for extended reach drilling and horizontal drilling. The most common alloy used is Ti-6AL-4V at a yield strength of 120,000 psi.

Aluminum drill pipe and titanium drill pipe are not covered by API or ISO standards.

ISO 10407 is the International Standards Organization (ISO) standard that replaces API RP7G and ISO 11961 replaces API Spec 5D. Other standards that address drill string components are the NORSOK Standards of which M-702 addresses drill string materials, components and the Industry Recommended Practices (IRP) Drill Pipe Committee of Canada. IRP for Critical Sour Drilling is a specification for drill string design and metallurgy for sour well drilling, while IRP6, Critical Sour Underbalanced Drilling, provides more stringent requirements for string design and metallurgy when underbalanced drilling is to be applied.

Causes and Prevention of Drilling Equipment Failures

Reports in the literature of BOP failures are rare, probably for two reasons. First, since these units represent the primary method of preventing potential blowouts with an uncontrolled kick in a well, they must be over designed and of good structural integrity. Second, fewer failures occur on surface equipment compared with the drillstem, which sees more severe environments in terms of corrosion and complexity of stress state. However, sulfide stress cracking (SSC) and brittle fracture of blowout preventer bolts has been reported in the past. For the most part, these were documented as being out of specification as far as API and NACE requirements.

Tool joints and drillpipe represent the area of greatest concentration over the past several decades, and thus, more is known and documented about their behavior. The first in-depth paper on this subject, "Causes and Prevention of Drill-Pipe and Tool-Joint Troubles," was written by R.S. Grant and H.G. Texter. This paper was last revised in 1948. No other comprehensive work on this subject has since been published, although other papers dealing with specific types of failures have been written. To introduce this multifaceted subject, purely mechanical failures will be dealt with before the actual drilling environment.

The stresses on a drillstring that is rotating during drilling—often in a deviated hole—are basically fourfold, three of which are shown schematically in Figure 3-4. There is a tension load caused by hook loads (weight of the pipe) and from the drill collars at the bottom of the hole. Depending on the number of drill collars used and the weight of the drilling mud, which adds buoyancy to the string, part of the drillstring will be in compression. The point at which the string

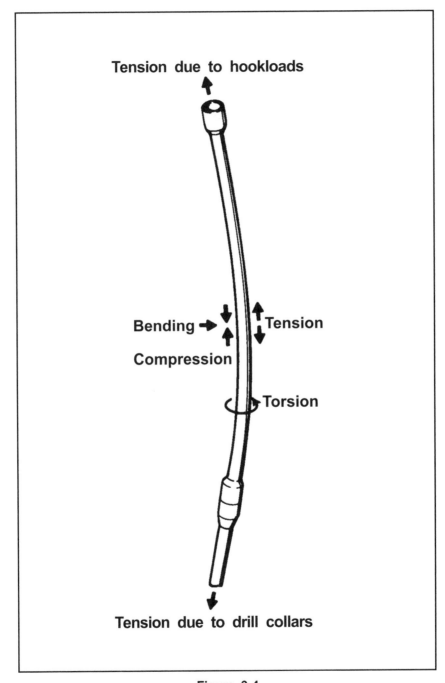

Figure 3-4
Three major stress conditions on drillstem: bending, torsion, and tension.

Figure 3-5
Drillpipe failure from tensile overload (after Grand and Texter).

changes from tension to compression is called the neutral point. Since drilling in compression decreases the life of the string faster than drilling in tension, the drill-collar weight is designed to move the neutral point as low in the hole as possible, allowing the largest portion of the string to be in tension. Bending stresses caused by drilling in a deviated hole cause cyclic compression and tension as the pipe rotates, alternating these two stress states. Finally, there is a torsional stress caused by rotation of the pipe when the bit is cutting into the formation. The fourth stress, not shown in Figure 3-4, is caused by vibration of the drillstem. This stress is difficult to quantitate and extremely complex. Vibration analysis is beyond the scope of this book, however, vibration can lead to fatigue failures of the drill string.

Twistoff is the mechanical failure of the pipe in torsion caused simply by overstressing the pipe; however, this term is often misused for any drillpipe failure that results in complete fracture of the pipe. Twistoff is more commonly used to describe fatigue failures. Torsional failure is rare but will occur if the bit becomes stuck and the rotary table continues to turn.

A more common failure than twistoff is tensile failure. This failure occurs when the pipe is pulled in two because of excessive stress on it. This happens most often when pipe is stuck in the hole and the drilling crew tries to pull on the pipe without monitoring the weight indicator. Pure tension failures are easily distinguished by the necking down (reduction) of the wall at the point of failure. The fracture will be circumferential and will produce a 45° angle along most of the surface. The OD of the pipe near the fracture will also have been reduced substantially. These features are shown in Figure 3-5.

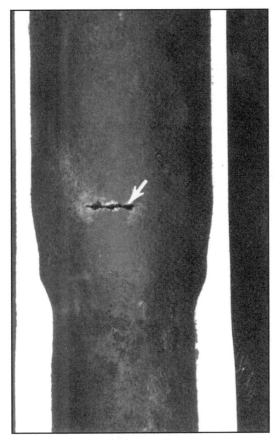

Figure 3-6
View of a washout (arrow) near the upset runout on the inside of the drillpipe.

Fatigue is the most common cause of failure in drillpipe and is variously called washout or twistoff in the field, depending on the appearance of the failure. A fatigue crack that has initiated in the pipe in the transverse direction, allowing drilling fluids to penetrate the wall and cutting out a hole, is called a washout. Figure 3-6 shows an example of a washout in drillpipe looking at the inside surface. If the fatigue crack propagates rapidly and the pipe parts, the failure is referred to as twistoff (see Fig. 3-7). Both of these terms are misnomers but remain part of the oilfield jargon but, in fact, are both the result of fatigue. Recently, it has been demonstrated that one of the primary reasons why drillpipe either parts or washes out is due to the fracture toughness of the pipe. Higher fracture toughness measured by Charpy impact produces washout whereas lower toughness causes twistoff. Figure 3-8 shows Charpy impact data of field samples for Grades E and X and also tool joints. It was determined from this work that a minimum Charpy impact of 40 ft-lbs at 75°F was sufficient to prevent twistoffs. The advantage of a

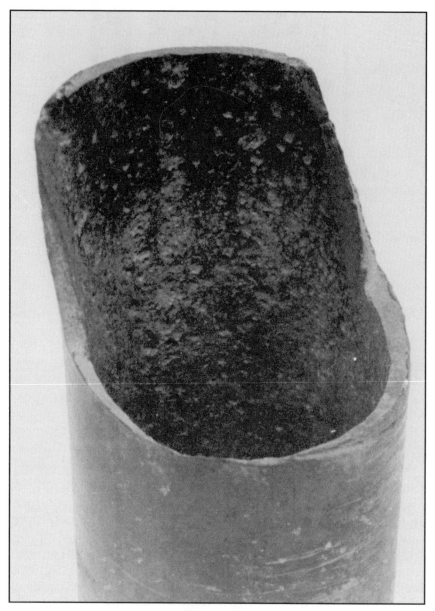

Figure 3-7
Corrosion-fatigue (twistoff) of drillpipe caused by internal pitting.

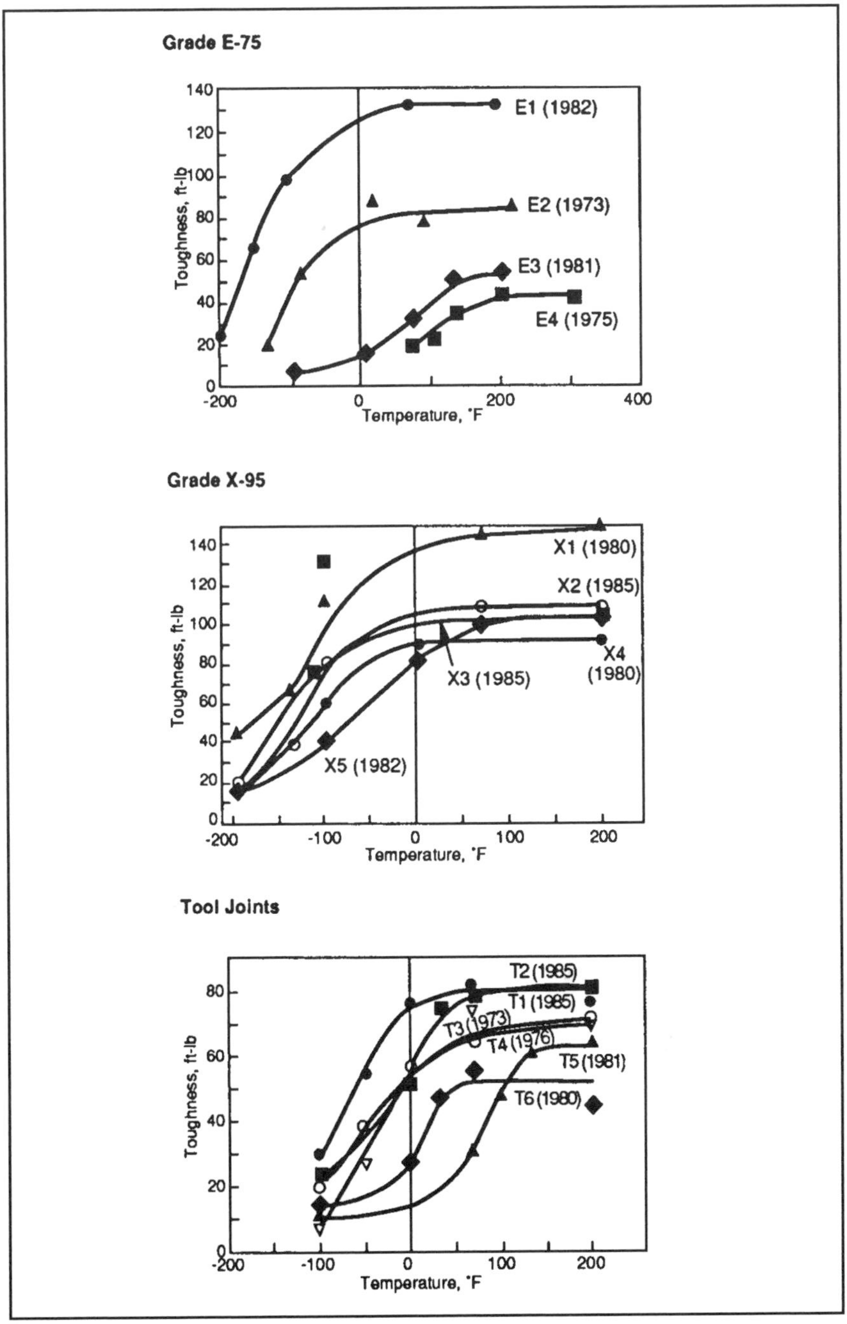

Figure 3-8
Charpy impact behavior of Grades E and X drillpipe and tool joints
(After Buscemi et al.).

97

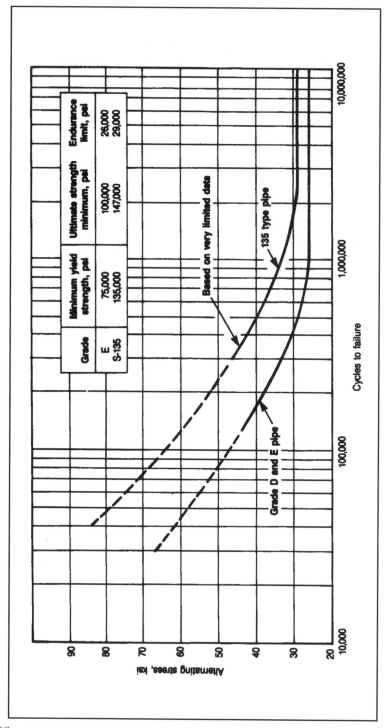

Figure 3-9

S-N curves for Grade E and Grade S-135 drillpipe; obtained by cyclic-bend full-scale test samples (after Mehdizadeh).

washout over a twistoff is the shorter time required for tripping a string rather than fishing for a twistoff. It is because of this work that the API and ISO standards included requirements for minimum Charpy toughness of the higher strength drill pipe grades.

There are three types of fatigue: pure fatigue, notch fatigue, and corrosion fatigue. Often, these types are not distinct since corrosion fatigue is initiated at pits that provide a notch for fatigue crack initiation. Furthermore, it is now well established that pure fatigue begins by micronotch formation within the metal. However, for discussion's sake each type will be described.

Pure fatigue was discussed in Chapter One and does not occur to any extent in the oilfield. What should be kept in mind is that fatigue damage is cumulative, and as such what appears to be good pipe after several holes may be close to crack initiation and failure. In fact, as Grant and Texter mention, drillpipe rotating at 100 rpm for just 10 days will have more than 1 million cycles imposed on it. In deep wells drilling time can run from months to more than 1 yr, imposing millions of stress cycles on a drillstring.

As discussed in Chapter One, the fatigue limit or endurance limit is, as a rule of thumb, 1/2 the tensile strength. Thus, it is commonly held that increasing the strength of a component will increase its fatigue strength. Figure 3-9 shows this to be true, but it is not practically significant. The tensile strength is increased almost 50%, while the endurance limit is increased only about 10%.

Fatigue strength is reduced in the presence of a notch, as shown in Figure 3-10. Notches act to raise the stress locally, often beyond the yield strength of the material. The effect of a notch is a function of its sharpness and orientation to the applied stress. Sharper notches increase the stress ahead of the notch root, making crack initiation easier than does a blunt notch. The depth of the notch is also a factor in fatigue life because deeper notches significantly reduce fatigue life in comparison to a shallow score mark. Slips or tongs are the most frequent causes of notches in drillpipe and often lead to fatigue failure, which initiates from the external surface of the pipe at the root of the notch.

Similar to notches, a rapid change in cross section from a heavy cross section to a thin cross section can lead to reduced fatigue life. Numerous drillpipe failures plagued the worldwide drilling industry in the mid-1980s with no obvious explanation. The fatigue failures were originating in the transition area of the internal upset where the drillpipe makes a transition from the tool joint upset (heavy section) to the drillpipe body (thin section). Subsequent research established that a short internal taper length, M_{iu}, decreased the fatigue life whereas a long generous taper increased the fatigue life. While finite element modeling and fatigue testing are required to determine the optimum length of M_{iu} for each size of drillpipe, Figure 3-11 shows the benefit of adequate internal upset length on the fatigue life of 5 inch IEU, 19.50 pound per foot Grade E drillpipe. A minimum M_{iu} of 80mm is most often specified but longer internal tapers in excess of 80mm have been shown to further increase the fatigue life.

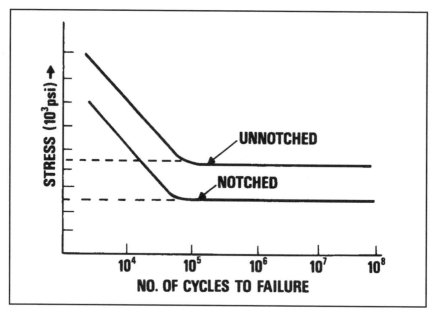

Figure 3-10
Effect of notches on fatigue resistance in steels.

Corrosion fatigue is the leading cause of drillpipe failure. This kind of failure is the result of the combined effects of a notch formed by a corrosion pit, which acts as a stress concentration, and fatigue, that is also assisted by the corrosive environment. As shown in Figure 2-8 in a corrosive environment the S-N curve has a distinct slope rather than an endurance limit, and failure will ultimately occur when the requisite number of cycles are attained. As in the case of notch fatigue, the sharper the notch (pit) bottom, the more severe the stress concentration and the shorter the fatigue life. This emphasizes the concept that corrosion fatigue is most often encountered in pitting environments. Since dissolved oxygen, chlorides, hydrogen sulfide, and carbon dioxide all promote pitting, it is easy to understand why drillpipe fails by this mechanism. As Grant and Texter showed for drillpipe

Table 3-4
Corrosion Fatigue of Drillpipe

Average Maximum Stress (psi)	Medium	Cycles to Failure (10^6)
31.500	Noncorrosive (air or distilled water)	2.20
31,500	Mildly corrosive (saltwater)	1.43
31.500	Corrosive (magnesium chloride)	0.86
31,500	Very corrosive (dilute HCl acid)	0.18

(After Grant and Texter)

100

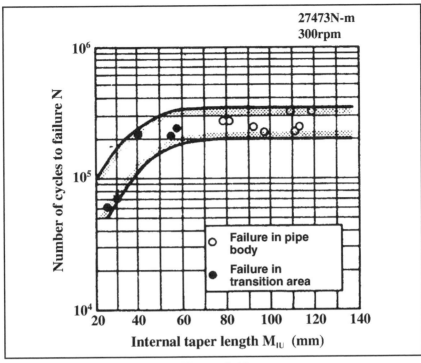

Figure 3-11

Effect of internal taper length on fatigue life of Grade E drillpipe
(after Tsukano et al.).

samples tested in bending fatigue, the number of cycles to failure diminished rapidly with the increasing severity of the environment (see Table 3-4). Another view of this effect of environment is presented in Table 3-5 from work by Mehdizadeh in which the affect of dissolved gases in saltwater on fatigue is described.

Table 3-5

Corrosion Fatigue of Drillpipe

Dissolved Gas in Saltwater	% Decrease from Air Endurance Limit
H_2S	20
CO_2	41
CO_2 + Air	41
H_2S + Air	48
H_2S + CO_2	62
Aerated Saltwater	65

(After Mehdizadeh)

As discussed earlier, an example of corrosion fatigue is shown in Figure 3-7. The long, flat surface at the top of the pipe is the site where fatigue cracking occurred. The cracking was initiated by a large pit on the inside surface at the center of the fatigue-cracked region. After enough cross-sectional area of the pipe had been cracked, the remaining portion was not sufficient to support the tensile load, so final fracture of the remaining pipe wall resulted from simple tensile overload. A similar kind of fatigue fracture can occur from the outside if corrosion or erosion from cuttings in the mud allow pitting to progress to the extent necessary for fatigue crack initiation.

The greatest advantage of the drilling process over petroleum production is the ability to alter the environment (i.e., the drilling mud) and reduce potential problems created by the environment. By the use of chemical inhibitors and scavengers, corrosion can be reduced substantially, increasing the fatigue life of the drillstring. Quite often, simple pH control can extend the service life of a drillstring. This enhancement by pH control is shown in Figure 3-12. Increasing pH from 6.6, which is characteristic of most oilfield waters, to 12.1 and 13.0 restores the threshold or endurance limit in an aerated saltwater solution. By removing dissolved oxygen in drilling muds, pHs of 10-11 are normally sufficient to regain the greater portion of fatigue life.

At present, there are essentially no practical metallurgical solutions to corrosion fatigue. Most remedies are plastic coating the drillpipe and/or chemically treating the mud to reduce corrosion. Increasing the strength of the pipe does not significantly increase the fatigue strength, as shown in Figure 3-9, and in fact can lead to other problems when associated with hydrogen sulfide. Aluminum and titanium drillpipe offer metallurgical alternatives and will be discussed later.

In the presence of hydrogen sulfide, high-strength drillpipe can fail by a hydrogen-stress cracking mechanism referred to as sulfide-stress cracking (SSC). This form of failure is caused by the absorption of hydrogen into the metal from the corrosion reaction of steel and wet hydrogen sulfide. While the actual mechanism of cracking is in much dispute, the parameters that govern susceptibility to SSC are well documented. These factors are strength, applied stress, pH, H_2S concentration, temperature, and microstructure.

Increasing strength and applied stress increase SSC susceptibility as do decreasing temperature and pH. The best microstructure for resistance to SSC at comparable strength levels is highly tempered martensite, while the least-resistant is a normalized structure.

As expected, S-135 pipe is quite susceptible to SSC, while X-95 pipe can be used when the drilling mud is treated to remove hydrogen sulfide. In high concentrations of hydrogen sulfide in which scavenging may not be completely effective, the lower grades, E and X, are best. Since SSC resistance of steels reaches a minimum at or near 25°C, the greatest problem with cracking occurs at the top of the

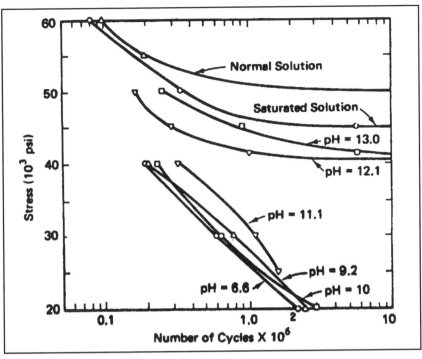

Figure 3-12

Effect of pH on corrosion fatigue in aerated saltwater (after McGlasson).

hole where high-strength pipe is most often run. To reduce this problem, tapered strings can be used to reduce the load on the top of the string, and thicker wall pipe can be run at the top to reduce the applied stress. Since X 95 steel has a hardness of 27-30 HRC and is often quenched and tempered, it usually stands a much better chance of resisting SSC than the higher-strength G 105 and S-135 steels. Figure 3-13 shows a typical SSC failure of S-135 pipe with the characteristic brittle fracture and the final ductile-shear lip. One very important consideration that is frequently ignored or forgotten is the high hardness of the tool joints. All the tool joints are of the same hardness which is essentially equivalent to S-135 drillpipe. Therefore, using lower strength drillpipe only reduces the potential of cracking of the pipe body not the tool joints. It is quite common in low strength drillpipe (E and X) for the tool joint pins to fail from SSC because they are the most highly stressed. Steel tool joints in general are particularly susceptible to SSC because of their higher strength. Most often pin failures occur where a fracture follows the circumference of the joint around the root of the last engaged thread. This region represents both the highest-applied stress and a stress concentration caused by the thread itself. Stress calculations and measurements have shown that the stress at the last engaged thread can achieve or exceed the yield

103

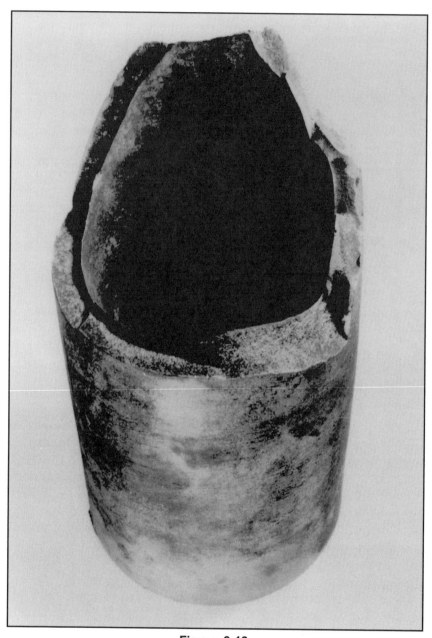

Figure 3-13
Sulfide stress cracking failure of S-135 drillpipe
(courtesy of G. Garwood).

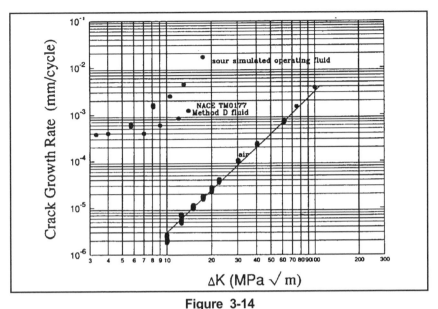

Figure 3-14
Fatigue crack growth rate in air (line) and in sour solution (after Hatcher and Szklarz).

strength. Although the boxes fail less frequently, they can be subjected to high hoop stresses; thus, cracking in the box typically occurs in a longitudinal direction. Drill collars fail in the same fashion as tool joints but less frequently since the applied stresses are lower from running on the bottom of the string.

Although hydrogen sulfide is most often derived from the reservoir, degradation of certain drilling muds can also produce hydrogen sulfide, thus contributing to SSC. Table 3-6 demonstrates the potential problems using lignosulfonate muds at high temperatures. Accompanying data to that in Table 3-6 by the same authors show that, even in high pH (>12.0) lignosulfonate mud, sulfide could be evolved because of decomposition of the mud (see Table 3-7). This decomposition tion has also been responsible for SSC failures of high strength casing when the mud was used as a packer fluid.

In addition to the potential for sulfide stress cracking when drill pipe and tool joints are exposed to H_2S, the fatigue performance of these components is diminished in the presence of H_2S but not only from corrosion, as previously discussed for H_2S, CO_2 and O_2, but due to the acceleration of the fatigue crack from dissolved hydrogen in the steel. Figure 3-14 shows the fatigue crack growth rate of steel drill pipe in the absence of H_2S and in the presence of H_2S. The faster crack growth rate is attributable to hydrogen assisted crack growth. Thus once fatigue crack initiation occurs in a sour environment the propagation rate will be much higher (several orders of magnitude) than in a drilling environment that does not contain H_2S.

105

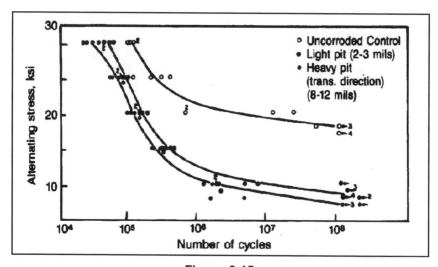

Figure 3-15

Effect of corrosion pitting on bending-fatigue properties of 2014-T6 sheet steel (after Person).

Table 3-6

Thermal Degradation of Lignosulfonates at High Pressures.

Lignosulfonate Solution*	A	B	C
Temperature (°F)	450	405	425
Pressure (psi)	12,000	10,000	10,000
Initial pH	8.3	8.5	8.3
Final pH	6.1	5.9	5.9
H2S (ppm)	15	2.5	20
Aging time (days)	16	16	16

* Solutions contained 10 parts per billion (ppb) lignosulfonate solubilized in a 0.43 ppb caustic soda solution. (After Bush et al.)

Table 3-7

Thermal Degradation of Lignosulfonates in High-pH Solutions.

Lignosulfonate Solution*	A	B	C
Temperature (°F)	375	375	375
Pressure (psi)	300	300	300
Initial pH	12.6	12.8	12.6
Final pH	8.1	8.2	9.1
H2S (ppm)	15	25	2.5
Aging time (days)	7	7	7

* Solutions contained 10 ppb lignosulfonate solubilized In 2 ppb caustic soda solution. (After Bush et al.)

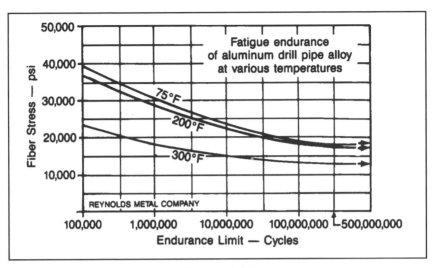

Figure 3-16
Fatigue strength of aluminum drillpipe at elevated temperatures
(after Boice and Dalrymple, © 1963, SPE).

One metallurgical alternative to steel that has not gained wide use in the industry, despite certain advantages over carbon and low-alloy steel pipe, is aluminum drillpipe. One of its chief advantages is its lighter weight, which allows for deeper drilling with a mixed string. Although the yield strength (58,000 psi) and tensile strength (64,000 psi) of 2014-T6 aluminum are below that for Grade E drillpipe, these factors have been overcome by using thick wall sections. From a bending-fatigue standpoint, comparing steel and aluminum loaded to the same deflections, the aluminum pipe can have a fatigue life significantly greater than steel. Aluminum is also more resistant to H_2S and CO_2 corrosion than steel pipe.

One of several disadvantages of aluminum drillpipe is its low resistance to muds with pH in excess of 10.5; increasing pH above this can cause serious corrosion. Chlorides can cause severe pitting, and as shown in Figure 3-15 can cause loss in fatigue resistance at levels greater than 180,000 ppm in salt muds. The endurance limit in this example has been reduced by more than 50%. Moreover, laboratory testing has confirmed that aluminum drillpipe is susceptible to stress-corrosion cracking in oxygenated brine muds even though in practice SCC has not been reported.

Another factor in the use of aluminum drillpipe is its behavior at elevated temperatures. Its fatigue strength is greatly reduced at temperatures of 300°F and greater (see Figure 3-16), so it is not recommended for long-term service above 250°F. However, this drawback is circumvented by using aluminum pipe in the top of the hole and steel pipe at the bottom of the hole, where the temperature is higher. Of course the static bottom-hole temperature is not the governing factor

107

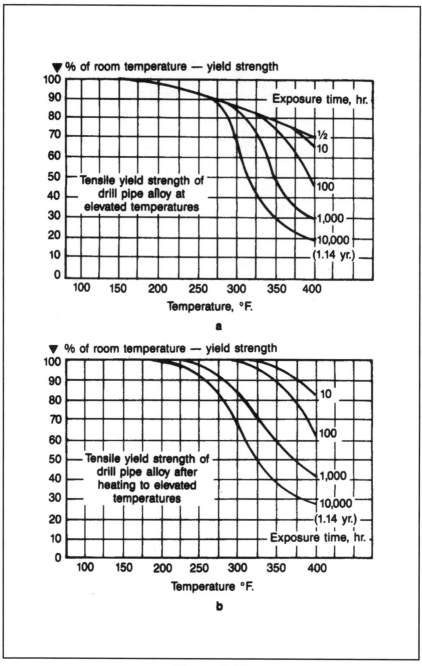

Figure 3-17

Yield strength of aluminum drillpipe (a) at elevated temperatures and
(b) after exposure to elevated temperature (after McGhee).

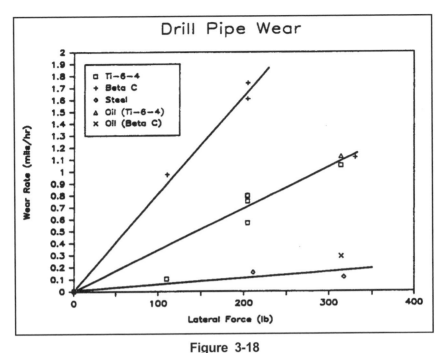

Figure 3-18

Titanium and steel drillpipe wear as a function of lateral force against
P-110 casing in water-base and oil-base mud.

during drilling since mud flow will create a certain degree of cooling, so circulating temperature is an important consideration on temperature limitations. Figure 3-17 shows how the yield strength is reduced when tested at high temperatures and at room temperature after exposure to high temperature.

Another problem with aluminum pipe is its lower abrasion resistance compared to steel drillpipe. Because of its lower strength and therefore hardness, aluminum does not resist abrasion or erosion from drill cuttings in the mud as well as steel pipe. This problem can be alleviated somewhat by reducing the solids content of the mud; however, wear against casing can still be a problem.

Steel tool joints present another area of concern because of the galvanic corrosion problem they present and because their threaded joint has a tendency to unscrew during drilling. Both problems have been encountered in practice.

Titanium drillpipe represents another metallurgical alternative to steel and aluminum drillpipe. Titanium has been considered for very deep wells because of the prohibitively high hanging load for steel. As mentioned earlier, titanium offers a high-strength to low-weight ratio advantage over steel and while it can be tool-jointed with titanium tool joints in practice steel joints are used. Titanium is quite corrosion resistant to most drilling muds and the presence of H_2S and

109

Figure 3-19

Multitude of fine cracks (white lines) and one large crack in the center of the photograph that are from heat checking on a steel tool joint. The cracks are highlighted by magnetic particles.

CO_2. Moreover, it has very good high-temperature strength for high bottomhole temperatures and excellent fatigue life in contrast to aluminum drill pipe.

One of the obvious disadvantages of titanium drillpipe compared to steel is the high cost. However, compared to the added cost of a large rig to handle steel pipe it may be competitive in some cases. An unexpected disadvantage of titanium drillpipe is its higher wear rate against steel casing compared to steel drillpipe and tool joints. Figure 3-18 shows the wear rate of two types of titanium drillpipe (Ti-6-4 and Beta C) against P 110 steel casing compared to steel drillpipe in both water-base mud and oil-base mud. The mechanism is both corrosion and wear. It is largely because of results such as these that titanium drill pipe is currently offered with steel tool joints.

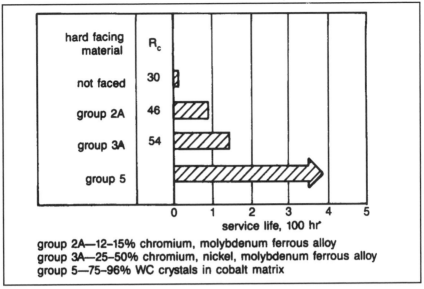

group 2A—12–15% chromium, molybdenum ferrous alloy
group 3A—25–50% chromium, nickel, molybdenum ferrous alloy
group 5—75–96% WC crystals in cobalt matrix

Figure 3-20

Wear resistance of various hard-facing alloys applied to tool joints of composition: 0.40% carbon, 1.5% manganese, and 0.2% molybdenum (after ASM, volume 1).

Tool joints most often suffer wear on the outside surface because of abrasion against the formation or casing during drilling in a deviated hole. Since the tool joint is larger in diameter than the pipe body, it has a greater tendency to rub the formation walls or casing than the body, although pipe-body failures have occurred when the pipe is crooked or when the deviation is so great that the pipe touches the walls. When tool joints are rotated under high lateral force against the hole wall, the temperature of the joint increases substantially because of friction. This localized temperature can be in excess of the lower critical temperature, eventually leading to heat checking of the tool joint as the joint is alternately quenched by the drilling mud and heated by friction. A network of longitudinal cracks form that can grow into longer cracks, offering sites for washout or further crack growth by fatigue or SSC. Figure 3-19 shows an example of heat checking of a tool joint.

The greatest reduction in torsional strength of a tool joint occurs by OD wear. This is caused both by lateral forces against the hole walls and by erosion from cuttings in the mud. Prevention of this type of problem is most often accomplished by hard facing (weld overlaying) the tool joint with an alloy that has greater wear resistance. Companies use either gas metal arc welding or flux core welding, adding tungsten carbide particles to the weld puddle to enhance the wear resistance. The advantage of adding tungsten carbide for wear resistance is

111

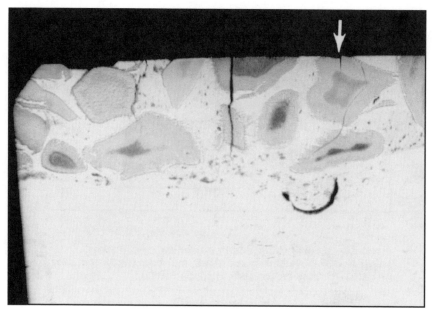

Figure 3-21
Cracks in tungsten carbide particles dispersed in hard facing on a drill collar.

evident from the bar chart shown in Figure 3-20. Service life is significantly increased when tungsten carbide hard facing is used versus other hard-facing materials. Tungsten carbide is graded by particle size with fine mesh on the order of 325-400 mesh particles up to coarse mesh at about 8-10 mesh. While the coarse mesh has very good abrasion resistance, the individual particles tend to fracture more easily than the fine mesh due to the brittleness of tungsten carbide.

Some manufacturer's and applicators use hard banding composed of chromium and molybdenum or nickel and boron but not containing discrete carbide particles. While hardnesses of 50-60 HRC can be achieved with these alloys their resistance to wear in the open hole may not be as good as those with carbide particles.

Figure 3-21 shows fracturing of large tungsten carbide particles in hard facing that resulted in failure of a drill collar. Similar failures may occur if the hard-faced piece is not properly preheated during welding and stress relieved after hard facing. Extremely high hardnesses are created in the heat-affected zone of the weld produced during the application of the hard face. If a post-weld heat treatment is not properly performed, premature failure of the drilling component will occur. The application of hard banding is like any other welding processes that requires the development of a qualified welding procedure specification (WPS). Many failures of hard banded tool joints have occurred simply because a WPS was not qualified and used

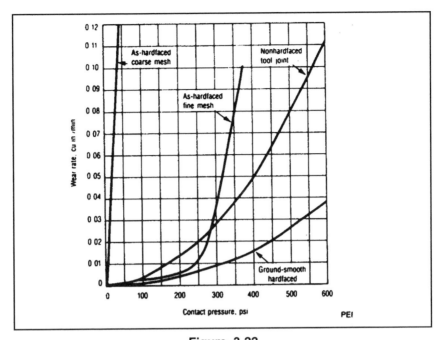

Figure 3-22

Casing wear rate as a function of contact pressure and type of hard facing (after Petroleum Eng. Int.).

Of course, one drawback of hardbanding is the increased wear on the casing. Casing wear must be a consideration when deciding on hard-faced or nonhard faced tool joints. Figure 3-22 shows a comparison of wear rates on casing for coarse mesh, fine mesh, and nonhard-faced tool joints. Note that hard facing that has been ground smooth produces the least wear on casing.

Other failures of tool joints not associated with metallurgy are inadequate makeup torque leading to erosion of the pin or box threads by drilling mud, called wobble, and thread galling caused by forced makeup of improperly engaged threads.

Although casing will be discussed in the next chapter, one problem specific to drilling is fatigue of casing. As discussed, casing wear can be a considerable problem during drilling operations. However, another frequent problem encountered after long-term drilling through casing is fatigue of the casing connections. The threads acts as stress raisers and this coupled with the alternating load of the drill string rotating against the casing frequently produces a fatigue failure. Significant casing wear is not necessary for this event to occur. Figure 3-23 shows a fatigue crack in an eight-round casing thread connection in K-55 casing.

Two recent developments have revolutionized drilling in the petroleum industry. These are coiled tubing (CT) drilling and drilling with casing. While both

113

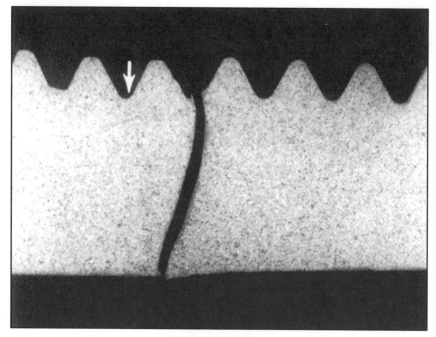

Figure 3-23
Cross section of 8-round casing threads showing progression of fatigue crack from thread root. Arrow indicates there are additional cracks in other thread roots.

have numerous advantages over conventional drill string assemblies the components are still manufactured from steels that have the same resistance to corrosion and fatigue as the conventional equipment. It is a common misconception in the drilling industry that by simply changing the product form from say threaded drill pipe to CT there is a commensurate improvement in SSC resistance, fatigue resistance, etc. Nothing could be more wrong. The CT steels have the same general resistance to SSC, fatigue and corrosion as do any of the other conventional steel equipment. Moreover, the use of casing for drilling significantly increases the potential for fatigue of the connections so that failures such as that shown in Figure 3-23 are more likely to occur.

Besides new drilling technologies the industry has begun a practice of disposing of drill cutting and waste drilling fluids by injecting behind casing into a suitable zone. While this procedure has had great success for the intended purpose of disposal it has also cause several casing failures. It is often forgotten, after well completion, that the intermediate casing in some wells is a high strength casing such as Q125 that while not susceptible to cracking in a drill environment can easily fail from stress corrosion cracking or SSC when exposed to drilling wastes.

Figure 3-24

Through wall fracture surface in Q125 casing showing the depth of a stress corrosion crack (dark elliptical area) that initiated at the OD.

Figure 3-24 shows a section of the full wall thickness of a section of Q125 casing that contained a deep stress corrosion crack that had initiated on the outside of the casing and propagated into the wall of the pipe. Stress corrosion cracks in other casing joints in this string propagated across the entire wall causing failures. The primary cause of the cracking was from the oxygenated degraded mud that also probably contained some H_2S as a result of sulfate reducing bacteria activity. Therefore, it is very important to consider the grade of the casing that will be exposed to the injected fluids and the actual properties of the fluids being injected and not simply assume that these fluids have remained the same as during drilling.

As should be evident, much effort still remains to improve the life of drilling components, especially the drillstem, in hostile drilling environments. Metallurgical considerations are of more importance in drilling today than ever before because of the deep drilling required to reach new reservoirs.

115

References

American Petroleum Institute. Specifications 5D, 6A, 7, and 16A.

American Petroleum Institute. Recommended Practice 7G.

American Society for Metals. "Properties and Selection of Metals " In Metals Handbook. Volume 1. 1961, p. 826.

Azar, J.J. "How O_2, CO_2 and Chlorides Affect Drill Pipe Fatigue." Petroleum Engineer International (March 1979), p. 72.

Boice, E.G. and R.S. Dalrymple."The Design and Performance Characteristics of Aluminum Drill Pipe." 38th Annual Fall Meeting. Paper 697. New Orleans, Louisiana: SPE of AIME, October, 1963, JPT.

Buscemi, C.D.; L. J. Klein; and G. B. Kohut. "Criterion Proposed to Reduce Drill Pipe Failures," Oil and Gas Journal, (Oct. 10, 1988), p. 64.

Bush, H.E.; R. Barbee; and J.P. Simpson. "Current Techniques for Combating Drill-Pipe Corrosion." API Drilling and Production Practice. 1966, p. 59.

Ferg, T.; B.D. Craig; and C. Aldrich, "The Degradation of Titanium Drill Pipe from Corrosion and Wear in a Drilling Environment", SPE Paper No. 23532 (1991).

Garwood, G.L. "Materials Selection for Downhole and Surface Equipment for Sour Gas Condensate Wells." Corrosion/73, Anaheim, California, 1973.

Grant, R.W. and H.T. Texter. "Causes and Prevention of Drill-Pipe and Tool Joint Troubles." API Drilling and Production Practice. 1941, p. 9.

Hatcher, P. R. and K. E. Szklarz, "Reduced Resistance to Cracking of a Sour Service Low Alloy Steel Subjected to Cyclic Loading in Simulated Operating and NACE TM0177 Environments", Corrosion 93, Paper No. 126, NACE, 1993.

McGhee, E. "What You Should Know About Aluminum Drill Pipe." Oil and Gas Journal (March 18, 1963), p. 168.

McGlasson, R.L. "Special Metallurgical Problems." Proceedings of the University of Oklahoma Corrosion Control Course, Norman, Oklahoma, September 1971.

Mehdizadeh, P. "Drill Pipe Failures: Where Do We Go From Here." Petroleum Engineer (September 1973), p. 52.

Person, N.L. "Fatigue Properties of Prior-Corroded Aluminum Sheet Alloys." Material Performance,14 (1975), p. 22.

Petroleum Engineer International, p.18 (March 15,1984).

Rollins, H.M. "What Do We Know About Drill Pipe Fatigue Failure." Oil and Gas Journal (April 18, 1966), p. 98.

Rollins, H.M. "Drill-Stem Failures Due to H_2S." Oil and Gas Journal (January 24,1966), p. 82.

"Steels for Conventional Energy Production and Transmission." Metal Progress, 108 (1975), p. 59.

Tsukano, Y.; H. Miyoshi; Y. Sogo; S. Nishi; and E. Takeuchi. "Optimum Design of Internal Upset Geometry of Drill Pipe for Longer Fatigue Life." Nippon Steel Technical Report No.44, p. 37 (Jan.1990).

Tuttle, R.N. "Deep Drilling—A Materials Engineering Challenge." Materials Performance, 13 (1974), p.42.

Williamson, J.S. and Bolton, J.B. Petroleum Engineer international" (September 1983), p. 54 and Petroleum Engineer International, (March 15, 1984), p. 18.

4

METALLURGY FOR OIL AND GAS PRODUCTION

The components discussed in this chapter are casing, tubing, sucker rods and pumps, Christmas tree components, and wire lines. As in the case of drilling, there are a multitude of special tools and equipment for oil and gas production, many of which have proprietary metallurgy. Although these specialty tools are important to the industry, they do not represent the same capital expenditure as tubing, casing, valves, etc., or the same potential for causing a catastrophic failure.

Production equipment receives more attention from a research and development standpoint Than other types such as drilling equipment simply because the life of a well may be projected to 20 years or greater in some instances. For such exceptionally long service under severe conditions, extraordinary measures to combat corrosion are often called for, including the application of corrosion resistant alloys. It is the recent progression and advancement of the industry from primarily carbon-steel components to high-alloy steels, stainless steels, nickel-base alloys, and titanium alloys that will be discussed in this chapter as well as the reasons for the necessity of such a transition.

117

Casing and Tubing

Casing, tubing, and drillpipe or, as they are often referred to in the industry, oil-country tubular goods (OCTG) are governed by the API under Specifications 5CT and 5D. The various API grades with their corresponding chemistries and mechanical properties are shown in Tables 4-1 and 4-2, respectively. The Group One grades represent the lowest strength, and the Group Four, the highest-strength grades. The specifications require manufacture of the steel by electric furnace, open hearth, or the basic oxygen process. The chemistry requirements are minimal for Groups One and Three, with only the phosphorus and sulfur restricted to a maximum of 0.030 wt% each. More control on chemistry is provided in Groups Two and Four.

Pup joints, casing, and tubing made to this specification can be either seamless or electric-resistance welded (ERW) depending on the particular grade. The ERW casing and tubing has to be either heat-treated after welding to a minimum temperature of 1,000°F (538°C) or processed so there is no untempered martensite. This latter requirement by API 5CT has created problems with some ERW that is not heat-treated after welding since it is quite difficult to determine that no untempered martensite is present.

API 5CT does not require a weld-seam heat treatment but many manufacturers heat treat the seam by induction heating to about 1,650°-1,850°F for less than 1 min, thus producing a normalized structure similar to the pipe body. The time at temperature (1,650°—1,850°F) is short enough that grain growth is not a problem. In fact, the induction heat treatment is so fast, the lower critical temperature may not be surpassed and the weld only receives a temper. This weld seam heat treatment has incorrectly been termed "seam anneal" when in fact the weld is not annealed.

Grade N-80 tubing and work tubing are required to be heat-treated full length and, if upset, re-heat-treated full length after upsetting. Grades J, K, and N casing and Grade J tubing are only required to be normalized if specified by the purchaser; otherwise they are supplied in the as-rolled condition. Grade J-55 tubing is typically not normalized full length after upsetting, which has been the source of numerous failures in CO_2 service over the years. This type of corrosion is referred to as ringworm corrosion and will be discussed later in this chapter. For the high-strength Groups Three and Four, the pipe must be either quenched and tempered or normalized and tempered and, if upset, full-length heat-treated after upsetting.

Couplings are required to be seamless and of the same grade as the pipe, meeting the mechanical requirement set forth in Table 4-2. However, Grades H 40 and J-55 pipe can be furnished with either J-55 or K-55 couplings.

Table 4-1 Chemical Requirements (By Weight Percent)

Group	Grade	Type	Carbon min.	Carbon max.	Manganese min.	Manganese max.	Molybdenum min.	Molybdenum max.	Chromium min.	Chromium max.	Nickel max.	Copper max.	Phosphorous max.	Sulfur max.	Silicon max.
	H-40	...	...	...	...	...	...	...	...	...	...	...	0.030	0.030	...
1}	J-55	...	...	...	...	...	...	...	...	...	...	...	0.030	0.030	...
	K-55	...	...	...	...	...	...	...	...	...	...	...	0.030	0.030	...
	N-80	...	...	...	...	...	...	...	...	...	...	...	0.030	0.030	...
	M-65	...	...	...	...	...	...	...	...	...	...	...	0.030	0.030	...
	L-80	1	...	0.43[1]	...	1.90	...	...	...	...	0.25	0.35	0.030	0.030	0.45
	L-80	9Cr	...	0.15	0.30	0.60	0.90	1.10	8.00	10.00	0.50	0.25	0.020	0.010	1.00
	L-80	13Cr	0.15	0.22	0.25	1.00	...	...	12.0	14.0	0.50	0.25	0.020	0.010	1.00
2}	C-90	1	...	0.35	...	1.00	0.25[2]	0.75	...	1.20	0.99	...	0.020	0.010	...
	C-90	2	...	0.50	...	1.90	...	NL	...	NL	0.99	...	0.030	0.010	...
	C-95	...	...	0.45[3]	...	1.90	...	...	...	...	...	...	0.030	0.030	0.45
	T-95	1	...	0.35	...	1.20	0.25[4]	0.85	0.40	1.50	0.99	...	0.020	0.010	...
	T-95	2	...	0.50	...	1.90	...	...	...	...	0.99	...	0.030	0.010	...
3}	P-110	...	...	...	...	...	...	...	...	...	...	...	0.030	0.030	...
	Q-125	1	...	0.35	...	1.00	...	0.75	...	1.20	0.99	...	0.020	0.010	...
4}	Q-125	2	...	0.35	...	1.00	...	N.L.	...	N.L.	0.99	...	0.020	0.020	...
	Q-125	3	...	0.50	...	1.90	...	N.L.	...	N.L.	0.99	...	0.030	0.010	...
	Q-125	4	...	0.35	...	1.90	...	N.L.	...	N.L.	0.99	...	0.030	0.020	...

[1] The carbon content for L-80 may be increased to 0.50% max. If the product is oil quenched.
[2] The molybdenum content for Grade C-90. Type 1 has no minimum tolerance if the wall thickness is less than 0.700 inch.
[3] The carbon content for C-95 may be increased to 0.55% max. If the product is oil quenched.
[4] The molybdenum content for Grade T-95. Type 1 may be decreased to 0.15% minimum if the wall thickness is less than 0.700 inch.
N.L. = No Limit. Elements shown must be reported in product analysis.
(courtesy API)

119

Table 4-2 Tensile and Hardness Requirements

Group	Grade	Type	Yield Strength Min. psi	Min. MPa	Max. psi	Max. MPa	Tensile Strength Min. psi	Min. MPa	Hardness Max.* HRC	BHN	Specified Wall Thickness Inches	Allowable Hardness Variation. HRC
1}	H-40		40,000	276	80,000	552	60,000	414	...	...		
	J-55		55,000	379	80,000	552	75,000	517	...	...		
	K-55		55,000	379	80,000	552	95,000	655	...	...		
	N-80		80,000	552	110,000	758	100,000	689	...	...		
	M-65		65,000	448	85,000	586	85,000	586	22	235		
	L-80	1	80,000	552	95,000	655	95,000	655	23	241		
	L-80	9Cr	80,000	552	95,000	655	95,000	655	23	241		
	L-80	13Cr	80,000	552	95,000	655	95,000	655	23	241		
	C-90	1.2	90,000	620	105,000	724	100,000	690	25.4	255	0.500 or less	3.0
	C-90	1.2	90,000	620	105,000	724	100,000	690	25.4	255	0.501 to 0.749	4.0
2}	C-90	1.2	90,000	620	105,000	724	100,000	690	25.4	255	0.750 to 0.999	5.0
	C-90	1.2	90,000	620	105,000	758	100,000	690	25.4	255	1.000 and above	6.0
	C-95		95,000	655	110,000	758	105,000	724	...	255		
	T-95	1.2	95,000	655	110,000	758	105,000	724	25.4	255	0.500 or less	3.0
	T-95	1.2	95,000	655	110,000	758	105,000	724	25.4	255	0.501 to 0.749	4.0
	T-95	1.2	95,000	655	110,000	758	105,000	724	25.4	255	0.750 to 0.999	5.0
3}	P-110		110,000	758	140,000	965	125,000	862	...	...		
	Q-125		125,000	860	150,000	1035	135,000	930	...	...	0.500 or less	3.0
4}	Q-125		125,000	860	150,000	1035	135,000	930	...	...	0.501 to 0.749	4.0
	Q-125		125,000	860	150,000	1035	135,000	930	...	...	0.750 and above	5.0

* In case of dispute, laboratory Rockwell C hardness test shall be used as the referee method.
(courtesy API)

Grades covered by Group Two have controlled chemistry and mechanical properties to provide greater resistance to sulfide-stress cracking however, C-95 is an exception to these requirements and is <u>not</u> a sour service grade. . The chemistry is considerably more restricted than for the other groups and also includes 9 Cr and 13 Cr compositions. The range of yield strength is much tighter for these grades such as L-80 versus N-80, the first of which has an allowable yield strength spread of 15,000 psi and the latter of 30,000 psi. Furthermore, the Group Two grades have hardness maxima and ranges of allowable hardness variations.

Heat treatment is also more detailed for Group Two. Heat treatment after upsetting and full-length heat treatment as in the other groups are required, along with minimum tempering temperatures. Cold working after the final tempering treatment is forbidden except for C-95 pipe, which is allowed up to a maximum of 3% compressive cold working after tempering.

Couplings are required to be seamless and of the same grade as the pipe, meeting all of the same chemical composition and mechanical properties as the pipe.

J-55 and K-55 are the most popular grades for tubing and casing, especially for shallow wells. Both usually are relatively high-carbon (0.45%) steels with a chemistry similar to AISI 1045 steel. They are provided in the normalized or as rolled condition but, because of the high carbon content, can reach strengths on the high end of the API requirement of 80,000 psi (552 MPa) and thus be equivalent to N-80 grade. H-40 grade is less frequently used; and with deeper wells requiring higher strength, burst, and collapse, its application has diminished in recent years.

Grades C-75, N-80, L-80, P-105, and P-110 are typically produced from C-Mn or C-Mn-Mo steels. The C-75 and P-105 grades were earlier API grades that are no longer part of the specification. C-90, and T-95 are made from steels based on 4130 steel and commonly modified with niobium, molybdenum, titanium, and/or boron.

Coupling stock often has the same general chemistry as the pipe but may contain slightly greater concentrations of molybdenum, titanium, boron, or manganese to increase hardenability since couplings have thicker walls than the pipe and must be able to achieve the same strength levels as the body.

Many non-API grades of tubulars are available for special applications. These range from high collapse strength casing, to low-alloy steels with restricted properties for hydrogen sulfide service, to nickel-base and cobalt-base alloys for deep, hot wells containing chlorides, hydrogen sulfide, and carbon dioxide. These latter alloys are referred to as corrosion-resistant alloys (CRA). Some of the more common of these alloys will be discussed later. The only CRA that API 5CT addresses is 13Cr, however, ISO 13680 covers a much larger group of CRAs.

At this point it is appropriate to briefly discuss seamless and ERW pipe. There are advantages and disadvantages in using either type, depending on the application. Any time a weld is introduced into a structure, it becomes a better candidate for failure than the base material, which has a more homogeneous structure.

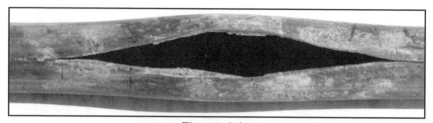

Figure 4-1a

Split along ERW seam in tubing caused by internal pressure and poor weld.
Note stitching on the left side of the split.

Figure 4-1b

Enlargement of left-hand portion of weld in Figure 4-1a.

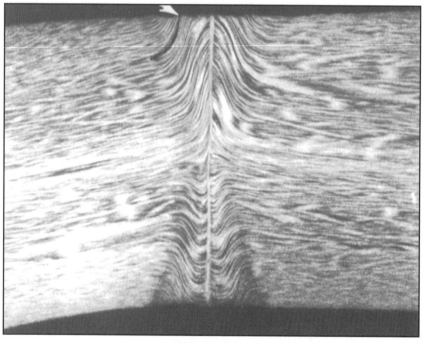

Figure 4-2

Hook crack (arrow) in ERW Casing. The vertical white line at the
center is the weld. Mag. 12X.

Figure 4-3

Fracture surface of an ERW showing black oxides in the weld
that interfered with good bonding of the weld.

The weld area by virtue of the welding process has a greater propensity for defects and, thus, a higher probability of failure than wrought base metal. However, properly manufactured and well-inspected ERW pipe has provided excellent service to the industry over many years and can be comparable to seamless. The key is careful control of the manufacturing of ERW and 100% inspection of the weldline.

Weld defects in ERW pipe arise from several sources. Foreign matter on the welding surfaces, such as oxides, short-circuiting the welding current, arcing electrical contacts, and excessive or insufficient upsetting during welding will produce regions of no weld. In the past many of these problems were the result of using low frequency welding. Now with the widespread use of high frequency welding (HFW) and high frequency induction (HFI) welding, ERW quality has been greatly improved. Figure 4-1a is an example of ERW tubing that was intermittently welded (stitching). It shows the stitching appearance in the enlargement (Figure 4-1b). Another common weld defect is hook cracks. These cracks form along the flow lines of the material that is upset during welding and are associated with nonmetallic inclusions that are deformed during upsetting. Figure 4-2 shows the cross-section of a weld with a hook crack originating at an inclusion.

Other problems with the ERW seam may arise during heat treatment after welding. Although the API requires a minimum heat treatment of 1,000°F (538°C) or processing in a manner such that no untempered martensite remains, hard spots can still be present. This, of course, reduces fracture toughness as well as SSC resistance. Also, during heat treatment of the weld, sufficient heat may not fully penetrate the wall thickness or misalignment of the induction heat zone with respect to the weld may occur. Unheat-treated welds can be quite hard and brittle providing an easy fracture path for failure that is not detectable until the pipe is run in the field. Figure 4-2 also shows the hourglass pattern of the heat-affected zone which is characteristic of an ERW that had not been heat treated. Figure 4-3 shows an example of black oxides along the weld line that interfered

123

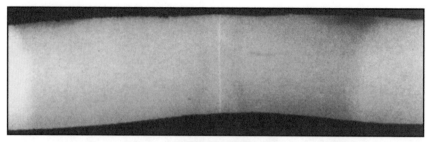

Figure 4-4

Cross section of properly heat-treated ERW displaying only the white ferrite line.

with the welding process and resulting in premature failure. Figure 4-4 shows a weld that was properly heat-treated, leaving only the tell-tale white ferrite line.

Improved manufacturing and better inspection techniques in the past few years have significantly reduced problems encountered with ERW pipe, making it competitive with seamless. Furthermore, ERW pipe has certain advantages over seamless. The surface finish is typically much better for ERW than seamless; thus coating application is less troublesome and less expensive on ERW pipe. The wall thickness and concentricity of ERW pipe is much more uniform than seamless, giving it better collapse resistance than seamless. Finally, it is less expensive than seamless pipe. However, the variability in quality from manufacturer to manufacturer is great and care should be taken in selecting the specific ERW to be used. For a majority of casing and tubing applications in the oilfield, ERW pipe is more than satisfactory if it has been properly manufactured, inspected, and tested.

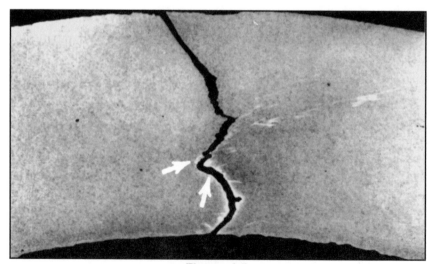

Figure 4-5

Macrograph of a section through the fracture origin of Q-125 seamless casing.

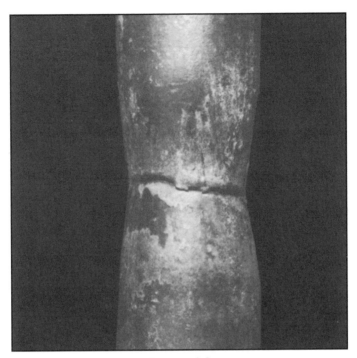

Figure 4-6
Tensile overload of P-105 tubing showing the necking-down of the pipe in the vicinity of the fracture. Mag. 3/4X.

The comments on ERW pipe should not be taken to imply there are no potential problems with seamless pipe. In fact, seamless pipe also suffers from manufacturing problems such as seams, scabs, cracks, etc. Figure 4-5 is an example of Q-125 seamless casing that fractured as a result of a seam that formed in the casing during hot working after piercing. Moreover, the surface condition of seamless can be quite poor as a result of hot rolling during manufacturing, thereby adversely impacting the application of coatings.

Regardless of whether the pipe is seamless or ERW, it can fail by modes of loading that are encountered in well operations. It is the requirement of the casing or tubing string designer to take into account tensile loading, burst, collapse, and connection jumpout. All of these modes are addressed by API bulletins and specifications. However, improper design or changes in the well environment can cause failures from these factors. Generally, failure from any one of these loading conditions are easy to identify.

Figure 4-6 shows the characteristic features of a tensile overload. Prior to complete fracturing at the center, the pipe OD and ID substantially neck down, displaying a high degree of ductility. This type of failure occurs simply from pulling the pipe apart.

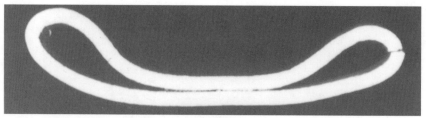

Figure 4-7
End view of a collapsed tubing section. Mag. 1X

A collapse failure also has very obvious features, Figure 4-7. In collapse, the pressure on the outside of the pipe is higher than inside so it collapses inward. Not all collapses are as complete as this and frequently just show a partial collapse of the pipe.

Burst is just the reverse of collapse with pressure on the inside of the pipe causing it to split open. The split is typically in the longitudinal direction.

Connection jumpout is one of the best understood and most common but least recognized problems in the industry. Figure 4-8 shows the undamaged pin threads next to the coupling of a 5-1/2-in., 15.5 pound per foot, K-55, 8-round connection. On closer examination, the thread dimensions, tensile properties, and overall dimension of the pin and coupling were in accordance with the API requirements. Excessive tensile loading is the most frequent cause for thread jumpout although the other factors such as a soft pin, and incorrect thread dimensions can also induce jumpout.

During heat treatment of casing and tubing, specifically during the quenching of steels, if the quench is too rapid or the steel too high in carbon or alloying ele-

Figure 4-8
Pin and coupling after jumpout of the pin. There was no damage to either the pin or coupling threads. Mag. 1/3X

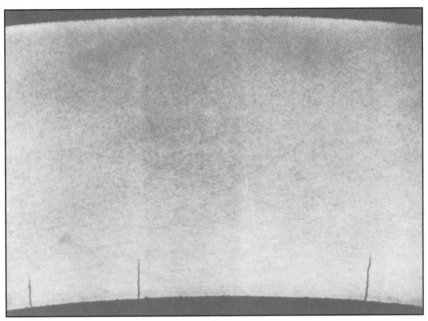

Figure 4-9a
Several quench cracks originating on the inside of C-140 casing.

ments, the pipe can crack. Quench cracking results when outer regions of the steel transform to martensite before inner areas in the workpiece do, such that stresses from the transformation of austenite to martensite cannot be accommodated and cracking results. Figures 4-9a and 4-9b show quench cracks in a C 140 grade casing material. Quench cracking has been observed in almost all API grades of casing and tubing that is quenched and tempered including L-80 13 Cr. Quench cracking usually originates at the OD since it is first to transform and the cracking is always intergranular.

Improper heating during upsetting to produce upset integral joint casing and tubing can lead to brittle failures in the upset. Figures 4-10 to 4-12 show the brittle failure in the upset after this N-80 tubing was run in the well and the microstructure characteristic of to high of an upsetting temperature. The white veins are ferrite when the steel became liquid along the grain boundaries and the gray islands are oxidation of the steel.

Another consideration in casing and tubing is fracture toughness. In the past this was not an important consideration because low strength pipe (e.g., J-55, K-55, etc.) was sufficiently tough at wellbore temperatures that fracture was not a problem. However, with the increasing use of these grades at arctic temperatures and the need to use casing with high collapse resistance, which translates to high

127

Figure 4-9b

One crack at higher magnification showing the intergranular nature, 400X.

strength, fracture toughness has become an important factor. Moreover, if the tubing or casing is not sufficiently tough then it may crack during normal well operations, for example, from the introduction of cold frac fluids, acid, etc. API 5CT recognized this need by requiring Charpy impact testing of Q-125 grade casing and specific minimum impact energies depending on wall thickness. At a very minimum, higher strength proprietary casing grades should also be impact tested to ensure adequate toughness for well control.

Figure 4-13 presents Charpy impact data for a typical K-55 casing as hot rolled. The fracture toughness is quite poor, displaying a ductile-to-brittle transition temperature well in excess of ambient. Normalizing has been shown to greatly improve toughness over the as-rolled condition. However, J and K are most often supplied in the latter condition.

While purely mechanical failures of tubulars such as collapse, burst, tensile failure, etc., occur, they are less common than corrosion. Until recently, corrosion in petroleum production was always handled by using plastic coatings and/or chemical inhibitors. However, internal plastic coatings for oil and gas production are not consistently reliable, often failing as a result of holidays in the coating or from wireline damage (see Figure 4-14) both of which accelerate corrosion or from

Figure 4-10
Brittle fracture in the threads of an upset connection.

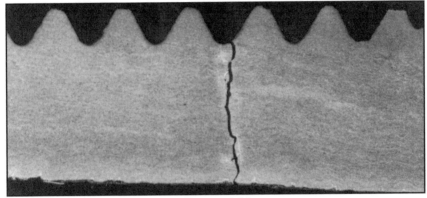

Figure 4-11
Macrography of the fracture shown in Figure 4-10.

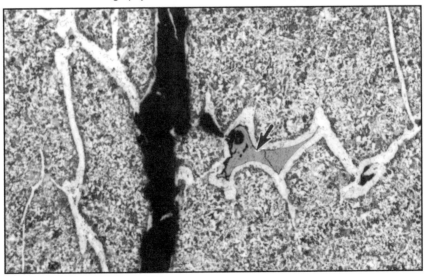

Figure 4-12
Close up of the fracture in Figure 4-11 showing the white areas of grain boundary liquation and the gray oxides (arrow) produced by overheating during upsetting. Magnified 100x.

129

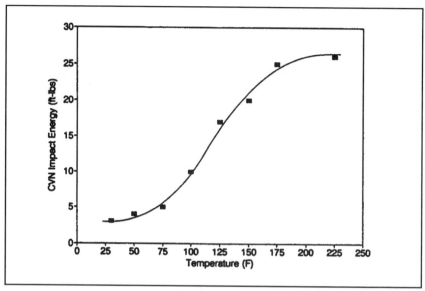

Figure 4-13
Charpy V-notch transition curve for a hot-rolled Grade K-55 casing.

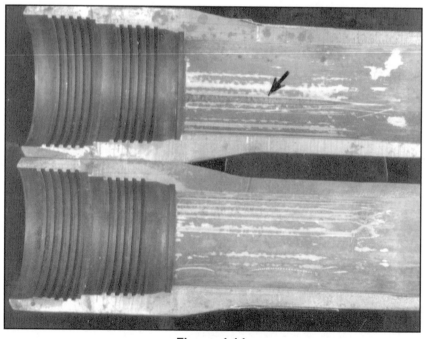

Figure 4-14
Wireline damage (arrow) of the plastic coating inside tubing
leading to selective corrosion.

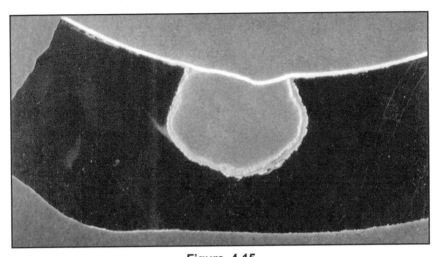

Figure 4-15
Section through tubing showing the intact plastic coating (white line at top) and the corrosion pit almost through the pipe wall caused by CO_2 corrosion.

gas and water permeation causing corrosion of the steel substrate (Figure 4-15). The permeation of the coating shown in Figure 4-15 by water and CO_2, while not disturbing the coating caused failure of the steel tubing string in just a few months. Moreover, with increasingly hostile well environments, the ability of coatings and inhibitors to withstand temperatures exceeding 375°F and pressures of 10,000 psi has been severely reduced. The only effective alternative for corrosion mitigation that remains is metallurgy. Although 9 Ni and 9 Cr steels had been used for tubing in the early 1950s, no further development occurred until the deep, high-hydrogen sulfide wells in Mississippi required alternative solutions to the standard coating/inhibitor program.

Produced oil and gas often includes corrodents such as hydrogen sulfide, carbon dioxide, and chlorides. It is quite rare in the production of these fluids that water is not present in at least sufficient amounts to cause corrosion. Pitting by hydrogen sulfide, carbon dioxide, and chlorides can become severe, and, when combined with high producing temperatures, corrosion rates on the order of several hundred mils per year (mpy) to an inch per year (ipy) have been observed. In addition to pitting attack, more catastrophic forms of failure such as sulfide-stress cracking (SSC) and in the case of stainless-steel and nickel alloy tubulars, stress-corrosion cracking (SCC) can occur.

Only those forms of corrosion attack that are metallurgically significant will be discussed. These are forms that can be affected by metallurgical solutions such as pitting, SSC, stress-corrosion cracking and general weight-loss corrosion.

131

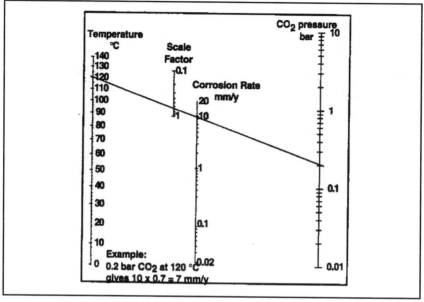

Figure 4-16

Calculation of corrosion rate as a function of CO_2 partial pressure and temperature taking into account the scaling at higher temperature. For example, at 120°C and 0.2 bar CO_2 partial pressure, the corrosion rate is 7 mm/y (After DeWaard and Lotz).

Inasmuch as possible, inhibitors are still the primary method for corrosion control in producing wells. When this approach is unsatisfactory or ineffective, the next step is an increase in alloy content of the tubulars. Although there has been some exposure of 9 Cr-1 Mo tubulars to aggressive environments, the resistance of this alloy is marginal. It is more common to use a stainless-steel grade such as AISI 420, which contains nominally 13% Cr.

Carbon dioxide in the produced gas or oil can lead to very rapid deterioration of alloys containing less than 12% Cr. DeWaard and Milliams were the first to quantify the severe weight-loss corrosion caused by carbon dioxide. Subsequent work by these authors and U. Lotz produced the nomograph shown in Figure 4-16. Corrosion caused by carbon dioxide is primarily a function of CO_2 partial pressure and temperature. This is more apparent from the equation developed by DeWaard, Milliams and Lotz:

$$\text{Log } V_{cor} = 5.8 - \frac{1710}{(T + 273)} + 0.67 \log P_{CO_2}$$

where:

V_{cor} = corrosion rate, mm/y
T = temperature, °C
P_{CO_2} = partial pressure of CO_2, bar

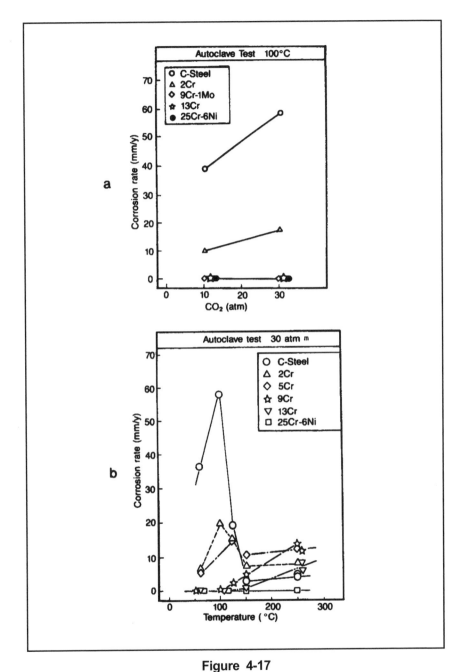

Figure 4-17

Effect of CO_2 Gas partial pressure on corrosion of chromium steels (a) and
effect of temperature on CO_2 corrosion rate of various chromium steels (b)
(After Sumitomo)

Figure 4-18
CO_2 corrosion of oil well tubing.

For example, assuming a partial pressure for carbon dioxide of 0.2 bar at a temperature of 120°C, the corrosion rate would be 7 mm/y. The equation is useful for those cases that extend beyond the nomograph although it is not strictly valid for high CO_2 partial pressures. However, it has been found to apply under some conditions and is useful for illustrating the potential severity of CO_2 corrosion. Thus for a deep well with a 20,000-psig bottom-hole pressure and 10% CO_2, the partial pressure would be about 2,001 psia (138 bar). If the bottom-hole temperature were 177°C (350°F), the calculated corrosion rate would be 2,663 mm/y (105,000 mpy). This value is unreasonably high and shows one of the limitations of the DeWaard approach. The equation does not consider the very important corrosion rate limiting effect of the formation of a protective or semi-protective iron carbonate ($FeCO_3$) layer on the steel. Nor does it take into account the produced water composition (e.g., calcium and bicarbonate content) that can have a profound affect on reducing the CO_2 corrosion rate. In addition DeWaard and others identified important contributions that reduce the effect of CO_2 such as the presence of an oil phase, the supersaturation of iron that can lead to scale formation, the presence of glycol and the effect of fugacity. In any valid CO_2 corrosion model all of these effects and more must be accounted for.

Figure 4-19
Ringworm corrosion adjacent to the upset in J-55 tubing.

Nevertheless, extremely high corrosion rates have been found in fields operating with high carbon dioxide partial pressures and high temperatures. The nomograph and equation still provide a means to approximate the severity of carbon dioxide corrosion and allow a quick, albeit conservative (worst case), analysis of the potential corrosive behavior of a carbon dioxide-containing system. Also, this method gives at least some semiquantitative information at low partial pressures of CO_2 versus the old (and still widely used)API rule of thumb that, for carbon dioxide partial pressures below 7, no corrosion occurs; between 7-30, moderate corrosion can be expected; and above 30, corrosion will be severe.

The original work of DeWaard and Milliams covered carbon dioxide partial pressure only to 1.0 bar. Work by others has extended the study of CO_2 corrosion above 1.0 bar, and their results are shown in Figures 4-17a and 4-17b. Since temperature and carbon dioxide partial pressure change with location in the tubing string, it is obvious the corrosion behavior will vary along the length of the string.

Figure 4-18 shows an example of CO_2 corrosion of an oil well tubing string. Corrosion by carbon dioxide, which forms carbonic acid when combined with water, is particularly severe in threads, connections, changes in metallurgical structure (e.g., welds and upsets), and changes in flow such as through connections and valves. Severe problems have been observed in gas production containing carbon dioxide when tubing and couplings of different grades are mixed. N-80 couplings connected to J-55 tubing always corrode preferentially to the J-55 grade and at fairly rapid rates. This appears to be a galvanic affect, although other experience shows that N-80 steel in the hole fails much faster than J-55 in wet CO_2 service. This may be the result of the quenched and tempered microstructure of N-80 steel, which is more susceptible to corrosion than the as-rolled structure of J-55. Considerable work has been done on the role of microstructure on CO_2 corrosion. It has been found that the cementite platelets in pearlite aid in anchoring a more protective $FeCO_3$ scale

As described before, ringworm corrosion is specific to upset J-55 tubing that has not been full length normalized. Figure 4-19 shows a typical example of ringworm corrosion caused by wet CO_2. This selective attack just beyond the upset is attributed to a galvanic effect between the different microstructure in the upset heat-affected zone and the nonaffected tubing body.

Corrosion of steel in the presence of carbon dioxide is a function of both chromium and nickel content as shown in Figure 4-20. At least 9% Cr is necessary to gain good corrosion resistance, but more often the threshold chromium content to ensure resistance is 12%. Thus 12-13% Cr steels represent the first step in applying metallurgy to tubulars for resistant to CO_2 corrosion. As was demonstrated in Figures 4-17a and 4-17b, the corrosion rate of steel in carbon dioxide is dramatically reduced with the addition of 9% Cr or greater to the steel. However, if the temperature is increased to 250°C (see Figure 4-17b), the 9 Cr steel corrodes at

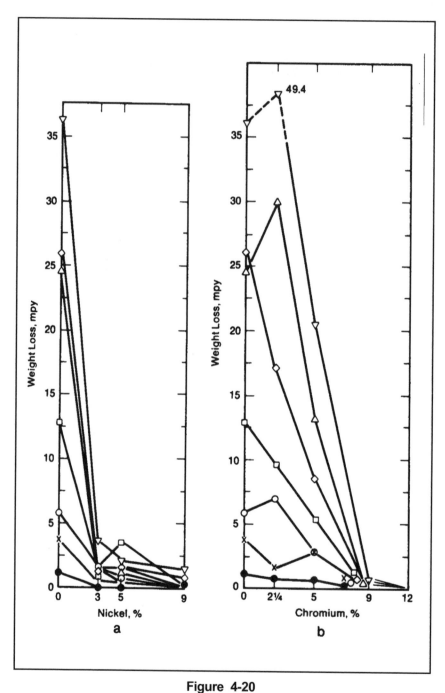

Figure 4-20

Effect of (a) nickel content and (b) chromium content on CO_2 corrosion of steels in gas condensate wells (After NACE Pub. No. 50-3).

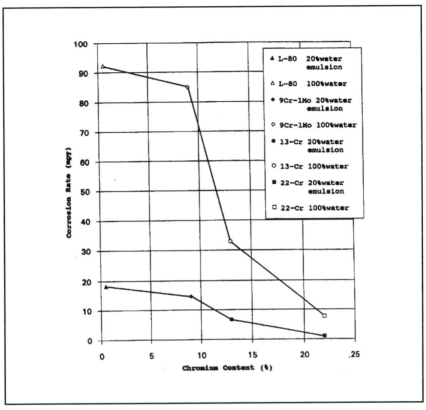

Figure 4-21

Corrosion rate of steels and stainless steels in oil/water mixtures
as a function of Cr content.

greater than 10 mm/y (395 mpy) while the 13% Cr corrodes much less and the 25 Cr-6 Ni (duplex stainless steel) corrosion rate remains almost zero. Thus increased resistance to CO_2 corrosion is a strong function of chromium content even at high temperatures and CO_2 pressure. Moreover, for oil wells that contain CO_2 the corrosion rate is a function of the water cut as well, Figure 4-21, but the same dependence on Cr still occurs as in gas wells.

To this point, the discussion of alloying for resistance to CO_2 corrosion is quite straightforward; however, as the environment becomes more complex, so do the metallurgical solutions. If chlorides are included in the carbon dioxide environment, as they almost always are in petroleum production, pitting corrosion and stress-corrosion cracking from chlorides becomes a concern for many alloys. Since stress-corrosion cracking typically initiates from pits on the surface of the alloy, pitting will be discussed in conjunction with SCC even though it must be kept in mind that failure can also occur strictly by pitting without associated SCC.

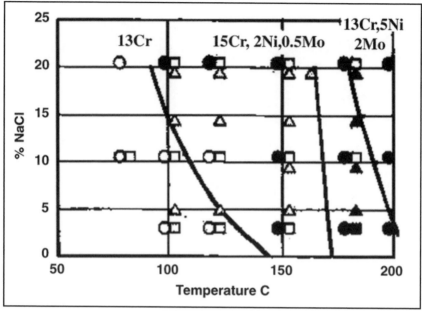

Figure 4-22

Corrosion map for alloy 13Cr and two S13Cr alloys as a function of temperature and NaCl concentration. Lines in figure indicate the limitation of safe use for these alloys (after Masamura et al).

As the temperature increases and the chlorides increase the straight 13 Cr steels begin to pit. By adding Ni and Mo to these steels the resistance to pitting is improved. The groups of 13 Cr alloys that contain Ni and Mo are referred to as Super 13 Cr stainless steels (S13 Cr), the more common of which are presented in Table 4-3. Figure 4-22 shows the relationship between 13 Cr and two S13 Cr alloys from a corrosion standpoint. Increased resistance at still higher temperatures is achieved with the duplex stainless steels.

The 22 Cr is a duplex stainless steel (a combination of austenite and ferrite) with approximately 6% Ni. These alloys have a two-phase structure as connoted by the name duplex. The phases are ferrite and austenite and are approximately balanced with 50% ferrite and 50% austenite as shown in Figure 1-36. Generally, with increasing chlorides and temperature the corrosion rate increases for S13 Cr but the 22 Cr shows much better resistance to corrosion. Table 4-4 presents some of the common duplex stainless steels. However, there is a penalty in changing from S13 Cr to 22 Cr. Duplex stainless steels (22 Cr and 25 Cr) cannot be heat-treated for strength but must be cold-worked. Above about 350°F duplex stainless steels can display unacceptable corrosion rates in high CO_2, high chloride wells. Increasing nickel content in these stainless steels can initially have a detrimental affect on SCC resistance. See Figure 2-10 which shows the minimum resistance to

138

Table 4-3 Typical Composition (wt%) of Super 13 Cr Alloys Compared to 13Cr

Alloy	C	Ni	Cr	Mo	Other
API 13 CR	0.20	--	13	--	--
SM 13 CRS	0.01	5	12	2	Nb
SM 13 CRM	0.01	4.5	12	0.7	
SM 13 CRI	0.01	2	11	0.3	
(Sumitomo)					
Kawasaki – HP1	0.02	4	13	1	--
– HP2	0.02	5	13	2	--
Corus	0.02	5	12	2	0.3V
DMV	0.02	5.5	13	2	
Vallourec	0.01	6	13	2	0.2 Ti

Table 4-4 Chemical Composition of Some Common Duplex Stainless Steels

Alloy	C	Cr	Ni	Mo	N	Cu	W
2205	0.02	22	5	3	0.1		
SAF 2507	0.02	25	7	3.5	0.3		
Zeron 100	0.02	25	7	3.5	0.2	0.7	0.7
25 Cr (DP3)	0.02	25	7	3	0.2	0.60	0.3
25 CrW (DP3W)	0.02	25	7	3	0.3	0.6	2

Table 4-5 Common Nickel Base Alloys

Name	Cr	Ni	Mo	Co	Cu	Other
Alloy 28	28	31	3.5	--	1	Bal Fe
Alloy 825	22	42	3	--	1	1 Ti, Bal Fe
Alloy 925	21	43	3	--	1	28 Fe, 2.1 Ti
Alloy 718	18	Bal	3	--	--	19 Fe, 5 Cb
Alloy 625	22	Bal	9	--	--	4 Cb + Ta
Alloy 725	21	Bal	8.5	--	--	3 Cb, 1.5 Ti
Alloy G 3	22	Bal	7	--	2	19 Fe
Alloy 2550	25	Bal	6	--	--	1.2 Ti, 18 Fe
Alloy G 50	20	Bal	8	1	1	18 Fe
Alloy C 276	15	Bal	16	1	--	4 W, 5 Fe

Table 4-6 SCC of Alloys in Various Brines at Different Temperatures and 7-Day Exposure

Alloys	CaCl₂					NaCl °F (°C)					MgCl₂				
	250 (121)	300 (149)	350 (177)	400 (204)	450 (232)	250 (121)	300 (149)	350 (177)	400 (204)	450 (232)	250 (121)	300 (149)	350 (177)	400 (204)	450 (232)
Ferralium 255[1] (25.6–5.17–3.3)*				025	025				25	025			5	025	025
Sanicro 28[2] (26.4–31.4–3.0)			2	025	025				025	025			5	025	025
Incoloy 825[3] (21.4–42.0–2.5)								0		025				05	025
Hastelloy G-3[4] (22.5–43.3–7.1)									025	025					025
Hastelloy C-276[4] (15.2–54.8–16.1)															025

* Values are for alloy content in the order, chromium-nickel-molybdenum

Note: 0, 2, 3, and 5 indicate cracks in the annealed, 20%, 30% and 50% cold-worked condition

[1] Bonar Langley Alloys Ltd.

[2] Sandvik

[3] Special Metals

[4] Haynes

(After Kolts)

SCC for Fe-Cr-Ni alloys at approximately 8% Ni. Thus, in increasingly severe environments containing chlorides at high temperatures, more resistant alloys must be selected that, according to Figure 2-10, will be primarily high in nickel content (>40% Ni) or nickel-base alloys. Many of the high-nickel and nickel-base alloys are not heat treatable and therefore must be cold worked to obtain the desired mechanical properties. Table 4-5 shows some of the common nickel based alloys. The group of alloys ranging from stainless steels to high nickel content iron-base alloys, nickel-base alloys, cobalt- nickel alloys, and titanium alloys has become known as corrosion resistant alloys or CRAs.

The SCC behavior of some of these alloys in high-temperature brines is shown in Table 4-6. The alloys are listed in order of increasing alloy content. The strong effects of nickel above 30% and molybdenum in reducing SCC are evident.

The addition of hydrogen sulfide to a system containing carbon dioxide and chlorides creates a complex environment for which tubular selection becomes quite difficult. Before discussing this problem, it is beneficial to examine the effect of wet hydrogen sulfide alone on steels.

Hydrogen sulfide in oil and gas production can be detrimental in two ways: it is an aggressive pitting agent, and it induces cracking in many alloys. The general weight-loss corrosion resulting from hydrogen sulfide corrosion is considerably less than that caused by carbon dioxide at the same partial pressure for several reasons. A semiprotective film of iron sulfide (FeS) sometimes forms on steel during corrosion however H_2S dissolved in water does not form a simple acid as does CO_2 (carbonic acid). Hydrogen sulfide also enhances pitting attack of many alloys, especially steels.

One of the greatest concerns facing the industry, however, is catastrophic cracking in hydrogen sulfide environments. This phenomenon has been determined to be a special case of hydrogen stress cracking that is more severe than for many other hydrogen-bearing environments because hydrogen sulfide poisons the hydrogen recombination reaction occurring at the cathode, thereby charging atomic hydrogen into the alloy. Sulfide-stress cracking (SSC) follows the same dependency on parameters as hydrogen-stress cracking. Thus, it has a temperature-versus-time-to-failure minimum at about room temperature. The significance of this to oil and gas wells is that susceptibility to SSC is greatest at the top of a casing or tubing string and on the surface equipment. As the applied stress and yield strength increase, the susceptibility to SSC increases. It is a common misconception that SSC is caused by the recombination of atomic hydrogen to form molecular hydrogen and that the resulting pressure from the H_2 produces cracking of the steel. This mechanism is correct for hydrogen induced cracking (HIC) that will be discussed in Chapter 6 but not for SSC. There is no one accepted mechanism for SSC. The two most prominent models are the lowering of the cohesive strength of iron-iron bonds by hydrogen atoms that then lowers the fracture stress or the enhancement of plasticity by hydrogen (Craig, ASM Handbook, vol. 13A).

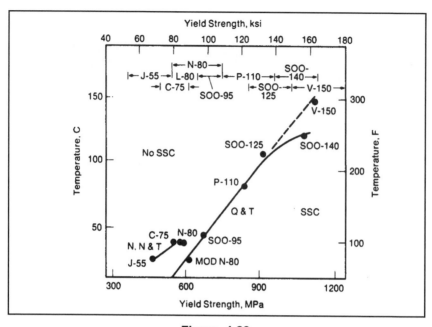

Figure 4-23

Effect of temperatures on sulfide stress cracking resistance of common grades of tubing and casing (After Kane and Greer, © 1977, SPE).

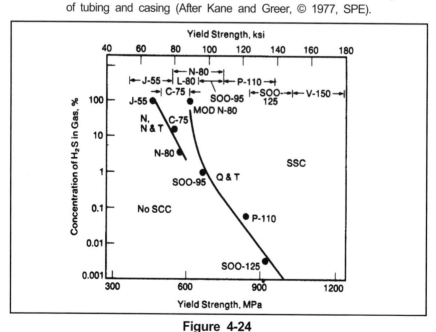

Figure 4-24

Effect of H₂S concentration on sulfide stress cracking of tubing and casing steels (After Kane and Greer, © 1977, SPE).

Handwritten margin notes (right side, rotated):

P110 OK for T > 175°F
Q125 OK for T > 225°F

NACE MR0175/ISO 15156
(Table A.3)

Figure 4-25
Sulfide stress cracking failure of L-80 grade tubing.
Note deep slip marks that assisted fracture initiation.

The effect of temperature on SSC of tubulars is shown in Figure 4-23. This figure also shows the effect of normalized and normalized and tempered J-55, C 75, and N-80 steel compared to quenched and tempered steels, reconfirming the effect of metallurgical structure on resistance. Furthermore, as the strength level increases, the temperature at which SSC does not occur increases. The practical benefit of this is that higher strength casing can be used deeper in a well where temperatures are higher without suffering SSC.

Figure 4-24 shows the effect of increasing hydrogen sulfide concentration on the SSC of common tubular grades. Again, the behavior of normalized and normalized and tempered steels is inferior to the quenched and tempered steels.

143

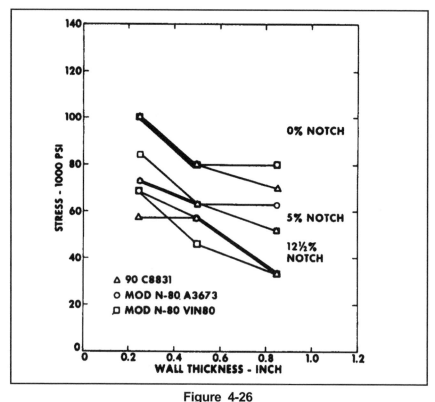

Figure 4-26
Effect of wall thickness and Charpy notch depth on threshold stress
for sulfide stress cracking (After Greer, © SPE).

Also, the high-strength steels tolerate less hydrogen sulfide before cracking. An example of a field failure of L-80 tubing by SSC is presented in Figure 4-25. Failure was principally the result of the deep slip marks shown on the OD of the pipe. Even highly resistant grades of tubing and casing can fail if improperly handled. Figure 4-26 shows the effect of notch depth and wall thickness on the threshold stress for SSC of L80 tubing. The two modified N-80 grades are similar to L-80 while the other is a C-90 grade. Increasing notch depth with increasing wall thickness can reduce the threshold stress for SSC by more than 50%; for example, compare a 5% notch in 0.250-in. material with a 12 1/2% notch in the same material at a thickness of 0.850 in.

The composition of steel is also quite important in determining resistance to SSC. Figure 4-27 compares the behavior of AISI 4130 low-alloy steel to that for C-Mn steels. The former steel has better resistance to SSC because of its greater hardenability and its resistance to tempering. This sluggish tempering behavior allows the 4100 series alloys to be tempered at higher temperatures than the carbon-man-

144

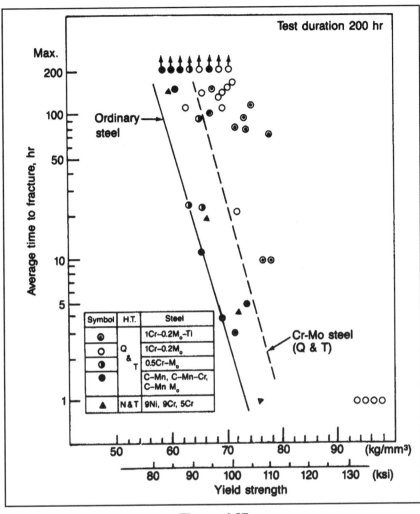

Figure 4-27

Sulfide stress cracking of commercial grades C-75, N-80, L-80, C-95
(After Ikeda et al.).

ganese steels to obtain the same hardness and mechanical properties. The higher-temperature tempering allows for more recovery of the microstructure and thus a uniform structure, which provides greater resistance to SSC.

It has been shown that a critical amount of molybdenum added to the steel can significantly improve the resistance to SSC for high strength steels. Using an AISI 4130 base steel, the addition of 0.5 – 0.8% Mo improves the SSC performance. It is for this reason that most T95 and C110 steels contain higher Mo contents than found in 4130 steel.

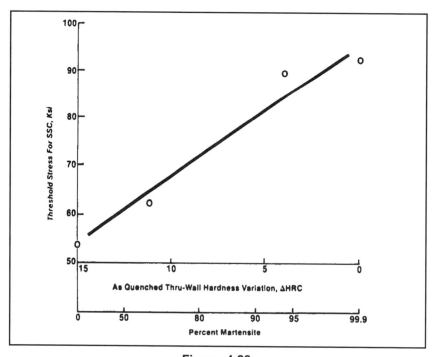

Figure 4-28
Relationship between percent of martensite and sulfide stress cracking
threshold for an AISI 4130 bar heat-treated to Rockwell C25 hardness
(After Greer and Holland, © 1980, SPE).

For many years there was a controversy over the role of nickel in steels and whether they reduced the SSC performance. Work by Craig and coworkers however, unequivocally demonstrated that there is no detrimental effect of Ni in steel, when the Ni content is held to 2% maximum and the steels are properly heat treated. Improper heat treatment (tempering above the lower critical temperature, A_1) is the most common cause for lowered SSC resistance of Ni containing steels. For steels containing more than 2% Ni, the proportional limit decreases with increasing Ni content so that SSC can occur at low fractions of the yield strength. However, this would not preclude the use of these steels for valve bodies and other components that are typically stressed to 50% of their yield strength or less. However, contrary to this complete understanding of the role of Ni in steels, as well as good field experience with Ni containing steels in H_2S, NACE MR0175 and ISO 15156 continue to arbitrarily restrict the Ni content of steels to 1% maximum.

The relationship of hardenability to SSC resistance is shown in Figure 4-28. The ability to achieve complete transformation to martensite is a function of hardenability of the alloy and the speed of the quench. The highest quality steels for SSC resistance have been quenched to near 100% martensite. The benefits of achieving

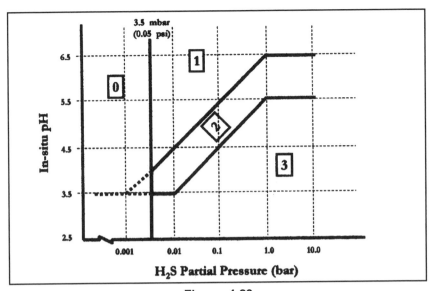

Figure 4-29
Regions that define sour and non-sour environments according to
NACE MR0175/ISO 15156 (© NACE International, 2004).

near 100% martensite during the quenching are so great, API 5CT requires a hardness test be performed and a minimum hardness on as-quenched C-90 and T-95 grade tubulars be attained in compliance with the following formula: HRC min = 50 x %C + 29. This minimum hardness represents a minimum of 90% martensite. (Note that carbon content of the steel is the sole factor in determining the as-quenched hardness.)

A generally accepted rule for resistance of carbon and low-alloy steels to SSC is to maintain the hardness below HRC 22. While there are exceptions to this rule, it has been very effective over the years and is satisfactory if no data or experience exists to contradict it for a specific application. Steels based on the 4100 series are acceptable up to HRC 26 provided they are tubulars. Higher alloyed materials can be exposed to sour (H_2S containing) environments at higher hardnesses. The acceptable hardness limits for many alloys to reduce the risk of SSC were first described in NACE Specification MR-01-75. This specification is frequently misapplied by oil company personnel to include weight loss corrosion from H_2S and other forms of environmental cracking such as SCC. MR-01-75 was effectively replaced in 2004 with the International Standard, ISO 15156. Figure 4-29 from that standard shows the regimes for SSC. This standard details the limitations for many alloys used in sour environments. Region 0 represents the non-sour region were no special precautions are needed when applying materials of various strengths. Regions 1, 2 and 3 are sour environments and specific details on suitable materials in these regions are described in the standard.

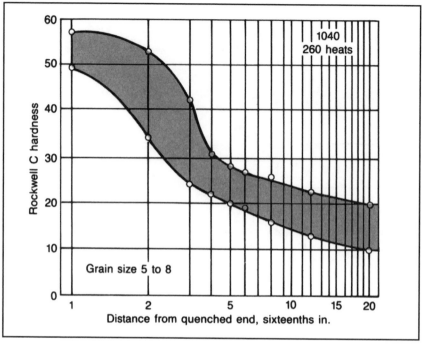

Figure 4-30

Hardenability band for AISI 1040 steels (After Metals Handbook).

These upper limits on hardness necessitate a maximum on the tensile strength and, therefore, yield strength of an alloy that can be used in hydrogen sulfide service. One means around the strength limitation is to increase the wall thickness of a tubular. Since stress is the force or load applied over a certain area (in this case, the cross-sectional area of the tube wall), increasing the wall thickness of the tubular can substantially reduce the applied stress, allowing lower-strength tubulars to be used. It must be kept in mind that increasing the wall thickness also increases the weight of the joint, thereby also increasing the applied load on top of the string. These two opposing factors must be balanced to arrive at an optimum string design for reducing the potential for SSC. The weight of the string can be partly offset by using a tapered string where possible (i.e., using successively smaller pipe toward the bottom of the string). It is always recommended to use the lowest strength tubular that can be accommodated when designing and running strings in sour service.

The increase in deep drilling has presented a terrific challenge to completion and production of these wells. Since the top portion of the string may be required to support 5-6 miles (8-10 km) of pipe, the yield strength of the material must be high or the wall thickness quite large. High yield strengths are more susceptible to SSC and require less hydrogen sulfide to promote SSC, therefore, heavy walls

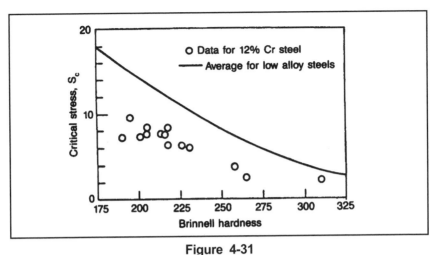

Figure 4-31

Comparison of the sulfide cracking tendency for 12% chromium versus low-alloy stee, S_c is a measure of resistance to SSC. Increasing S_c is equivalent to increasing resistance to SSc (After Treseder and Swanson).

are often the choice. This presents the problem of producing tubulars of L-80 through C110 in heavy-wall sections, with a uniform microstructure and hardness across the wall.

Heavy-wall, low-alloy tubulars and couplings are often produced from 0.750 to 1.50 in. wall thickness. To achieve the desired properties in this kind of section thickness, the hardenability of the alloy becomes important. As discussed in Chapter One, the first step is a more rapid quench. This entails a water quench that, in some mills, is applied just to the external surface of the tubes. In other steel mills, both external and internal water quenching are performed. Looking at the end-quench data for 1040 steel (e.g., J-55) shown in Figure 4-30, the depth at which an external water quench will produce significant hardening is less than 3/16 in. Above and beyond the as-quenched hardness, there must also be allowance for loss in hardness caused by tempering. Therefore, to obtain a fully martensitic structure and to allow sufficient hardenability such that tempering will not result in a product below needed strength levels, an alloy steel is required. Most tubulars that are used with large wall thickness and/or that require the desired SSC resistance are based on the AISI 4130 grade low-alloy steel. To compare the effect of alloying while keeping carbon constant, Figure 1-28 shows an end-quench hardenability curve for AISI 4140H in which the carbon content is kept constant. Compared to Figure 4-30, the hardness at 3/16 in. in the middle of the band for 1040 is HRC 33, whereas for 4130 the depth at which HRC 32 is achieved is about 1-7/8 in. Also, if the quench is inside/outside, the effective thickness to obtain HRC 32 is doubled. Thus the power of alloying elements

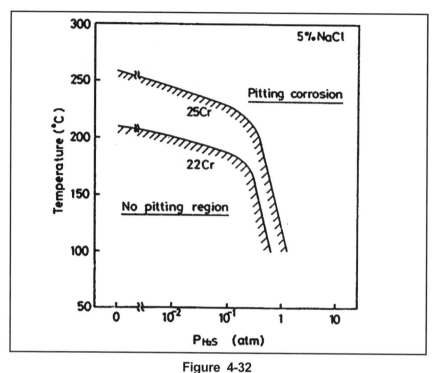

Figure 4-32

Influence of partial pressure of H₂S and temperature of pitting behavior of duplex stainless steels (After Sumitomo).

in enhancing hardenability is tremendous. Those mills that have only an external quench capability often increase the carbon and manganese content or use alloying elements such as chromium, boron, or titanium to increase the hardenability.

In spite of attempts to push the usable strength of steel tubulars to higher limits in hydrogen sulfide, the threshold remains around 100 ksi. In fact, all low alloy steels heat-treated to yield strengths in excess of about 135 ksi fail rapidly when exposed to hydrogen sulfide. Based on the earlier discussion of increasing resistance to corrosion and SSC with increased alloying, it would be expected that 13% Cr would have greater resistance to SSC than a low-alloy steel. Figure 4-31 shows this assumption to be incorrect, and that AISI 410 (12 Cr) or AISI 420 (13 Cr) stainless steel actually is more susceptible to SSC than the low-alloy steels. This is usually attributed to the difficulty in producing a completely tempered martensitic structure. Quenching followed by a single temper often leaves a significant amount of untempered martensite that can cause a reduction in resistance to SSC. Thus, a double temper is required with the second temper specified at 50°F less than the first. Still, the resistance of 13 Cr to environments containing H₂S is marginal, especially in the presence of chlorides. The S13Cr alloys have proven to be

150

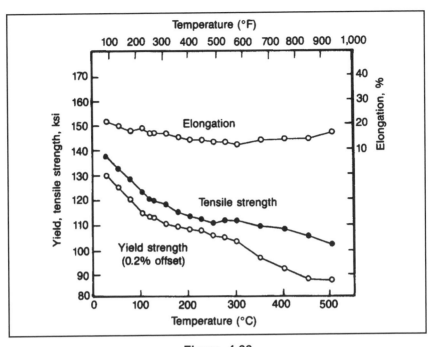

Figure 4-33
Effect of elevated temperature on mechanical properties of
duplex stainless steel (After NKK).

only marginally better in H_2S than 13 Cr but for all intents and purposes they are the same.

The duplex stainless steels offer better chloride-stress cracking resistance than austenitic stainless steels and enhanced weight-loss corrosion resistance from CO_2 than 13% Cr steel. They also show increased SSC resistance; however, this resistance to SSC is limited to low concentrations of hydrogen sulfide on the order of 1.0 psia or less for the 22Cr duplexes and about 3 psia for the super duplexes. Of course, this depends on the amount of cold work as well as other factors. As the hydrogen sulfide content increases, the suitability of duplex stainless steels diminishes (Figure 4-32), so high-nickel alloys must be utilized—especially when chlorides are also present in the environment.

Another consideration when using duplex stainless steels is that they are most often used in the cold-worked condition. Moreover, when subjected to high well temperatures, a certain amount of recovery occurs, leading to loss in strength (see Figure 4-33). This loss in strength is common for many but not all of the cold worked CRA materials.

The behavior of CRAs in complex well environments has been extensively studied, and CRA tubulars have been run in many wells.

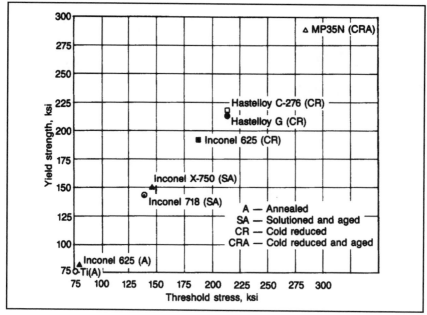

Figure 4-34

Yield strength versus threshold stress for SSC for highly alloyed materials. None of the alloys failed in the NACE test (data from Watkins and Greer).

Figure 4-34 shows the threshold stress for SSC of some of the more common CRAs as a function of yield strength. These alloys were tested in the NACE solution (oxygen-free water containing 5% sodium chloride, 0.5% acetic acid, and saturated with hydrogen sulfide) at room temperature. None of these alloys failed in 30 days of exposure when stressed to 98% of their yield strength. Based on the information shown in Figure 4-34, it would appear that MP35N and the other alloys are essentially immune to failure in hydrogen sulfide. However, these materials are not totally immune to failure in aggressive well environment.

In fact, at temperatures above ambient up to bottomhole temperature, which currently can approach 500°F, cracking and corrosion of CRAs are necessary considerations. It has been found that cracking of CRAs at elevated temperatures in CO_2, H_2S, chlorides, and free sulfur cannot simply be distinguished as SCC or SSC. Therefore, cracking of CRAs in aggressive wells or surface equipment is often referred to as environmental cracking (EC).

The selection of a suitable CRA tubular for a specific well environment depends on many factors such as gas composition, water chemistry, pressure, temperature, flow rates, risk, economics, etc. These factors are dealt with in more detail elsewhere (see for example, B.D. Craig, SPE Monograph).

Generally, the ranking of CRAs according to corrosion resistance is as follows

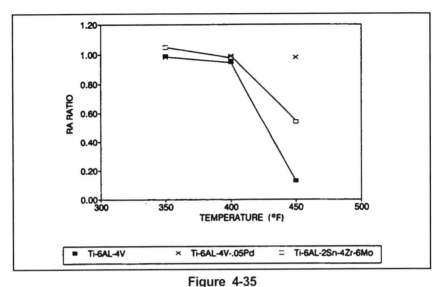

Figure 4-35

Environmental cracking of three Ti alloys measured as reduction in area ratio versus temperature (After Sumitomo).

in increasing order of resistance: martensitic stainless steels (13% Cr and S13 Cr), duplex stainless steels, high nickel content iron-base alloys (e.g., Alloy 28, Alloy 825), nickel-base alloys with low molybdenum (e.g., Alloy 2550, G-3), nickel-base alloys with high molybdenum (Hastelloy C-276), nickel-cobalt alloy (e.g., MP35N) and titanium alloys. The last three alloy groups are generally equivalent although the Ti alloys have better resistance to the wellbore environment than the others. Figure 4-35 shows the environmental cracking resistance of several titanium alloys under simulated sour well conditions.

The advantage of some titanium alloys over many nickel-base alloys is that they can be heat-treated to very high strength levels (>150,000 psi yield) so that thinner wall tubulars can be run at a lower cost than a comparable thick wall nickel alloy. However, the acid resistance of titanium alloys is poor compared to the nickel alloys, and their fracture toughness is considerably less than for nickel base alloys.

If not properly manufactured, stainless steels and nickel alloys may contain a variety of phases that are detrimental to the performance of these alloys. Some of these phases are carbides ($M_{23}C_6$, M_7C_3, M_6C, MC, where M = Cr, Fe, Mo, Ti, Nb, etc.) and nitrides (Cr_2N) or compounds such as sigma, mu and Laves phases. These latter compounds can have a deleterious effect on the fracture toughness as well as the corrosion resistance of the stainless steel and nickel alloys in which they form. This problem was mentioned in Chapter 1 where the deleterious acicular delta phase that precipitated in Alloy 718 was mentioned as the cause of a tubing hanger failure in the North Sea.

153

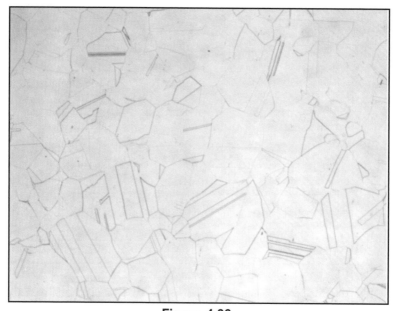

Figure 4-36

Microstructure of solution-annealed Hastelloy C-276 showing a single phase with essentially no carbide precipitation. Mag. 100X.

Sensitization as discussed in Chapter Two can occur in many of these alloys and reduce their corrosion resistance. Figure 4-36 is an example of solution annealed Hastelloy C-276 tubing prior to final pilgering for size and strength. Figure 4-37 shows a similar nickel-base alloy in the same condition that reveals significant grain boundary carbide precipitation. The latter microstructure is far less suitable for exposure to a corrosive environment than the C-276 in Figure 4-36.

Figure 4-38 shows the same alloy in Figure 4-36 after pilgering to achieve the desired strength. Note the elongated grains and the small parallel lines (twins) that are indicative of a cold-worked alloy.

Hydrogen-stress cracking is a potential problem in service for alloy tubulars since many of the other components in a system may be carbon steel (i.e., casing, hangers, etc.). Coupling between these alloys and steel may lead to hydrogen charging of the CRA. Nickel alloys show greatest susceptibility to HSC around room temperature.

Stress-corrosion cracking (SCC) can also become a problem for CRAs as the temperature increases. This aspect was discussed earlier in Table 4-6 which demonstrates the effect of cold work and temperature on SCC. Table 4-7 substantiates this SCC problem with data from tests in a much more severe environment.

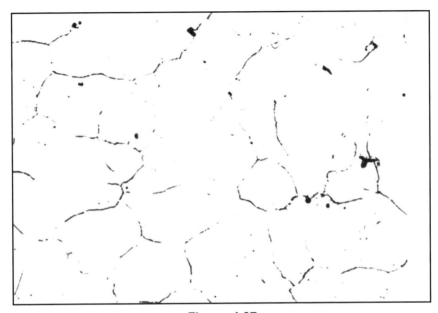

Figure 4-37

Microstructure of a nickel-base alloy similar to C-276 showing severe carbide precipitation along the grain boundaries. Mag. 100X

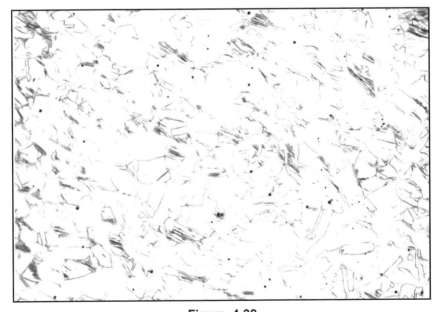

Figure 4-38

Micrograph of the same alloy as shown in Figure 4-36 after cold working to increase strength. Mag. 100X

155

Table 4-7 Stress-Corrosion Cracking of Nickel- and Cobalt-Base Alloys (C Ring Specimens Tested in Aqueous Solutions Containing 25% NaCl, 0.5% Acetic Acid, 1 g/L Sulfur, and H_2S)

Material	%Trans. Y.S.	Test Temperature, °C (°F)					
		175 (35)		205 (400)		290 (550)	
		70	90	70	90	70	90
Hastelloy Alloy C-276 (37% CR)		0	X	X	X	X	X
MP35N (59% CR)		X	X	X	X	X	X
Hastelloy Alloy G (59% CR)		...	...	X	X	...	...

O = Passed
X = Failed
Time to failure by SCC was 100 days in some cases. Test duration needed to obtain data shown in this table was 150 days.
(After Kane and Boyd)

Table 4-8 Comparison of the Longitudinal and Traverse Tensile Properties of Cold Worked Hastelloy G50 (After Haynes).

Temp, °C	0.2% Yield, ksi		Tensile, ksi	
	Long	Trans	Long	Trans
25	107.6	102.9	126.9	121.6
93	101.5	97.0	119.7	113.4
204	91.5	85.1	110.4	113.3
316	89.8	83.8	98.4	98.4

The effects of increasing temperature and applied stress are evident. Although these data indicate somewhat poor resistance of nickel- and cobalt-base alloys to HSC and SCC, it must be kept in mind that these are laboratory tests and therefore intentionally more severe than actual conditions. Moreover, the test environment contains elemental sulfur which is known to cause SCC of many alloys. They are meant to examine parameters that affect cracking behavior in a relatively short testing time. The fact is that many of the alloys discussed have been used successfully in field applications. What is important to gather from this discussion of CRAs is that many factors affect corrosion and cracking resistance, and when an alloy must be selected for a particular application, all of these factors must be considered.

One alternative to solid CRA components is the use of CRA clad over carbon and low-alloy steel. While these materials are available, the industry has been slow to adopt them, especially for downhole applications. Clad tubing has been run and performed successfully in a few instances. The obvious cost advantage over solid CRA should provide an impetus for further use in the future.

From the different possible corrosion-related failure mechanisms discussed, It is evident that the design of a tubular string must take into account all of these factors.

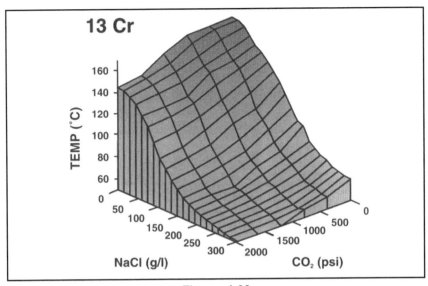

Figure 4-39

The corrosion resistance of 13 Cr martensitic stainless steel in CO_2/NaCl environments in the absence of oxygen and H_2S (Courtesy of the Nickel Institute).

At the top of the hole where the string may be close to ambient temperature, failure by SSC is most probable, while at the bottom of the hole where the temperature is greatest, chloride cracking is of primary concern. Between these two extremes, failure may occur by either or both mechanisms. Pitting attack and general weight-loss corrosion will be greatest near the bottom of the string because of temperature. But since water may not drop out as a liquid until farther up the string, these problems can be expected almost anywhere in the well.

One can appreciate from this discussion of tubulars that no set rules exist for materials selection for tubing and casing. Furthermore, many corrosion mechanisms may be operative at the same time, so each must be considered and the likelihood of its contribution weighed against the cost of alloying to avoid failure.

In addition to the corrosion resistance of various CRAs, the variation in mechanical properties of cold worked CRAs with direction in the tube must be considered during string design. The difference in yield strength and tensile strength from the longitudinal direction to the tangential or transverse direction is referred to as anisotropy. All alloys generally possess some degree of anisotropy however, cold working tends to exacerbate anisotropy. Table 4-8 shows this behavior for Alloy G50. The degree of anisotropy varies considerably depending on the alloy and the amount of cold working it has been exposed to in order to achieve the desired mechanical properties. The difference between longitudinal and transverse properties can reach 10% or more.

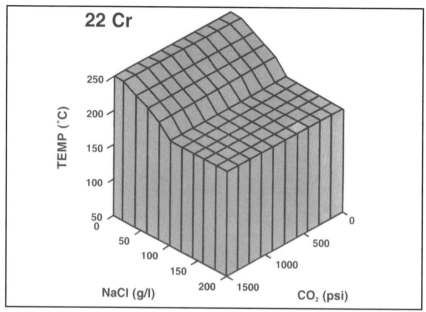

Figure 4-40

The corrosion resistance of 22 Cr duplex stainless steel in CO_2/NaCl
in the absence of oxygen and H_2S (Courtesy of Nickel Institute).

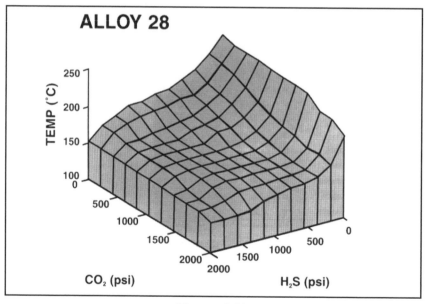

Figure 4-41

The corrosion resistance of Alloy 28 in H_2S/CO_2 environments
in the absence of elemental sulfur (Courtesy of Nickel Institute).

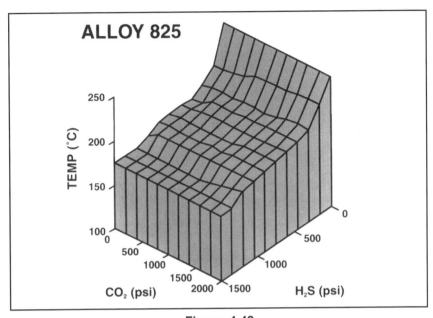

Figure 4-42
The corrosion resistance of Alloy 825 in H_2S/CO_2 environments in the absence of elemental sulfur (Courtesy of Nickel Institute).

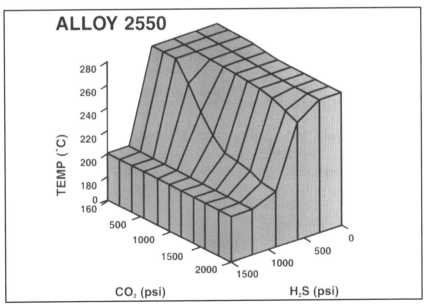

Figure 4-43
The corrosion resistance of Alloy 2550 in H_2S/CO_2 environments in the absence of elemental sulfur (Courtesy of Nickel Institute).

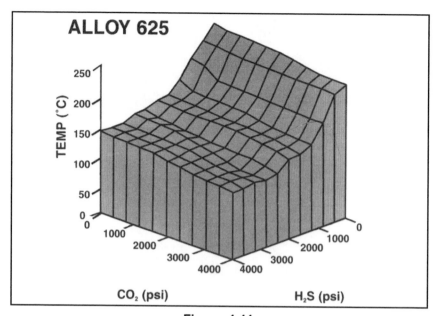

Figure 4-44
The corrosion resistance of Alloy 625 in H_2S/CO_2 environments in the absence of elemental sulfur (Courtesy of Nickel Institute).

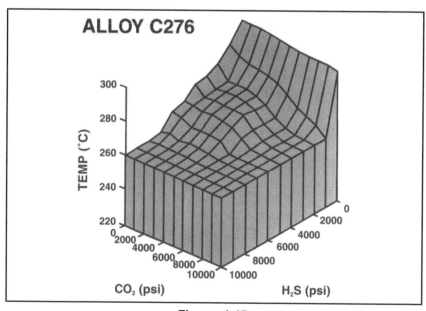

Figure 4-45
The corrosion resistance of Alloy C276 in H_2S/CO_2 environments in the absence of elemental sulfur (Courtesy of Nickel Institute).

Both anisotropy and the potential loss in yield strength and tensile strength where exposed to well temperatures (referred to as well aging) must be included in the tube properties when designing strings for burst, collapse and axial loading.

In the final analysis the selection of CRAs for specific well applications is a complex function of the many variables discussed in this chapter. However, it can be helpful, especially during the economic evaluation phase of a new well or field, to have a general idea of the CRAs that may or may not be suitable for an application. Figures 4-39 to 4-45 provide a general guideline for selecting CRAs based on well conditions. Within the shaded areas of each diagram the corrosion rate for that alloy is less than or equal to 2 mpy (0.05 mm/y) and the alloy is resistant to SSC and SCC.

Expandable Tubulars

Before leaving the subject of casing and tubing it is important to mention the increasing uses of expandable tubulars. Solid expandable tubulars were primarily developed to minimize the number of casing strings in wells and reduce the telescoping effect of conventional well completions. To date the majority of expanded casing has been ERW casing with an 80,000 psi minimum yield strength. In some cases a P110 grade has been used. Expansion proceeds by one of two methods. One method uses hydraulic pressure and an expansion cone that is pumped to the bottom of the string then swaging begins from the bottom up as the cone is tripped out of the hole. The other method uses a rotary expansion tool that runs top down through the casing. This expansion results in a significant amount of plastic deformation of the original casing. The wall thickness is reduced while the length of the casing increases. The expansion of the casing will increase the burst strength of the casing but lower the collapse strength (referred to as the Bauschinger Effect). These two methods produce differing degrees of strain hardening so that the resulting mechanical properties will be different. In addition to the reduction in collapse resistance, expanded tubulars will suffer from a process called strain aging that can adversely affect the fracture toughness of the tubulars and further diminish their resistance to SSC (Mack and Filippov). Since uniform expansion is desirable, ERW casing is used more often because of its more uniform wall thickness compared to seamless casing.

Many of these issues have been considered and investigated however much more work needs to be done to alleviate concerns over the final properties of the tubulars. The important concerns that remain are: the integrity and leak tightness of the expanded threaded connections, the effect of expansion on burst, collapse and axial load of casing; and the effect on the corrosion resistance of tubulars, especially the SSC resistance.

Sucker Rods

Sucker rods represent another kind of downhole equipment that frequently fails. The movement of sucker rods results in a cyclic load on the whole string and each rod individually as a result of the up-and-down stroke during pumping. In one complete cycle of the rod string, the rods go through several stress cycles because of the acceleration and deceleration of the string and the elastic elongation of each individual rod. The maximum stress occurs on the upstroke and the minimum stress on the downstroke. The loading on the entire string and on each rod individually is fatigue.

Sucker-rod metallurgy and properties are covered under API Specification 11B and the polished rod under 11D. The chemical and mechanical properties are reproduced from the API in Table 4-9.

Table 4-9 Chemical and Mechanical Properties of Sucker Rods

Grade	Chemical Composition	Tensile Strength, psi Min.	Max
K	AISI 46XX	85,000	115,000
C	AISI 1036*	90,000	115,000
D	Carbon or alloy **	115,000	140,000

* Not restricted to AISI 1036 steel
**Any composition that can be effectively heat treated to the minimum ultimate tensile strength
(After API 11B, table 2-1)

A compilation of mechanical and chemical properties of some of the commercially available sucker rods is shown in Table 4-10. Additional processing is included for some rods to increase the fatigue performance. This may be done by means of induction-hardening the surface or by shot-peening the surface. These two treatments place the surface in compression—in some cases as high as 125,000 psi for the induction hardening—which produces a case hardness of BHN 475-50. Compressive stresses of 67,000 psi have been measured after shot peening.

Couplings and subcouplings for pin-pin rods have essentially no chemical composition requirements and limited mechanical property requirements under the API. Class T couplings must be manufactured a hardness range of Rockwell C 16-23. The sulfur content must not exceed 0.050%, which is the only chemical composition requirement.

Couplings are available in quenched and tempered AISI 4640 steels, which is case hardened to HRC 50-60 for wear resistance or spray metal coated with nickel-base powders (containing chromium, boron, and silicon) to a minimum thickness of 0.010 in. with hardnesses exceeding HV 595.

Polished rods used at the top of the string and run through the packing are manufactured from 1045 piston steel, ground and polished; 4140 low-alloy steel; cold-drawn bronze; cold-drawn Type 304 stainless steel; or Monel. They are also supplied with a hard facing or are chrome-plated.

Depending on the source of information, from 60-80% of all sucker-rod failures occur in the body; the remainder occur in the connections. These failures are predominantly the result of corrosion fatigue, as would be expected from the cyclic nature of their application. Figures 4-46 through 4-48 show examples of sucker-rod corrosion that resulted in corrosion-fatigue failures.

Figure 4-46
CO_2 corrosion of a sucker-rod body showing localized attack and plateaus common to this form of corrosion.

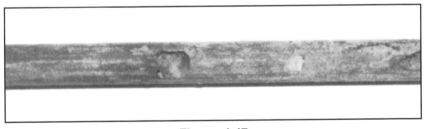

Figure 4-47
Pitting attack of sucker-rod body from H_2S.
Note random large pits with little other corrosion of the body.

Figure 4-48
Row of pits along one side of a rod leading to corrosion-fatigue failure.

Table 4-10 Chemical Composition and Mechanical Properties of Common Commercial Sucker Rods

Manufacturer	Designation	Alloy	C	Mn	P (Maximum)	S	Si	Ni	Cr	Mo	Other
API GRADE C (carbon steel)											
Weatherford	S-60	1029M	0.22-0.29	1.00-1.35	0.025	0.040	0.15-0.30				
Weatherford (Corod)	CD	1036M	(0.34)	(1.33)			(0.26)				
Upco	35	1536	0.30-0.37	1.20-1.50	0.040	0.040	0.15-0.30				
Norris	30	1536M	0.30-0.39	1.10-1.40	0.040	0.045	0.20-0.30				0.02-0.07V
API GRADE K (nickel-molybdenum alloy)											
Weatherford	S-59	46XX	0.14-0.22	0.55-0.75	0.025	0.035	0.15-0.35	1.65-2.00		0.20-0.30	
Upco	45	4621M	0.20-0.25	0.60-0.80	0.025	0.035	0.20-0.30	1.60-2.00		0.15-0.25	
Norris	40	4621M	0.18-0.25	0.60-0.80	0.035	0.035	0.15-0.35	1.65-2.00		0.15-0.25	0.03-0.07V
API GRADE D											
Carbon steel											
Weatherford	X-67	1029M	0.22-0.29	1.00-1.35	0.025	0.040	0.15-0.30				
Upco	75	1541	0.36-0.44	1.35-1.55	0.030	0.030	0.15-0.30				
Chrome-molybdenum alloy											
Upco	75	4142	0.39-0.46	0.65-1.10	0.040	0.040	0.20-0.35		0.75-1.20	0.15-0.25	
Norris	78	4142M	0.38-0.45	0.80-1.00	0.035	0.035	0.15-0.30	0.45 max.	0.80-1.10	0.15-0.25	
Norris	90	4320M	0.18-0.24	0.80-1.00	0.025	0.025	0.20-0.35	1.15-1.50	0.70-0.90	0.20-0.30	
Special alloy											
Weatherford	S-87	3130	0.22-0.29	0.70-1.00	0.025	0.040	0.15-0.35	0.70-1.00	0.41-0.65	0.20-0.30	
Norris	97	4330M	0.28-35	0.70-0.90	0.035	0.35	0.15-0.30	1.65-2.00	0.70-0.90	0.20-0.30	0.03-0.07V
MISCELLANEOUS											
Weatherford	EL	Special	0.38-0.42	1.00-1.30	0.040	0.040	0.15-0.30	0.30 Max	0.55-0.85	0.24-0.55	

Notes: M-modified.

Table 4-10   (continued)

Manufacturer	Designation	Yield Strength, 1,000 psi	Tensile Strength, 1,000 psi	Elongation 8 in., %	Reduction of Area, %	Brinell Hardness	Heat Treatment
API GRADE C (carbon steel)							
Weatherford	S-60	90/105	100/115	13 min	55 min	207-235	Quenched & tempered
Weatherford (Corod)	CD	100 min	115 max		50-60	250-260	Quenched & tempered
Upco	35	60 min	90/115	18-23	50-60	190-205	Normalized
Norris	30	60 min	90/115	15 min	45 min		Normalized & tempered
API GRADE K (nickel-molybdenum alloy)							
Weatherford	S-59	90/105	100/115	13 min	55 min	207-235	Quenched & tempered
Upco	45	68/80	85/100	18-25	60-70	175-207	Normalized & tempered
Norris	40	60 min	90/115	16 min	55 min		Normalized & tempered
API GRADE D							
Carbon steel							
Weatherford	S-67	110/125	120/140	11 min	55 Min	248-277	Quenched & tempered
Upco	75	90/110	120/140	15 min	45 Min	241-280	Normalized
Chrome-molybdenum alloy							
Upco	75	100/115	120/140	10-15	50-65	241-280	Normalized & tempered
Norris	78	85 min	115/140	10 min	45 min		Normalized & tempered
Norris	90	115/125	140/150	10 min	45 min		Normalized & tempered
Special alloy							
Weatherford	S-87	115/130	125/140	12 min	55 min	248-280	Quenched & tempered
Norris	97	90/100	115/125	14-18	50-60	235-250	Normalized & tempered
MISCELLANEOUS							
Weatherford	EL*						Induction case hardened

* General properties not applicable due to differences in case and core properties.

165

Figure 4-49
Tong marks on shoulder of rod jut below coupling that resulted in a fatigue failure.

Occasionally, failure is the result of tensile overload and will display the necked-down area in the region of fracture. This is, of course, caused by exceeding the tensile strength of the rod and is commonly the result of pulling a subsurface pump that is stuck in the tubing.

Mechanical fatigue from improper rod handling is another frequent cause of failure. In this case, nicks and notches from tools induce sufficient stress concentrations to enhance fatigue cracking as discussed in the chapter on drilling. Figures 4-49 and 4-50 show failures related to mechanical damage.

Depending on the environment a sucker rod is subjected to, heat treatment and chemical composition of the rod can have significantly different effects on the fatigue life. In environments in which hydrogen sulfide is present, corrosion fatigue may be accelerated by the effects of sulfide stress cracking or hydrogen-enhanced fatigue-crack growth. Thus, rods with hardnesses above HRC 22 may not perform as well as lower-strength rods. In fact at high strength, rapid fracture

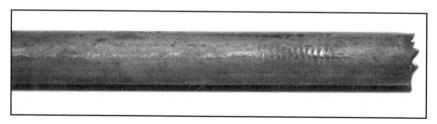

Figure 4-50
Tool marks on body caused notches that ultimately led to a fatigue failure.

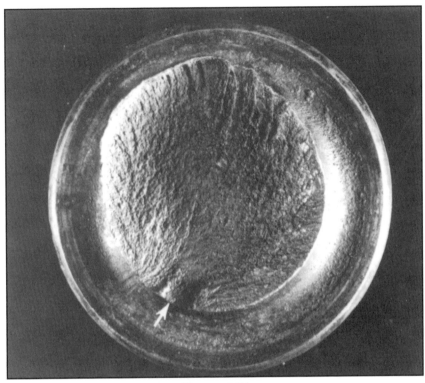

Figure 4-51
Fracture surface of induction-hardened rod from SSC.
Arrow indicates fracture origin.

by SSC can occur with essentially no fatigue. Figure 4-51 shows an Induction-hardened rod that has failed by SSC. Table 4-10 illustrates that higher strength rods in hydrogen sulfide can give poor performance. The addition of alloying elements such as chromium and molybdenum (e.g., 1036 versus 4142) does not increase service life as might be expected but can act to decrease it. In fact, much work on corrosion fatigue of carbon steels versus low-alloy steels shows that minor amounts of alloying do not increase fatigue resistance, nor do they enhance corrosion resistance. This is because there just is not enough alloy present to provide resistance to pitting, which is one of the initiating factors in corrosion fatigue.

In sweet wells in which only chlorides and carbon dioxide are present, some evidence indicates low-alloy steels may have an advantage over carbon steels (e.g., 1036 steel) from a corrosion-resistance standpoint. Figure 4-52 shows the reduced corrosion of AISI 4340 and 3235 steel compared to 1036 steel in a sweet environment. In practice, however, little difference is usually found in the corrosion-fatigue resistance of carbon and low-alloy steels. There are few high alloy

167

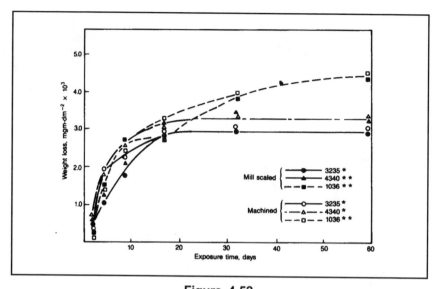

Figure 4-52
Weight-loss data for AISI 3235, 4340, and 1036 Steels.
*Hot-rolled normalized and tempered. ** Hot-rolled and normalized
(After Snape and Van Rooyen, © ASME).

rods available (see Table 4-9), and little information exists on their behavior in corrosive wells. More often fiberglass rods are used for corrosion resistance than are corrosion resistant alloy rods.

One method to promote corrosion resistance and increase corrosion-fatigue life has been plasma-arc spraying of a 316 stainless steel coating on Grade C or D rods. In this process, particles of the stainless steel are carried by an arc plasma

Table 4-11 Classification of Sucker-Rod Steels According to API Specification in Relation to Their Corrosion-Fatigue Performance in H_2S + CO_2 + Brine

Material	Heat Treatment	UTS, ksi	Hardness Rockwell C	Corrosion Fatigue Life at 36,000/12,000 psi Stress		Min. UTS, ksi API Spec	API Class
				No. of Cycles x 10⁶	Service Life Months[1]		
1036	N	102	8	8.63	13	90	C
4621	N&T (1,000°F)	89	10	5.19	7.5	82	K
1036	Q&T (1,000°F)	124	21	9.10	13.2	115	D
1036	Q&T (900°F)	137	29	4.72	6.8	115	D
4142	N&T (1,000°F)	127	27	5.96	8.5	115	D
4340	N&T (1,000°F)	134	28	3.73	5.4	115	D

[1] Equivalent service life of a polished sucker rod at a rate of 16 cpm.
(After Mehdizadeh)

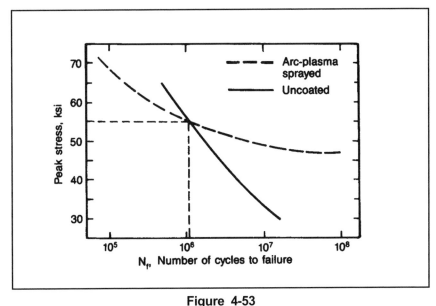

Figure 4-53

Enhancement of fatigue life for arc-plasma-sprayed 316 stainless-steel rods over uncoated Grade C rods (After Chen and Mehdizadeh).

stream to the surface of the rod, where they immediately solidify. This is followed by the application of a fusion bond epoxy top coat. The total coating thickness is typically on the order of 16-17 mils. Laboratory testing (see Figure 4-53) shows the beneficial effect of this process when the coated rods are subjected to an environments containing hydrogen sulfide, carbon dioxide, and brine. The coated rods can be subjected to a much higher peak stress than uncoated rods, and a true threshold behavior returns to the coated rod. However, above 55 ksi peak applied stress, the brittle 316 coating cracks and fatigue resistance is reduced compared to the uncoated rod. Using a fatigue-life criteria of 10^7 cycle, it is evident that a 40% increase in peak operating stress is available by using the coated rod. However, the bonding strength of the coating is the limiting factor in performance of plasma-sprayed rods, so care must be taken when running higher-strength rods.

Sucker-rod couplings can be another source of rod string failures. Improper makeup of the couplings to the rods can result in coupling fatigue failures. Looseness of the joint allows fatigue crack initiation at the root of the coupling thread next to the last engaged thread of the pin. A typical fracture surface in a coupling is shown in Figure 4-54. Another frequent cause of coupling failure is externally initiated. For example, hammering the coupling, pipe-wrench jaw marks, corrosion, or wear can produce notches that initiate fatigue cracks from the outside surface of the coupling, as shown in Figure 4-54.

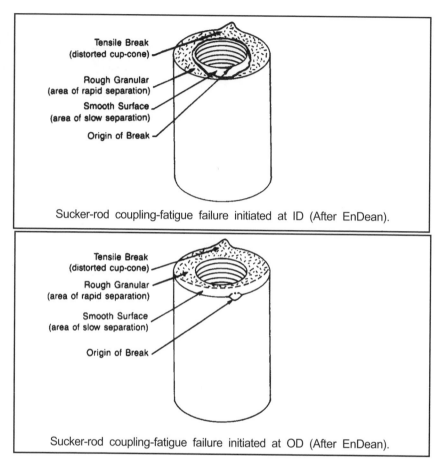

Sucker-rod coupling-fatigue failure initiated at ID (After EnDean).

Sucker-rod coupling-fatigue failure initiated at OD (After EnDean).

Figure 4-54

Less often, failure of the pin can occur if the joint is overtorqued. This will usu-ally be quite apparent when the joints are being made up, and failure will occur in the shoulder of the rod.

Wear and corrosion resistance can be dealt with metallurgically by using spray metal couplings. API Specification 11B designates two grades of couplings: T (bare metal) and SM (spray metal). The hardness of the former must be in the range HRC 16-23 and the spray metal on the later greater than HV 595.

The use of bare metal and spray metal coupling and rods is at the center of a predicament in rod-pumped wells. In many rod-pumped wells for numerous rea-sons the rods slap against the tubing and/or the couplings rub against the tubing. Either the tubing, rods, or couplings then preferentially fail by rapid metal loss.

This is frequently and incorrectly blamed on wear and a hard surfacing or spray metal is applied to the couplings or rods for wear resistance. Of course this just transfers the problem to the tubing. In actual fact, these problems are not primarily wear or erosion but rather corrosion accelerated by wear. As the rods slap the tubing or the couplings rub against the tubing they locally remove the semi-protective corrosion product layer and/or the corrosion inhibitor leaving bare metal behind that quickly corrodes. After each stroke, more bare metal is available for corrosion in preference to those areas that are still covered with corrosion product and/or inhibitor. Accelerated corrosion then ensues until failure of the rods, couplings, or tubing occurs. Although centralizers and rod guides would reduce tubing wear from couplings and rods, there is a reluctance by workover crews to run this type of equipment. Care should be taken not to create one problem while solving another.

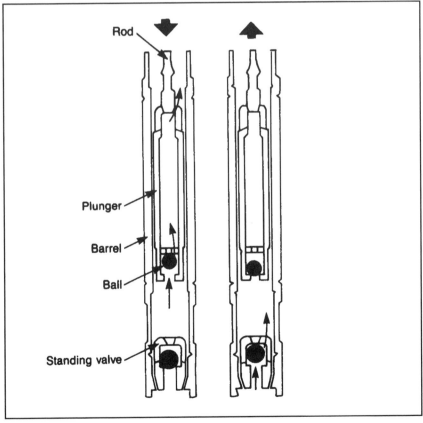

Figure 4-55

Sucker-rod tubing pump showing the different components (After Bruton).

171

Subsurface Pumps

The two most common subsurface pumps are electric submersible pumps (ESP), sucker-rod pumps. Sucker-rod pump requirements are detailed in API Standard 11AX, but little information is provided about the metallurgy. Most pumps fail by corrosion and/or abrasion. There are three basic types of subsurface pumps: rod pumps, tubing pumps, and casing pumps. Just as the designators imply, the first operates by inserting the pump into the tubing string and landing it on a hold-down. For the second, the pump barrel and standing valve are installed as part of the tubing string, and the third is like the first except it is installed on the sucker-rod string and run in the casing without using tubing. A typical rod pump is shown in Figure 4-55 with the various parts designated.

Table 4-12 gives the chemistries of the most common alloys used for barrels and plungers in sucker-rod pumps. Although this is by no means complete, it does represent a majority of those alloys used in the manufacture of subsurface pumps.

Since carbon-steel components corrode rapidly In even slightly corrosive environments containing hydrogen sulfide and/or carbon dioxide, it is common to chrome plate many surfaces, including the pump barrel. However, chromium plate is porous, quite hard, and easily cracked, which leads to a severe galvanic effect at the breaks. The resulting galvanic corrosion can be rapid and catastrophic. Figure 4-56 shows an example of this problem on a pump plunger.

Electroless nickel plate can have exactly the same type of problem. This strong galvanic couple can be overcome by plating over an alloy such as brass, monel, or stainless steel that is closer in the galvanic series. Pump plungers are often sprayed with a material like Colmonoy No. 6 (chromium boride and chromium carbide in a nickel matrix) for wear resistance. More recently titanium boride and silicon carbide coatings have been effectively used.

Wear is one of the most common causes of failure of subsurface pump components, so many of the parts are surface treated with spray metal or by nitriding, carburizing, and plating. Because of this mixed metallurgy and the desire to use as economical a base metal as possible, galvanic corrosion is the primary corrosion problem in rod pumps, although SSC can also be a problem with heat treatments that produce high hardness. Specific information on selection of alloys for sucker-rod pumps Is available in NACE Standard MR-01-76, "Metallic Materials for Sucker Rod Pumps for Oilfield Corrosive Environments."

ESPs are typically constructed of carbon steel or 9Cr-1Mo housings with 416 or 410 stainless steel heads and bases. The impellers are generally made from Ni Resist (cast iron). For more corrosive applications duplex stainless steels are used for housing and impellers and heads and bases.

Table 4-12 Chemical Composition of Most Common Alloys Used for Subsurface Rod Pump Barrels and Plungers

Alloy	C	Mn	Si	Element (wt%, max.)	
				S	P
1015	0.18	0.60		0.05	0.04
1020	0.23	0.60		0.05	0.04
1025	0.28	0.60		0.05	0.04
1035	0.38	0.90		0.05	0.04
1040	0.44	0.90		0.05	0.04
4130	0.33	0.60	0.35	0.04	0.04
4615	0.18	0.65	0.35	0.04	0.04
4640	0.43	0.80	0.35	0.04	0.04
8645	0.48	1.00	0.35	0.04	0.04
Nitralloy N	0.27	0.70	0.40		
Nitralloy 135	0.40	0.70	0.40		
4–6 Chrome	0.10	0.60	0.50	0.04	
303 SS	0.15	2.00	1.00	0.15 min.	0.20
304 SS	0.08	2.00	1.00	0.03	0.045
70–30 Brass					
85–15 Brass					
443 Admiralty brass					
Monel R405	0.30	2.00	0.50		
Monel R400	0.30	2.00	0.50		
Gray cast iron	3.30	0.70	2.40	0.12	
White cast Iron	3.20	0.60	0.50	0.12	0.05
Eutectic cast Iron	3.70	0.60	2.00	0.05	

(After Bruton)

Christmas Tree and Wellhead Equipment

The Christmas tree represents the primary surface control of a well. Figure 4-57 shows a typical tree of which there are numerous variations, depending on temperature, pressure, and produced fluids, The two means of flow control are valves and chokes. Most often, Christmas-tree valves (e.g., wing, master, and swab) are gate-type valves. Since chokes are of similar design, the following discussion will refer to general aspects of both because the metallurgical requirements for fracture and corrosion resistance will be essentially identical. Christmas-tree components are covered by API Specification 6A (ISO 10423). Most valve bodies to be used in noncorrosive environments at temperatures from -20 to 250°F are constructed of ASTM A 487 Grade 4 steel, AISI 4130, or 8630 modified steel, either forged or cast. The bonnets are made from wrought material of the same composition, usually 4140 steel, as are the stem and gates. Seats typically are also made

173

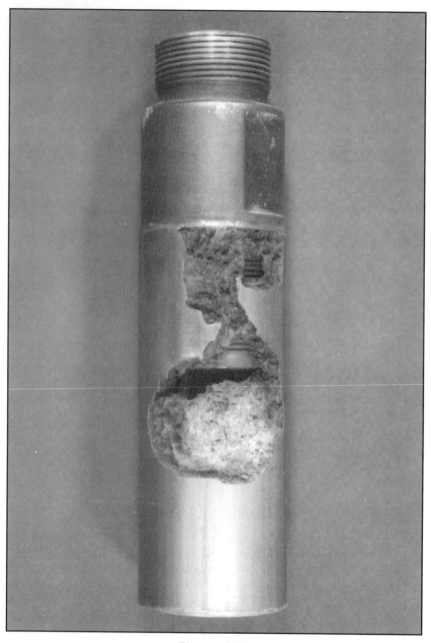

Figure 4-56
Rod pump punger failure as a result of breaks in chrome plate leading
to galvanic corrosion of low-alloy steel plunger body.

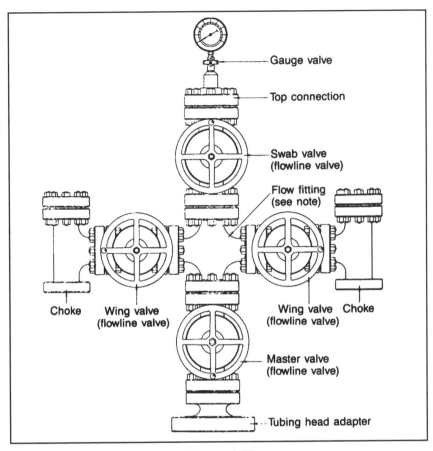

Figure 4-57

Typical Christmas tree (After API Specification 6A).

of 4140 steel, although there are some variations from manufacturer to manufacturer. Gates are usually molydisulfide coated or plated with nickel or chromium.

For application in corrosive environments, a variety of metallurgy is available from manufacturers depending on the particular conditions of the well. When SSC is a potential problem and NACE MR-01-75 (ISO 15156) requirements are mandated, the body and bonnet are often made of 8630 modified, 4130 or 2-1/4 Cr-1 Mo quenched and tempered to a maximum hardness of Rockwell C 22. The gate and seats are made of Type 410 or 17-4PH stainless steel. Sometimes seats are overlayed with Stellite No. 6 or a flame sprayed tungsten carbide coating for wear and corrosion resistance. Historically stems were made of 410 stainless steel, Monel K500, or 17-4 PH precipitation hardening stainless steel. In very sour service all of these stem materials have failed from SSC. Therefore, for sour service stems ISO 15156 now basically only allows 4130, Alloy 718 or Alloy 725.

In environments in which only carbon dioxide is present but in concentrations expected to be quite corrosive, Type 410 stainless steel, ASTM A217 CA-15 (cast stainless equivalent to wrought 410), F6NM (forged equivalent to 410) or CA6NM (ASTM A487) are used for body and bonnet, especially when low temperature impact toughness is required. Type 410 stainless-steel gates and seats are also installed. The gates are often coated with molydisulfide and/or are hard surfaced or nitrided since carbon dioxide is notorious for increasing corrosion in areas of high wear or velocity. Stems are made of either 410 stainless steel or 17-4 PH. In high CO_2 concentration, solid 316 stainless steel trees have been successful.

If both hydrogen sulfide and carbon dioxide are present but pressure is low, the body and bonnet are usually made of 410 stainless steel, (CA-15 or CA6NM), with 410 stainless steel or Monel K500 gates and seats and either Alloy 718 or 725 stems. All parts have controlled hardness conforming to NACE MR-01-75/ISO 15156.

For low-temperature applications such as arctic service, notch toughness is the most important criteria. To meet API 6A impact requirements, alloys such as 8630 modified, 4130, 2-1/4 Cr-1 Mo, or F6NM stainless quenched and tempered must be used for all pressure containment components. In cases in which hydrogen sulfide and carbon dioxide or a combination of the two are present, F6NM, duplex stainless steels or Alloy 625 clad steel are used.

Even with the wide selection of materials available for aggressive environments, these low-alloy steels and stainless steels are not adequate for many highly corrosive environments. As shown in Figure 4-39, 13% Cr stainless steel offers limited resistance to elevated temperature carbon dioxide corrosion. For higher concentrations of carbon dioxide and associated brines at elevated temperature, more protection is needed. In some fields that produce carbon dioxide, type 316 stainless steel bodies and bonnets have been successful because of high velocities through the tree, and temperatures have been low enough to avoid stress-corrosion cracking. However, the achievable strength of austenitic stainless steel components is low, so when high-pressure wells or very corrosive wells are completed, either a heat-treatable CRA must be used for components or corrosion resistant overlays must be applied. The former is often cost prohibitive in most cases although solid duplex stainless steel and Incoloy 925 trees have been made and installed. A more cost effective solution to the use of solid CRA components is to clad the wetted areas with CRA but use a heat-treatable low-alloy steel shell.

Weld overlaying of 4130 or 2-1/4 Cr-1 Mo steel base metal is performed using gas metal-arc welding (GMAW) more commonly known as metal inert-gas (MIG) welding with Inconel 625 wire. All surfaces that will be wetted by the corrosive stream are overlayed and then ground smooth. This type of procedure has several built-in problems that must be examined for each application. For instance, weld dilution will form an alloy at the steel/overlay interface with properties entirely different from either the base metal or welding wire. It has been found,

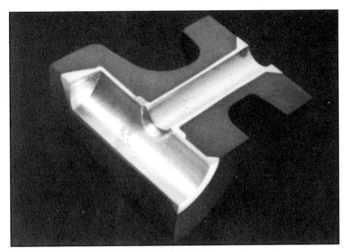

Figure 4-58
Section through a CRA clad steel valve.

however, that when using Alloy 625 filler metal for cladding, an iron concentration in the top layer of up to 10-15% maximum is acceptable and does not compromise the corrosion resistance. The heat-affected zone can also become quite hard and susceptible to hydrogen stress cracking or reduced fracture toughness. If overlaying is incomplete, small anodes of low-alloy steel will be coupled to a large cathode of alloy metal that presents a serious galvanic-corrosion problem. In contrast to these potential drawbacks, weld overlay trees have successfully functioned in very severe environments for over 20 years with no reported failures.

An alternative to weld overlay is to hot isostatically pressed (HIP) nickel-base alloys into low-alloy bodies. The application of the HIP process to valve bodies allows development of a good metallurgical bond with the base metal and with the assurance of uniform microstructure, properties, and thickness of the CRA. Almost any alloy can be HIPed, and work has been done on a variety of common engineering alloys such as Inconel 625, Hastelloy C-276, and MP35N. Inconel 625 is the most common material for HIP clad and these components have been as successful as the weld overlay components.

The advantage of the HIP-clad valves is the resultant wrought structure of the alloy material, which is more homogeneous and thus less susceptible to localized corrosion as is the cast structure of a weld overlay. Furthermore, interfacial dilution extends only about 0.05 mm into the clad, whereas on overlays it ex tends on the order of 3.2 mm. However, problems have been encountered in the past with incomplete removal of the steel cans necessary to the HIP process. Remnants of steel on the surface of the CRA can compromise the performance of the clad. Figure 4-58 shows a section of a clad valve body. The higher cost of HIP cladding compared to weld overlay has essentially elimiated this process from the marketplace.

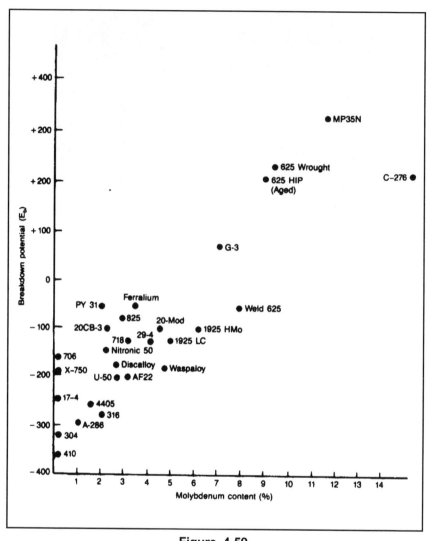

Figure 4-59
Resistance of various alloys to localized corrosion (E_b) as a function of molybdenum content in 11Wt% NaCl brine with 500 psi of CO_2 at 250°F (121°C) (After Bednarowicz).

The resistance to localized attack in a CO2-Cl environment as a function of molybdenum content of an alloy is shown in Figure 4-59. These alloys were examined for potential cladding in valves. As is evident, increasing resistance to pitting, which is described by the breakdown potential, occurs with increasing molybdenum content. The very high resistance to pitting of Inconel 625 explains why it is preferred for cladding.

Failures of valve components in hydrogen sulfide systems have occured in stem material of hardness that meet those recommended by the NACE MR-01-75 specification. Inconel X-750 was a common alloy used for stem construction until frequent field failures caused by SSC required its replacement with Alloy 718, which has performed much better. Valve stems made of Monel K500 that were heat treated in accordance with MR-01-75 have also failed by SSC at hardnesses below the HRC 35 maximum imposed by MR-01-75. In addition, valve bodies made of 410 stainless steel with hardness greater than HRC 22 and bonnets made from Ledloy A at a hardness of BHN 174 have failed in hydrogen sulfide environments. Neither of these, however, met the MR-01-75 requirements.

Few valve body failures have occurred because of environmental cracking, primarily because body and bonnet sections are quite thick for pressure containment; therefore, applied stresses are lower, which reduces the potential for cracking. However, there have been some failures of 410 stainless steel tree valves from SSC even though the material met the HRC22 maximum required by MR0175/ISO 15156. Bodies more often fail from corrosion in stagnant areas that allow fluids that contain hydrogen sulfide, carbon dioxide, and/or oxygen to accumulate.

Chromium or nickel plating (electrolytic or electroless) is not always beneficial. Gates are often plated for corrosive production service or waterflood service. If the plate becomes damaged or microcracks form, as is often the case in high flow areas, severe pitting attack follows at the base of the crack—again caused by a galvanic effect when the base metal is a low-alloy steel. Systems containing dissolved oxygen are particularly susceptible to galvanic attack.

In those cases where corrosion resistance must be combined with good erosion resistance, hard facing using plasma transferred arc (PTA)-applied Tribaloy, or Stellite coatings such as T-800 and No. 4, respectively, are suitable. Also, detonation ("D") gun-applied LW45 has been successfully used for severe service. More recently, coatings applied using the high velocity oxy-fuel (HVOF) process have been successful. Selection of a corrosion-erosion resistant hard facing for gates and slats is best accomplished by testing the product in the actual or simulated environment.

One other area in which valves are commonly used is in waterfloods. Here, water is injected into the ground for secondary recovery of oil, and it is common for injection pressures to reach 4,000 psi. Since the water is gathered from a source well or surface source such as tanks, oxygen is a prime culprit in corrosion. If produced water is commingled with other water for injection, hydrogen sulfide and carbon dioxide may also be present. Chlorides and suspended solids, which may imparl a high degree of abrasion and erosion, especially to valve components, are usually added to these corrodents.

Bodies and bonnets for waterflood valves are constructed of quenched and tempered 4130 or 4140 steel, while gates are made variously of chromium or nickel-plated low-alloy steel such as 4130, 316 stainless steel, or 17-4 PH stainless steel. Stems are usually made of 17-4 PH stainless steel in the H1150 condition, while seats are made of 316 or 17-4 PH stainless steel.

Most problems in waterflood service are corrosion of the body and gates, erosion of the seats, and erosion-corrosion of the body. Plated gates have short lives if the water is oxygenated—again from galvanic corrosion between the noble metal plating and the low-alloy steel base metal. The same occurs in the body and bonnet when they are plastic coated, usually with a baked phenolic. Local breaks in the coating result in failure because of pitting of the base metal.

NACE International has compiled tables for easy access to information on the metallurgy of valves and components to be used in waterflood service. The particular limitations and uses of these alloys are described in detail in NACE Recommended Practice RP-04-75 and should be consulted prior to any selection. The tabulated conditions are for aerated water containing more than 10 ppb oxygen: nonaerated, less than 10 ppb; with H_2S, more than 1 ppm, and without H_2S, less than 1 ppm.

One other component of Christmas trees that frequently require special metallurgy are chokes. Chokes are frequently subjected to erosion from liquids or solids in the flow stream, abrasion and/or cavitation. Abrasion is associated with surfaces sliding against each other and is accelerated by particles between these surfaces. Cavitation is wear damage caused by the formation and collapse of vapor bubbles in a fluid. These bubbles can create pressures on the order of 200,000 psi when they collapse, severely damaging the metal surface. Thus chokes are subjected to extremely severe wear and the choice of materials to resist these forms of wear are not always obvious. For example, increasing hardness does not always translate to increasing erosion resistance since there is often a corrosion component to the attack; therefore, the most resistant material may be softer than other alloys but more corrosion resistant. It has been found that for excellent erosion and abrasion resistance, tungsten carbide with very low nickel binder content and ceramics are the best. Cobalt binders for tungsten carbide are not recommended since they are susceptible to leaching and SCC in produced fluids. For cavitation resistance in liquid service, stellites and nickel chromium alloys followed by stainless steels, tungsten carbide, and ceramics are best.

Subsea Christmas Trees

Subsea Christmas trees and wellheads are described in API 17D/ISO13628-4 which has many similarities to API 6A. However, one of the significant differences between surface and subsurface equipment is the exposure of relatively high strength fasteners to sea water and cathodic protection (CP) systems. Many factors need to be considered when selecting fasteners for subsea applications.

Subsea equipment is usually constructed from many different materials which are not inherently immune from corrosion in sea water, and which depend upon CP for their long term service. While it is not necessary for the more highly alloyed materials to be polarized to the same negative potentials as carbon steel to prevent localized corrosion, it is normally impractical to electrically isolate them from the main carbon steel structure. In fact, it is necessary to go to great lengths to ensure that all metallic components are electrically continuous. Typical practices include the use of continuity straps, disc washers beneath bolt heads, the removal of paint from contact surfaces.

Corrosion can take many forms which will affect the stability of the clamping force and the life of the bolts. Mechanical failure and fatigue can be accelerated or made more likely by corrosion. The galvanic series determines the potential of metals in sea water with those at the top of the galvanic series being anodic compared to those listed towards the end of the chart. Aluminum for example is anodic in the presence of steel and steel is anodic in the presence of stainless steel.

One of the most common problems dealing with bolted joints in subsea application is corrosion. Materials requirements to resist corrosion by seawater have increased in recent years especially for use in the exploration and extraction of oil and gas from beneath the ocean floor. A major problem in all this is the corrosivity of the seawater. Corrosion is usually localized, such as pitting and crevice corrosion. If carbon steel is used, normally a protective coating must be applied or protected with a CP system or both.

Pitting, crevice corrosion and hydrogen from the cathodic protection system need to be considered when selecting materials for subsea bolting. Cathodic protection is utilized to protect subsea equipment from corrosion. In cathodic protection with sacrificial anodes, there are always parts of the object where the potential is more negative than the reversible potential of hydrogen evolution, so significant hydrogen evolution always takes place. Under such circumstances corrosion of the anodes generate hydrogen on the cathodes which may then be absorbed by the alloys that are the cathodes and protected by the CP system. The ingress of hydrogen into a component, is an event that can seriously reduce the ductility and load bearing capacity of the fastener, causing cracking and catastrophic brittle failure at stresses below the yield stress of the material.

The most common low alloy steels used for subsea bolting applications are:ASTM A193 B7 or ASTM A320 L7. The chemistry for both materials are identical with ASTM A320 L7 requiring low temperature impacts. These materials are not corrosion resistant and will require the use of CP for corrosion resistance in subsea applications. With subsea equipment, CP is utilized to provide corrosion protection for the structural components. CP will result in some adverse effects that are generated with its use. For example, atomic hydrogen can be absorbed into the surface of the fastener during cleaning, pickling or electroplating operation. Likewise hydrogen can be created at the cathode of a corrosion cell. For subsea applications there are several options that may be utilized for the protection of alloy steel. These options can include the use of coatings for the corrosion protection in seawater or the use of the CP. With the use of coatings, intimate contact with the CP system is not so important providing the flange connections are also low alloy materials. PTFE is a typical coating for low alloy bolting material under CP. The coating is often specified to preserve the bolt surface prior to installation and, with to aid assembly. If PTFE coating is used, care must be taken to ensure electrical continuity between the bolting and the assembly. In cases however, where a coating is not used, it is important that the CP is effective over the full length of the bolt. Each bolt must be connected to the CP system. NORSOK Standard M503 provides a recommendation for electrical continuity.

In many application the use of socket head cap screws are utilized for areas where the area is limited. Standard socket head cap screws are normally purchased per ASTM A574. Cap screws purchased to that specification are manufactured in a hardness range of HRC 38-45. For subsea applications bolts with this high hardness range will be susceptible to hydrogen stress cracking (HSC) by the CP system. In cases as this, consideration should be given to purchase the bolts to lower hardness range (HRC 22 maximum).

When the environments are more aggressive and higher alloy materials are utilized for subsea equipment, selection of bolting becomes critical. Choices for such applications can include using alloy bolting with the understanding that proper CP is utilized on each bolt or a selection of a corrosion resistant alloy bolt may be possible. Corrosion resistant alloys (CRA) are used for bolting in any situation where the CP of low alloy bolting would be considered inadequate. Crevice and pitting and corrosion are also of major concern when selecting fasteners for subsea applications. Pitting is characterized by attack at small discrete areas. The attack can appear quite minor at the surface but have a larger cross section area deeper in the metals. These pits can propagate quickly leading to perforation. Where pitting may be an issue, a pitting resistance equivalent (PRE) formula has been developed which is:

PRE = % Cr + 3.3 % (Mo + 0.5W) + 16 % N

Even though PRE expressions are based on laboratory tests they provide a basis for comparing alloy compositions and thus selecting alloys. A PRE of 40 or greater is normally considered a requirement for immunity to pitting and crevice corrosion in aerated sea water at ambient temperature. Table 4-13 provides PRE (also PREN) values for some common corrosion resistant alloys used for bolting. It should be noted however, that the PRE expression is not an indication of resistant of the alloy to hydrogen embrittlement (HSC). For example, Grade 660 material with a PRE value of 16.8 has been found to be immune to HSC whereas materials such as super duplex are more prone to embrittlement under the same conditions. Table 4-14 shows special considerations required in selecting corrosion resistant alloys for subsea bolting. Typical applications of CRA bolting with advantages and disadvantages of each are as follows:

Super Duplex Stainless Steels (i.e. UNS S32750 or UNS S32760)

The advantage of S32760 and S32760 include strength levels up to ASTM A193 B7M (yield strength of 80,000 psi) with good ductility. Higher strength can be achieved by work, however this is not recommended if the bolting is to be exposed to CP. Super duplex stainless steels have complete corrosion resistance to sea water and have PRE values exceeding 40 which minimizes pitting and crevice corrosion.

The main disadvantage of super duplex is their susceptibility to HSC when exposed to CP. The following precautions are recommended if duplex steels are to be used for bolting:

- Super duplex stainless steels should be in the solution treated condition.
- The hardness should be limited to 280 HBN
- Material should be impact tested to demonstrate freedom from precipitation of deleterious third phases
- Bolt threads should be formed by rolling

Precipitation Hardened Austenitic Stainless Steels

ASTM A453 Gr 660, a precipitation hardened austenitic stainless steel, has been used a bolting material for subsea connections. Its strength is equivalent to that of A193 Gr L7 or B7 materials and has been found to be immune to HSC. Because of the low PRE however this material is not fully corrosion resistant to sea water and will thus require at least at least partial CP to minimize pitting.

Nickel-Based Alloys

Alloy 625 has been used as CRA bolting material. It has moderate strength in the solution treated condition (YS 65,000 psi) and is completely resistant to sea water (PRE > 45) Higher yield strength up to 105,000 psi may be achieved by precipitation hardening or cold work.

Alloy 718 has high strength where the yield strength is greater that 145,000 psi in the precipitation hardened condition, but with a PRE of 26 and cannot be considered fully corrosion resistant in sea water.

Titanium

Titanium alloys are considered immune to corrosion by sea water. The higher strength alpha-beta alloys can be heat treated to strengths in excess of 145,000 psi. However, care must be exercised if titanium is used in a system subject to CP since many of the Ti alloys are very susceptible to hydrogen damage.

Table 4-13 Common Corrosion Resistant Bolting Materials

Common Name	UNS	% Cr	%Ni	%Mo	PREN
316L	S31603	18	12	2.5	22.6
254 SMO	S31254	20	18	6	42.2
Grade 660	S66286	15	25	1.25	16.8
22% Cr	S31803	22	5.5	3	30.5
25%Cr	S32760	25	7	3.5	37.7*
Alloy 925	N09925	21	44	3	27.8
Alloy 625	NO6625	22	60	9	46.4
Alloy 718	NO7718	19	53	3	26.2
Alloy 500	NO5005	0	65	0	N/A

Table 4-14 Special Consideration for Subsea Applications (CP & HSC)

Material	CP Needed	Susceptible to HSC
316 SS	Yes	No
22 Cr Duplex	Yes	Yes
Gr 660	Yes	No
Alloy K-500	Yes	Yes
25 Cr Duplex	Possibly	Yes
Alloy 625	No	Rarely
Alloy 718	No	Rarely

Wirelines

Wirelines are used for servicing downhole equipment, setting downhole valves, and running measurement tools such as calipers and logging tools. Wirelines are covered by API Specification 9A and are constructed of plow steel, improved plow steel, or extra-improved plow steel and coated with zinc by electrodeposition or hot galvanizing.

Plow steel has a composition similar to AISI 1067 steel and has a tensile strength exceeding 240,000 psi; improved plow steel, which is produced from AISI 1075 steel, has a strength of 250,000 psi or higher. This high strength is achieved by heat treating and cold drawing in a process termed patenting.

Heat treatment and cold work produce a very fine pearlitic microstructure that is aligned in the lengthwise direction of the cable, imparting a very high yield and tensile strength to the cable as well as a high degree of anisotropy. These cables are also treated with a corrosion-inhibitor compound that is effective in many environments. However, this type of treatment, as well as wellsite chemical inhibition, is not totally effective against corrosion, and environmental cracking can often occur, especially in hydrogen sulfide-containing environments.

Table 4-15 Stress Corrosion Cracking of Wireline Materials

Materials	Lab (93°C)	Field (93°C)	Lab (149°C)	Field (149°C)	Lab (177°C)	Field (204°C)
AISI 316	F	F	F	F	…	F
18-18-2	F	P	F	P	…	F
Uranus 50	NF	NF	F	F	F	F
SAF 2205	NF	…	F	…	F	F
Uranus B6	NF	NF	F	F	F	F
2RK65 (Sabdvik)	NF	NF	F	NF	F	F
Sanicro 28	NF	…	F	…	F	F
Carpenter 20Cb-3	NF	…	NF	NF	F	F
Incoloy 825	NF	…	NF	…	F	F
Hastelloy G	NF	NF	NF	NF	…	F
Alloy 718	…	NF	NF	NF	…	F
Pyromet 31	NF	…	F**	…	F	F
Inconel 625	…	…	NF	NF	…	F
Inconel 617	…	…	NF	NF	F	F
Hastelloy C276	…	NF	NF	NF	F	F
MP35N	…	…	NF	NF	NF	NF
…	…	…	…	…	…	…

[1] Environment
  — Field (NaCl + MgCl$_2$ + CaCl$_2$ with 11% H$_2$S and 40% CO$_2$ gas for 30 days)
  — Lab (NaCl with 100% H$_2$S gas for 7 days)
NF = No failure
F = Failure
P = Pitted but no failure
F** = three of six specimens failed
(After Vaughn and Chaung)

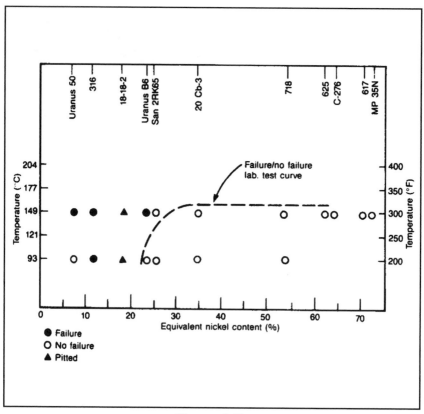

Figure 4-60

Effect of equivalent nickel content on stress-corrosion cracking resistance of wireline materials in field environments (After Vaughn and Chaung).

Monel K500 wirelines have been successfully run in western Canada, but in areas of high hydrogen sulfide and high temperature, dealloying can be significant.

Since the diameter of most wirelines is between 1.68 and 2.34 mm, a small reduction in cross section caused by corrosion can produce failure. Type 410 stainless steel has been used; but because of the high strength required and the stresses on the wireline, it too fails in hydrogen sulfide-bearing environments. The austenitic stainless steels, when highly cold worked, are susceptible to chloride stress-corrosion cracking as well as sulfide stress cracking; therefore, they are not good candidates for this type of service. Since almost all oil and gas wells contain water with chlorides, the use of chloride cracking-sensitive materials should be excluded from wireline service. Some wirelines made of austenitic stainless steels have failed by chloride stress-corrosion cracking when temperatures exceeded

180°F. The author has analyzed failures of a chromium-modified Hadfield manganese-steel wireline (11% Cr, 8% Mn, 2% Ni and 0.80% C) that failed by SSC in a sour well in Wyoming.

In fact, because of the very high tensile strengths required for wireline wire, few alloys are suitable for service in the presence of chlorides and hydrogen sulfide. This is evident by the data presented in Table 4-15 from work by Vaughn and Chaung. The tensile strength of all of the alloys tested was approximately 220 ksi. Under the most severe circumstances—a laboratory solution—the only alloy resistant to environmental cracking was MP35N. This is summarized in Figure 4-60, which relates the cracking sensitivity to nickel content. This behavior explains why MP35N is currently being used for wirelines in extremely severe service and why, to dale, no failures of MP35N wirelines have been reported.

The conductor material in these MP35N armored cables is usually nickel-clad copper, ASTM B-355 class 10. Other armor materials currently available are 18-18-2, Uranus 50 (a duplex stainless steel), and Uranus B6, which is fully austenitic. All three alloys are described in Table 4-15 and show less-satisfactory performance than MP35N. At lower temperatures such a 93°C, these should be acceptable alloys and more economical than MP35N.

Gravel-Pack Screens

Gravel-pack screens are used to control sand production that eventually leads to erosion. Figure 4-61 shows the cross section of a screen used for corrosion testing that is a segment of an actual screen. The inner tube is perforated J-55, K-55, or N-80 grade pipe with the outside wire forming the screen being 304 stainless steel, 316L stainless steel, Carpenter 20, Alloy 825 or Monel 400. These are spot welded to runners on the base tube. The most common problem with these screens is simply erosion of the fine wires, which leads to large holes in the screen.

One other failure mode is stress-corrosion cracking (SCC)caused by the completion fluids in the wellbore. $CaBr_2$, $CaCl_2$, and $ZnBr_2$ are used to complete wells, and at high temperatures (≥200°F), they can cause SCC. This is especially true for the $ZnBr_2$/304 stainless-steel combination. (See Figure 2-15)

Corrosion in Packer/Completion Fluids

While considerable work has been performed regarding the effect of packer/completion fluids on corrosion and cracking of both steels and CRAs, much of the work has either been incomplete or misrepresented the actual environments that properly considered have the potential for great damage to these materials. There are several specific concerns with packer fluids, even for carbon steel equipment:

Figure 4-61
Cross Sectional view of gravel-pack screen showing the attachment
of the wire to the base tube.

1. The corrosivity or aggressiveness of these fluids (typically brines), by themselves.

2. The detrimental effect of certain additives to the fluids (eg, thiocyanate) made by the supplier.

3. The effect of charging the packer fluid with CO_2 and/or H_2S from the production, by way of connection or packer leaks, on the fluid corrosivity.

4. The effect of a vapor space above the packer fluid that may contain oxygen.

5. The effect of tong and slip marks on the tubing outside surface on localized corrosion and/or stress corrosion cracking (SCC) in the above two environments.

Most of the research to date in this area has addressed only the first considera-tion noted above not recognizing that the latter factors are common to most wells and are significant to the severity of the system. Moreover, clear brine suppliers have demonstrated in controlled short term tests that the inhibitor package pro-vided with the brine is sufficient to reduce corrosion to a low level for carbon steel and 13Cr. However, these tests were most often not run in brines charged with H_2S or CO_2 nor is it known how long a life the inhibitors have and how inhibitive they were in the presence of acid gases. As expected the corrosion rate for carbon steel (N-80) increases with temperature and brine density. For uninhibited brines the following corrosion data based on 30 day exposure at 177°C were observed (Ezzat et al):

Table 4-16

Brine	Density (lb/gal)	N80 (mpy)	13 Cr (mpy)
NaCl	10.0	0.9	Not Tested
KCl	9.7	1.6	Not Tested
NaBr	12.5	0.2	Not Tested
KBr	11.4	0.3	Not Tested
$CaCl_2$	11.6	1.3	Not Tested
$CaBr_2$	14.2	9.7	Not Tested
$ZnBr_2/CaBr_2$	19.2	28.8	3.9

While the initial corrosion rates after a few days are high in uninhibited clear brines, it has been found that over the long term the rates diminish to acceptable values even without inhibitors except for the heaviest brines $CaBr_2$ and $ZnBr_2$. Several trends that have been confirmed in other studies. For the same density and anion, the brine with a double valent cation is often more corrosive than a single valent cation ($CaCl_2$ versus NaCl). Moreover, the bromides are often more aggressive than the chlorides and corrosion increases with brine density.

A study of several alloys in NaBr and $CaCl_2$ confirmed the complexity of the brine/acid gas system (Frick). The following two tables from that work show rel-atively low corrosion rates especially for the higher alloyed CRAs but a variety of responses to crack propagation as measured by the double cantilever beam (DCB) method. As demonstrated, cracking can occur at both ambient and elevated tem-peratures. However, these results are somewhat complicated by the fact that the low temperature tests were performed with 1.38 MPa H_2S and 2.93 MPa CO_2 while the high temperature tests were at 6.89 MPa H_2S and 4.14 MPa CO_2.

Table 4-17 Corrosion Rates of Alloys in Coupon Experiments (mm/y)

Alloy	NaBr 24°C	NaBr 232°C	CaCl$_2$ 24°C	CaCl$_2$ 232°C
C-90	0.12	0.95	0.02	1.52
9Cr	0.05C*	1.22CP**	0.01C	1.48CP
13Cr	0.04C	1.25CP	0.02C	1.25CP
22Cr	nilC	0.01	nil	0.04C
28	nilC	0.01	nil	0.02C
625	nil	0.01	nil	0.01

* Crevice attack

**Pitting attack

Table 4-18 Cracking Susceptibility
(DCB Results in MPa√m: C-Ring Failures Underlined)

Alloy	NaBr 24°C	NaBr 232°C	CaCl$_2$ 24°C	CaCl$_2$ 232°C
9Cr	> 81.7	> 85.1	> 68.2	> 80.8
13Cr	_33.1_	>119.7	_25.8_	< 86.3
22Cr	**106.6_	_27.5_	< _34.8_	_28.6_
28	> 114.7	< 78.6	> 124.3	> 108.7
625	* 67.8	84.3	* _68.1_	51.1

< indicates branching of the crack
> indicates no crack growth
* indicates specimen was steel coupled
** indicates interrupted test (possible invalid result)
_ indicates one C-ring failure

Few studies have been published that consider the detrimental effects of acid gases on clear brines. Most of the studies have been concerned with 13Cr, 22Cr and 25Cr stainless steels. In general, it was found again that the higher the brine density and the greater the use of multivalent and multi-brine salts (CaBr$_2$/ZnBr$_2$) the higher the corrosivity of the brine and the tendency for SCC.

In anticipation of CRA completions for the T-Block in the North Sea various CRAs were tested in 11.5 pound/gal (ppg) NaBr and 11.5 ppg CaCl$_2$ at 135°C with 40 bar CO$_2$ and 0.02 bar H$_2$S (Cheldi et al). No cracking of samples was observed for the NaBr brine but pitting and crevice corrosion of 13Cr and Super 13Cr was observed. As expected, the CaCl$_2$ fluid was more aggressive, producing pitting and crevice corrosion in almost all the alloys (13Cr, Super 13Cr, 15Cr and 22Cr) and cracking in all but the 13Cr and 22Cr alloys.

Other studies (Battelle) however, have found that the NaBr and CaCl$_2$ fluids produced SCC at ambient temperatures while the CaBr$_2$/ZnBr$_2$ mixture was the more detrimental fluid at high temperature.

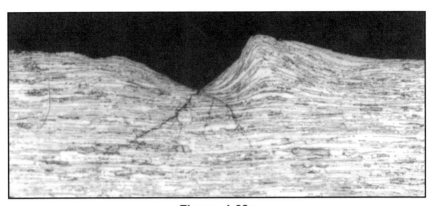

Figure 4-62a
SCC propagating from the bottom of a slip mark in 22Cr tubing
exposed to CaCl₂ at 300°F. Mag. 100X.

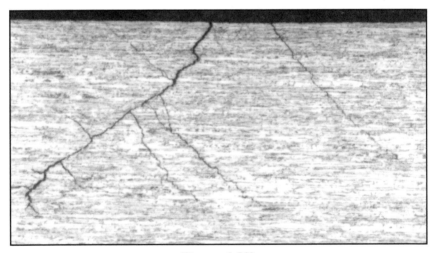

Figure 4-62b
SCC on the same sample shown in Figure 4-62a but originating
on the free sruface.

Figure 4-62a shows an example of SCC emanating from the bottom of a slip mark on 22 Cr tubing that was exposed to 12.4 lb/gal $CaCl_2$ brine with CO_2 at 300°F and no H_2S however, thiosulfonate was present. The fluid was also completely deoxygenated. Figure 4-62b shows that SCC also occurred on the same 22Cr sample in the same environment without any slip or tong marks present, demonstrating the aggressiveness of this environment and that notches from slips and tongs are not required to initiate SCC. Table 4-19 shows the results of laboratory testing in a completely deoxygenated 12.4 lb/gal $CaCl_2$ brine fluid under 500 psi CO_2 with thiosulfonate. Both stainless steels were susceptible to SCC in this environment. What is extraordinary about the SCC of 13Cr is that common belief

191

is martensitic stainless steels do not suffer SCC in a chloride environment. Thus this type of failure is contrary to conventional wisdom.

Table 4-19 Stress Corrosion Cracking of CRAs in $CaCl_2$

Alloy	Temperature, °F	SCC
13Cr	70	Yes
13Cr	300	Yes
22Cr	300	Yes

Field Experience With Packer/Completion Fluids

Generally there have been few problems with CRAs and packer fluids considering all of the completions of this type. However, those failures that have occurred have been significant. Pitting corrosion from oxygenated packer fluids has been frequently observed for 13Cr and one sulfide stress cracking failure of 13Cr tubing as a result of gas charging of the packer fluid has been documented (Hashim and Craig). Three duplex stainless steel failures have been reported in the literature, one where sea water was the packer fluid (Silence et al) and two where $CaCl_2$ was the fluid (Mack et al and Mowat et al). There have also been undocumented failures of Super 13 Cr tubing from SSC as a result of the degradation of thiocyanate in the fluid and other undocumented failures of DSS from $CaCl_2$ packer fluids.

In conclusion while there have been several problems with packer/completion fluids and CRAs there is no existing guideline for what fluid is best or acceptable in combination with a certain type of CRA. Moreover, much of the existing data are conflicting. Therefore, it is the best policy to minimize potential problems by using the least aggressive packer fluid possible.

Acidizing

Acidizing has been performed in the petroleum industry for many years and contrary to popular belief there have been significant failures of steel tubing and equipment as a result. Figure 4-63 shows the worm eaten type of acid attack on steel tubing. Another frequent problem encountered during acidizing is illustrated in Figure 4-64. A 9Cr-1Mo nipple just above a safety valve had been in sour gas service for many years when the well was acidized causing the nipple to fail from SSC in the threads (Figure 4-65). The sudden production of H_2S from the acidification of FeS plus the low pH caused SSC to occur. However, with the advent of CRAs concern over the resistance of these CRAs to acidizing prompted several studies that confirmed the need for planning and care during acidizing of wells completed with CRAs.

Figure 4-63

External corrosion on tubing from acid job.

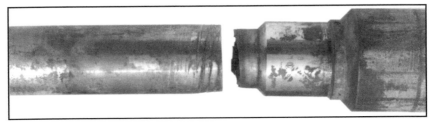

Figure 4-64

Sulfide stress cracking in the threads of a nipple after an acid job.

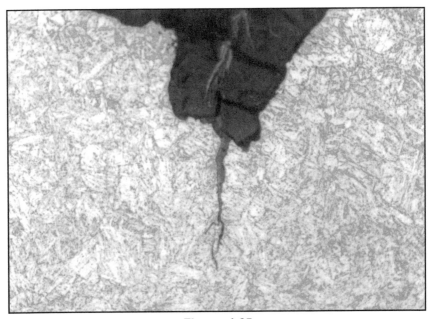

Figure 4-65

Close up of the fracture in the thread root of the nipple shown in Figure 4-64.

193

In the past the most common acids for well work were HCl and HF. Typical concentrations are 15% HCl, 12% HCl and 12% HCl plus 3% HF. However, acid strengths up to 28% HCl are also used. The acid companies commonly use inhibitors in the acid to reduce corrosion during the acid treatment but these are short-lived inhibitors that have a life of approximately 10 hours. Moreover, fluid returns after acidizing often have spent acid that is still quite corrosive without benefit of an inhibitor. A serious misconception has arisen in the industry that spent acid is not corrosive since the pH is often in the range 2-3 which is higher than the active acid pH near 1. Nothing could be more wrong and in fact many failures of equipment (both CRAs and steel) occur during acid returns and not during the acid job itself.

One study confirmed the aggressiveness of these acids and concluded (Kane and Wilhelm):

1. Acidizing can cause severe weight loss corrosion, localized corrosion and SCC of CRAs.

2. The behavior of CRAs in inhibited acids is specific to the alloy, acid composition and environmental conditions.

3. The prevalent mode of attack in the inhibited active acid is general corrosion while in spent acid SCC is prevalent especially at high temperatures.

The dramatic corrosion rates observed on CRAs in spent HCl acid can be seen in Table 4-20 (de Mello Joia).

Table 4-20 Comparison of Corrosion (mpy) in Active Acid Plus Inhibitors to Spent Acid at 80°C

Alloy	Inhibited 5% Acetic + 7% Formic + 1.5% HF	Spent Acid
P110	23	2434
13 Cr	54	762
S13 Cr	94	940
15 Cr	49	475
22 Cr	24	44
316	25	6

This comprehensive study performed by de Mello Joia and coworkers compared the corrosion rates of steels and CRAs in inhibited line acids and then spend acids. Table 4-21 presents similar work that demonstrates the significant jump in corrosion from the spend acid. Inhibited active acid was shown to produce acceptable corrosion rates especially considering the short exposure time for most acid jobs.

Table 4-21 Results After Exposure to Spent Acid at 110°C

Alloy	Ave Corrosion Rate (mm/y)	
	pH 0.2	pH 1.0
13 Cr	—	4710
22 Cr	692.5	20.1
25 Cr	13040	0.03
22 Cr/25 Ni	149	0
825	27.0	7.7

As expected the higher nickel alloys are more resistant to acid attack but certainly not immune. Table 4-22 shows the results of tests in uninhibited acids as a function of temperature for three nickel based alloys (Ahluwalia et al).

Table 4-22 Corrosion Rates After Exposure to Uninhibited Acids (mm/y)

Temp °C	15% HCl			12% HCl +3% HF	
	G-3	G-50	C-276	G-3	G-50
66	1.8	1.4	0.7	0.9	1.4
93	7.9	5.1	1.7	17.3	8.2
121	46	28.6	6.5	NT	NT
149	521	175	NT	445	207

NT = Not tested.

It can be seen that uninhibited acids are quite corrosive, however, most acid companies have now developed inhibitors specific to certain acid/CRA combinations. Some oil companies are reluctant to use these aggressive mineral acids. Most recently there has been a trend to use either a combination of organic acids (acetic, formic, etc) and mineral acids or just organic acids to stimulate wells. This trend is beneficial to hardware used on wells. However, many companies still periodically employ 28% HCl acid that often causes severe damage to equipment such as the hardfacing on valve gates, Figure 4-66.

Coiled Tubing

Traditionally coiled tubing (CT) was used primarily for acid jobs and well work overs. However, in recent years the applications of CT have greatly expanded into areas such as drilling, completions and flowlines. While well work remains the primary use for CT, its use for well completions has become significant. Two distinct size groups of CT are currently being used, the smaller of which are the umbilical and the larger of which are for well completions.

195

Figure 4-66
Blistering of the thin hardfacing on an Alloy 625 gate
after acidizing with 28% HCl.

Small diameter tubing is generally thin wall low pressure tubing with outside diameters in the range of 6 to 25mm. It is frequently used for hydraulic control lines in wells, for delivering chemicals to the bottom of wells or combined in bundles for subsea umbilicals for well control or field applications. Similar arrangements are used for subsea umbilicals and pipeline bundles. The variations are infinite and depend on the particular applications and needs for specific fields. These small diameter tubing products and applications are increasingly important for the oil industry especially in the deep water fields now being developed.

The larger CT (3/4 inch to 6-5/8 inch OD) includes CT for well workover and drilling operations and in their larger diameters (4 inch to 6-5/8 inch) it is used for flowlines. The discussion here however is restricted to CT applications for well completions. The composition, properties, manufacturing and testing of CT is specified in API RP 5C7. CT is almost always made from carbon steel and is thus limited in service life due to fatigue and corrosion. A typical string of CT is only suitable for 50-70 well operations, then it must be discarded. The industry generally considers this a commodity product and is not interested in greater service life at a significantly greater cost (i.e. CRAs). Steel CT generally comes in grades 70, 80, 90 and 100; these values represent the minimum yield strength in ksi. CT is manufactured in the same way that ERW pipe is made except that it is not cut into specific lengths but reeled onto a reel. The tubing is periodically welded together using a bias weld to produce the long continuous lengths.

The use of CT for well work results in fatigue loading from the reeling and unreeling and the combined action of internal pressure. Thus as can be expected from fatigue failures in drill pipe and sucker rods, CT fails most often from fatigue, or more specifically corrosion fatigue. Several studies have been performed to evaluate corrosion and corrosion fatigue of CT as if this product were expected to display characteristics significantly different from other steel products in drilling and production. As has been demonstrated and can be predicted, CT behaves just as other steels do in the presence of H_2S, CO_2, O_2 and acids. Moreover, fatigue life models have been developed to predict the life of CT, which except for environments such as nitrogen or other non-corrosive conditions, are certainly unreliable. There is a great need in the petroleum industry to effectively model corrosion fatigue, not only for CT, but as shown for drill pipe and sucker rods, corrosion fatigue is the primary cause of failure.

There is another factor that is often forgotten when using CT for permanent completions as velocity strings. When, for example, a 1.25 inch OD x 0.109 inch wall thickness CT velocity string is run inside a 2-7/8 inch, 4.7 pound/ft conventional tubing string, the wall thickness is almost 1/2 that of the original string. Even though the corrosion rate in the well may not change with the introduction of the CT string, the service life may be shorter by 1/2 simply as a result of the reduced wall thickness. In actual fact the life maybe even shorter as a result of the higher velocity in the CT.

The use of CT will continue to grow in the industry and should increases as the availability of CRA CT increases. Recently, one supplier of CT has begun to offer an austenitic stainless steel CT referred to as QT-16Cr that has been very effective in combatting corrosion in velocity strings. This CRA available up to 90 ksi yield promises to broaden the applications of CT.

Effect of Mercury on Production Equipment

While signs of mercury (Hg) in natural gas streams were noted many years ago it did not become a recognized problem until large gas fields in Asia and elsewhere began producing large quantities of Hg for which handling became a potential health problem. Moreover, there were associated corrosion and cracking problems with the production and gas treating equipment. Subsequent investigations by several operators found that Hg production in natural gas streams is indeed quite common. Failure of equipment by Hg can occur by corrosion or liquid metal embrittlement (LME), neither requires the presence of water.

LME results in either a loss of ductility of a solid metal or fracture below the normal yield stress when it is under tensile stress and its surface is wetted by some lower-melting liquid metal. The fracture surface is typically brittle in appearance with intergranular cracking although transgranular cracking can occur, as evidenced by research into monocrystals and metallic glasses. Fracture surfaces appear to have a coating of the liquid metal (maybe only a monolayer), i.e. it is not necessary to saturate the bulk solid metal by the liquid by a diffusion mechanism. The precise mechanism has not been elucidated, but "adsorption-induced embrittlement" is favored, where atomic bonds at a crack tip are broken by the presence of the liquid metal atoms.

Intimate contact of the liquid with the solid is required – even an oxide film is sufficient to prevent interaction of the solid and liquid. Thus, plastically deformed surfaces with fresh metal exposed or stress raisers which lead to easy rupture of surface protective films are likely initiation points for LME cracks. Surface films, which are removed by erosion or abrasion by sand, may also expose underlying fresh metal surface to mercury.

Susceptibility to LME is often unique to specific combinations of metals and the purity of the liquid or solid metals are critical (e.g. pure copper is not embrittled by mercury, but copper alloys are highly susceptible). Only micrograms of liquid Hg can cause the effect in susceptible couples. There is an empirical rule (sometimes broken) that LME is a problem when the solid has little or no solubility in the liquid and forms no intermetallic compound.

Mercury embrittlement is usually intergranular, with little indication of crack branching or striation to indicate slow crack propagation. In fact fast crack growth rates of 10-100cm/s have been estimated from tests – these fast speeds and the low activation energy for this type of cracking being distinguishing features of LME compared to other types of stress corrosion cracking.

In general there is a brittle to ductile transition as the temperature is raised. Severe embrittlement occurs near the freezing temperature of the liquid and behavior becomes more ductile as the temperature is raised (although some materials show a precise transition temperature rather than a gradual shift from brittle to ductile behavior). This implies that 'hot' operational conditions are less likely to lead to embrittlement than 'cold' shut-down conditions.

Mercury forms a liquid solution with specific metals primarily aluminum, tin, gold, silver and zinc. Of these only aluminum has practical industrial significance. The aluminum oxide layer protects the aluminum surface. Where mercury can breach the aluminum oxide and wet the underlying surface the rate of amalgamation depends on the microstructural condition. Certain alloys and welds can be particularly rapidly affected. The result of amalgamation of these aluminum alloys is a loss of mechanical strength, particularly of welds.

This is a specific problem of certain metals exposed to high temperature mercury (typically above 500°C) where dissolution of the surface takes place. This has been extensively investigated in the context of using metals as liquid coolants in nuclear plants but such high temperatures are not found in gas production facilities.

A special type of corrosion can arise in the case of mercury in contact with specific metals such as aluminum and tin in the presence of moisture. In this case the first step is the formation of an amalgam. Amalgam corrosion is the combined action of mercury and moisture and only occurs at temperatures where liquid water can exist. The main difference between this and simple amalgamation is that the corrosion propagates with minute amounts of mercury. A feature of this form of attack is the production of hydrated aluminum oxide and hydrogen corrosion products. Corrosion regenerates the reactant (Hg) and the reaction is therefore self-propagating. Regenerated mercury amalgamates with aluminum and the amalgam reacts with water. The reaction rate is extremely fast with a rate of penetration of in excess of 1000 mm/yr. When observed the hydrated aluminum oxide corrosion products grow as filaments from the surface appearing very dramatically and rapidly.

A laboratory study has reported that dimethyl mercury can corrode carbon steel. It is stated that the corrosion is exacerbated in the presence of H_2S (Wongkasemjit). There are no reports of dimethyl mercury being identified as the cause of corrosion in service conditions.

Carbon and Low Alloy Steels Exposed to Hg

Plain carbon steels are virtually unattacked by liquid mercury under non-flowing or isothermal conditions. Moreover, field experience with carbon steel piping and vessels has been very good without any loss of integrity.

Testing of A516 Gr70 steel at room temperature in mercury resulted in slight decreases in reduction in area and lower fracture stresses (although they were above yield) compared to tests in air (Krupowicz, 1989). The LME effect was very much less pronounced than in AISI 304 stainless steel. No corrosion or amalgamation of the surface of the steel by mercury was noted.

For normal grades of steel only in the most extreme conditions of having a pre-existing sharp notch and/or excessive plastic deformation or fatigue loading initiating a crack, would there be any risk of LME due to Hg. There is not a problem of having reduced yield strength, so the presence of mercury does not impact the design basis for the plant. At normal temperatures the embrittlement would be expected to be very limited in carbon and low alloy steels; significantly less than the effect on AISI 304 stainless steel.

Stainless Steels and Nickel Alloys in Hg

There are several references to problems with Type AISI 304 stainless steel both in terms of corrosion and LME.

Type 304 stainless steel was exposed to 0.5molar sodium chloride with mercuric chloride added and lasted for 28 days at room temperature (Brown et al) Above 1ppm of mercury ions the metal loss started to rise quite significantly and at 100ppm of mercury the metal loss was about 10 times greater than in a mercury free solution. The experiments also investigated cracking in these environments, but no cracking was detected in Type 304 stainless steel up to 100ppm of mercury in 0.5molar sodium chloride.

Type 304 stainless steel showed a distinct reduction in the area when tested in mercury and sensitization has reduced the time to failure as compared to the as-received material. The fracture surface of the sensitized material showed more intergranular regions, whereas the as-received material had a mixture of brittle fracture regions and some areas of ductile rupture.

Type 316, 316L and 321 do not show any significant difference between the behavior of the as-received material in air, or in mercury, or in mercury after sensitization heat treatment.

It has been suggested (Krupowicz, 1993) that materials can be grouped such that Type 316L, 316, 321 stainless steels and Alloy 800 are not sensitive to LME but Type 304L, 304 stainless steels and Alloy 600 were quite susceptible to LME. It was speculated that molybdenum had an important role to play in a controlling metal embrittlement fracture resistance of stainless steels but this is not obvious from the composition of these steels.

Over a period of time it was noted that corrosion of carbon steel downhole tubing was becoming a problem in the Arun wells in Indonesia. Drake et al. investigated the use of 13%Cr, 22%Cr and 25% Cr stainless steels as optional materials under the downhole conditions. In addition, copper plated 22%Cr and 25%Cr was used to determine if copper (used for plating the threads for anti-galling) had an effect when in contact with mercury. At all of the test temperatures (135°C,163°C, 177°C) the 22%Cr and 25-28%Cr stainless steels showed no evidence of cracking whatsoever. Corrosion rates of less than 0.0025mm/yr were detected. The copper plating however was removed by exposure to these conditions. 13%Cr steels did not crack in any of the conditions. There was some etching, corrosion and pitting observed in the tests at 135°C and at 163°C. The 13%Cr steel tested at 177°C exhibited very high corrosion rates of 2.26mm/yr in the vapor phase and 2.87mm/yr in the liquid phase.

While there is relatively little information on the performance of 13%Cr tubing in mercury, there is substantial field experience with over 300 wells in the Groningen field completed with L80 13%Cr in gas producing 180µg/m³ of mercury. No corrosion or cracking problems have been noted since installing 13Cr tubing although there is no evidence for liquid mercury being present in this field.

Valve springs and valve stems of Monel 400 have been found to experience LME on exposure to raw natural gas containing approximately 100µg/m³ of elemental mercury (Wilhelm). Mercury was present on the surfaces by adsorption from the gas and/or condensate. Because of the high susceptibility of Monel 400 to LME, only very low mercury levels were sufficient to produce failure by cracking. It is noted that the degree and rate of attack of Monel increases with temperature.

It is reasonable to conclude that in less severe strain conditions (without the substantial plastic deformation produced in the SSRT) there would be no observation of mercury embrittlement, and in a practical situation the nickel alloys (with the exception of Monel 400) would retain sufficient ductility to avoid any catastrophic embrittlement failure.

Alloy 600 showed a similar behavior to type 304 stainless steel with a significant drop in the reduction in area when comparing samples tested in air to those tested in mercury and a notable reduction in the time to failure in the sample that was sensitized compared to the as-received material tested in mercury. The sensitized material showed distinct intragranular cracking.

Alloy 800 showed only minor effect of testing in mercury and heat treatment. The variation in time to failure and reduction in area values measured is probably within the general scatter of the test method and so this material would appear to have very good resistance to liquid mercury embrittlement.

Aluminum Alloys + Hg

In the presence of mercury and moisture, the protective oxide film on aluminum and its alloys breaks down resulting in catastrophic oxidation at ambient temperatures. The phenomenon is characterized by the growth of "trees" of aluminum hydroxide.

Furthermore, mercury embrittles both pure and alloyed aluminum, reducing the tensile strength by about 20%. This reduction in strength is a distinct difference compared to the behavior of stainless steels and nickel alloys, which (with the exception of Monel) show no reduction in tensile properties even in alloys that are susceptible to embrittlement. Ductile behavior is resumed in aluminum and its alloys above 200°C.

There are many references to service failures of aluminum alloy equipment and very little mercury is needed to cause fractures (English and Kobrin).

Severe corrosion was encountered in a 63S aluminum alloy pipeline carrying water condensate with a small amount of hydrocarbons. Analysis (presumably of the surface of the metal) indicated a mercury concentration of 4-15µg/in² (0.62-2.32µg/cm²) this indicates the ability of mercury to accumulate as liquid droplets even from a low concentration in the environment. Contamination of mercury was so great that globules of mercury could readily be seen at a magnification of 50 times.

Wilhelm discussed the effect of elemental mercury on engineering materials used in ammonia plants. Because of the low temperatures required in these plants there is extensive use of aluminum alloys. He cites experiences (in 1990) of degradation of aluminum piping and cold box (gas liquefaction) equipment. The concentrations of elemental mercury and mercury compounds in process equipment can give rise to corrosion and also liquid metal attack if inappropriate combinations of moisture, alloy and mercury occur. He investigates the fact that the metal surface acts as a catalyst in the ammonia environment forming mercury nitride (Hg_3N_2) and related complexes. There is a possible risk of formation of unstable (explosive) compounds when ammonia and mercury vapor are combined.

A well established mercury corrosion problem occurred at a natural gas plant in Skikda, Algeria in 1974 (Boumaza). Corrosion occurred on an aluminum coil heat exchanger in the liquefaction train of the natural gas processing plant. The problem was resolved by passing clean dry heated natural gas (70 °C) through the cryogenic section to desorb mercury before shutdowns.

Amalgam corrosion was experienced on aluminum heat exchangers (Alloy 6061) in a gas containing 0.001-0.65µg/Nm³ of mercury (Wilhelm). Corrosion occurred just above 0°C, which only arose during plant shutdowns when liquid water could be present. Loss of efficiency in mercury removal systems (described by Lund) led to failures upstream of welds in aluminum cold boxes about one month later.

To avoid mercury damage to aluminum equipment in LNG plants (eg. the cryogenic heat exchanger) mercury is removed in a molecular sieve. The Santa Barbara Extraction Plant in Venezuela had a mercury gas concentration of 1.3mg/Nm3 max to avoid corrosion in the cryogenic plant (Traconis et al). Operating guidelines for optimization of the functioning of mercury removal equipment using sulfur-impregnated carbon beds to achieve 0.002mg/Nm³ are described by Lund.

Tests on alloy 5083 indicated that ionic solutions containing hydroxide ions caused oxide film breakdown on specimens, but the occurrence of LME cracking was dependent upon mercury ions in the solution. In contrast, in neutral or slightly acidic solutions, the presence of ionic mercury was insufficient to cause LME cracking even when specimens were plastically strained while contacting the mercury containing environment. Thus mercury and hydroxide ions were found to act synergistically to cause LME at the relatively low mercury concentrations that were tested. Work by others on this same alloy showed the same susceptibility and it was concluded that mercury attack would be greatest during heat up or cooling from room temperature to cryogenic temperatures when considering the use of these alloys in ethylene plants.

It was noted that the fractures in pure mercury consistently occurred immediately after yielding; specimens tested in 0.1mol potassium mercuric iodide (K_2HgI_4) exhibited variations in fracture loads dependent on the pH. The purpose of these tests was to show that in an alkaline solution there is ionic reduction and plating of elemental mercury which is then able to embrittle the substrate equivalent to the situation where liquid mercury is present. In neutral or acidic solutions this step of plating out of elemental mercury does not take place and hence these solutions do not cause LME.

A plate and fin heat exchanger with Alloy 3003 plate elements and welded aluminum Alloy 5086-0 was found to have suffered LME cracking at girth welds in the Alloy 5086 (Turissini et al). The reference does not indicate any attack on the Alloy 3003 or SS 304L piping. Heat exchangers made of Alloy 3003 brazed with Alloy 4004 have not leaked whereas higher magnesium content welds in pipe or headers made of Alloy 5083 have shown LME.

Any steps taken to increase the wetting of the aluminum alloy surfaces with mercury increased the ability to penetrate the natural defects in oxide film and attack the underlying base metal. Examples were plating with nickel and plating with copper or applying ultrasonic vibrations to the samples. Impurities in the mercury or in the metal forming grain boundary precipitates also increased the sensitivity to mercury attack. This may explain why the 5083 alloy (alloyed with Mg) is much more sensitive to mercury attack than 3003 alloy. Treatments which thicken the oxide layer such as steam treating or anodizing improve the resistance to LME. Shot peening was also effective although not necessarily a practical approach for bulk equipment, particularly for heat exchangers.

English and Kobrin noted that in general the higher strength aluminum alloys such as the 5000 and 6000 series are more susceptible than the lower strength alloys like 3003 and 1100. They also note the requirement for the aluminum oxide film to be penetrated, which may occur as a result of many factors including erosion or abrasion or the presence of wetting agents such as copper and zinc. Relatively low stresses can propagate mercury induced transgranular attack causing brittle failure in an otherwise ductile material. While mercury in the vapor phase is not believed to be capable of embrittling aluminum alloys it is possible for mercury to accumulate at low points in process plant, behind butt weld backing rings and other places, and cause problems despite low initial concentrations in feed stocks.

Other Alloys

In practical service there have been no cases reported which can be attributed to embrittlement or cracking of titanium by liquid mercury. Titanium and its alloys are highly resistant to practically all inorganic salt solutions including those of mercury over a pH range 3-11 and to temperatures well in excess of boiling. Corrosion of Grade 2 by saturated mercuric chloride at 100°C is recorded as an insignificant 0.001mm/yr.

Various alloys have been tested in sustained load test in liquid mercury and produced no evidence of attack or cracking. However, embrittlement has been observed in slow strain rate test on Titanium Grade 29 with severe plastic deformation.

There is a certain amount of confusion in the laboratory test literature concerning the tendency of copper to be embrittled by mercury. Some papers indicate copper is embrittled by static tensile or rotating fatigue testing and others indicate that there is no embrittlement.

Copper zinc brasses show reduced fracture stress and reduced fatigue strength in mercury. It seems that the embrittlement process takes place through the grain boundaries, minimizing the grain boundary area making crack propagation easier. It has been observed that single crystals of 70% copper, 30% zinc brass were not embrittled.

Increasing the zinc content up to 40% makes the brasses more easily embrittled by mercury with cracks following the zinc-rich beta phase. Various other copper alloys with a variety of alloying elements have been investigated and premature fatigue testing and embrittlement during tensile testing is commonly reported. Copper aluminum alloy was found to be embrittled by mercury if it was deformed during contact, illustrating the typical need for plastic deformation observed in other alloys.

Cracking was found in a bundle of admiralty metal tubes in a condenser carrying service cooling water internally and hydrogen gas containing hydrogen sulfide on the outside. Cracking of the tubes was noted and the tubes were found to have a roughened surface with numerous longitudinal cracks following the grain boundaries. The areas of the cracks were found to contain mercury.

A bronze impeller in a pump handling tri-ethylene glycol (TEG) corroded in only 3 months service. The surface of the impeller was found to be contaminated with a substantial amount of mercury.

While the detail of the literature is somewhat confusing, the general impression received is that copper and its alloys are susceptible to mercury embrittlement. In practice the Aluminum alloys have failed from embrittlement by Hg more than any other alloys described here.

Acid Gas Injection

Although this subject is strictly a gas processing topic it frequently falls to completion engineers to design and complete acid gas injection wells that are used by the gas processing side to dispose of acid gases removed from the natural gas stream during processing. The gas streams are typically a combination of H_2S and CO_2 with some water vapor.

The ability to model the phase behavior of these acid gas injection streams has been quiet good and is the key to materials selection for the acid gas injection equipment. If the associated water is found to be entirely soluble in the acid gas stream or the stream is dehydrated then corrosion from H_2S and/or CO_2 will not occur. However, if the potential for a liquid water phase is moderate to light then corrosion maybe a problem. Contrary to oil and gas production containing H_2S and CO_2 the conditions are not as severe since the acid gas stream will contain little or no chlorides and the temperatures are often far lower than in deep wells. Therefore, carbon steels and stainless steels are often used for acid gas injection equipment with great success. It is customary and prudent however, to specify that all acid gas injection equipment be purchased to and fabricated in accordance with ISO 15156 (NACE MR0175). Since SSC can occur very quickly even during a minor upset where liquid water precipitates.

There has been considerable experience with acid gas re-injection in Canada and the US so that the materials of construction are very well established from years of injection.

There are three major components in an acid gas re-injection system: compression, flowline and injection well.

Compressors

Generally, the first stage of compression will receive gas at its water dewpoint and become undersaturated through the compressor and on the discharge side due to the temperature rise through the compressor. As such the compressor cylinders and metallurgy of the first stage compressor is typically carbon steel (or ductile iron for the cylinders) to NACE MR0175/ISO 15156. For the remaining stages of compression the interstage coolers and knockout drums and piping are either Type 316L stainless steel or a combination of stainless steel and inhibited carbon steel. The difficulty in selection of stainless steels between stages of compression arises over the question of whether any or how much chloride may carry over and the potential for SCC. This issue is dealt with differently by many companies.

Injection Flowline

The materials for the injection flowline are decided based on whether the acid gas is fully dehydrated at this point and will not drop out water on the way to the injection well or not. Since there will be essentially no chlorides at this point the choice becomes carbon steel or 316L stainless steel. Most often the flowlines are made from carbon steel and welded to me MR0175/ISO 15156. No other special precautions are taken.

Injection Well

The injection tree is typically steel trimmed with stainless steel. Frequently the lower master valve is clad with Alloy 625 to guarantee that the well can always be shut in. In some cases only the seat pockets are inlaid with Alloy 625 and the seats and gates and stems are Alloy 625 or 718. A subsurface check valve is placed at the bottom of the tubing string to prevent back flow of the acid gases. The tubing string is either J55 or L80 and may be bare or some companies prefer to internally plastic coat the tubing.

References

Ahluwalia, H., V. Ishwar and G. Petersen, "Corrosion Characteristics of G50 Alloy (UNS N06950) - An Improved Material for Sour Gas Applications", Corrosion/91, Paper No. 19, NACE (1991).

American Petroleum Institute. Specifications 5CT, 6A, 9A, and 11B.

American Society for Metals. Metals Handbook. Volume 1. 1961.

ASM Handbook Vol 13A Corrosion, Sections on Environmental Induced Cracking, 2003

Battle, J.L.; T.V. Miller: and M.E. True. "Resistance of Commercially Available High Strength Tubular Goods to Sulfide Stress Cracking." Materials Performance, 14 (1975), p. 11.

Bednarowicz, T.A. "ELectrochemical Polarization to Determine the Localized Corrosion Behavior of Various Materials Used for heavy Section Wellhead Equip ment in a 121°C-3.5 MPa CO_2-NaCI Environment." Corrosion/82, Houston, Texas: NACE, 1982.

Boumaza, A., Auoadene, B, Session II, Paper 3, 10th International Conference on Liquefied Natural Gas, Kuala Lumpur, Malaysia, 25th May 1992.

Brennan, J.R. "Metallurgy of Sucker Rod Pumps." Paper presented at Western States Corrosion Seminar. San Dimas, California: NACE, May 1968.

Brown M.H., Binger W.W. and Brown R.H., "Mercury and its Compounds – A Corrosion Hazard", 8th Annual NACE Conference March 10-14 1952

Bruton, B.R., "Selection of Metallic Materials for Subsurface Pumps for Various Corrosive Environments." Proceedings of the University of Oklahoma Corrosion Control Course. University of Oklahoma and NACE, September 1971.

Chen, E.Y. and P. Mehdizadeh, "Corrosion Fatigue Life of Arc Plasma Stainless Steel Sprayed Sucker Rods." Materials Performance, 19 (1980), p. 14.

Connell, J.G. and R.M. Shapiro. "Logging Operations in Sour Gas Wells." Symposium on Sour Gas and Crude. Tyler, Texas: SPE of AIME, 1974.

Craig, B.D., "Sour Gas Design Considerations," SPE Monograph, 1992.

Craig, B.D., J.K. Brownlee and T.V. Bruno, "The Sulfide Stress Cracking of Nickel Steels", Corrosion, vol 48, p. 90, 1992

de Mello Joia, C.J.B., R. Brito, B. Barbosa, F. de Moraes, A. Pereria and L. Marques, "Performance of Corrosion Inhibitors for Acidizing Jobs in Horizontal Wells Completed with CRA Laboratory Tests", Corrosion 2001, Paper No. 01007, 2001.

DeWaard, C. and U. Lotz, "Predictions of CO_2 Corrosion of Carbon Steel", Corrosion '93, Paper No. 69, NACE, 1993.

Drake D.E., Sutanto H., Colwell J.A., Stiegelmeyer W.N., "Corrosion Resistance of Materials Under Arun Field , Indonesia, Conditions Part I", Corrosion 1990 NACE Las Vegas USA, 1990

EnDean, H.J. Champion News, Champion Chemical Company, Houston, Texas (July 1975).

English J.J. and Kobrin G., "Liquid Mercury Embrittlement of Aluminum", Materials Performance pp62-63 February 1989

Fowler, E.D. and A.F. Rhodes. "Checklist Can Help Specify Proper Wellhead Material." Oil and Cas Journal (January 24, 1977), p. 62.

Greer, J.B. "Metal Thickness and Temperature Effects in Casing and Tubing Design for Deep, Sour Wells." 47th Annual SPE Meeting, San Antonio, Texas, 1972.

Greer, J.B. and W.E. Holland. "High Strength Heavy Wall Casing for Deep Sour Gas Wells." 55th Annual Fall Meeting of the Society of Petroleum Engineers. Dallas, Texas, September 1980, JPT 1981.

Ikeda, A.: S. Nagata; T. Tsumura; Y. Nara; and M. Kowaka. "Development of High Strength Oil Country Tubular Goods Highly Resistant to Sulfide Stress Corrosion Cracking." Hollywood, Florida: API, 1977.

Kane, R.D. and J.B. Greer. "Sulfide Stress Cracking of High Strength Steels in Laboratory and Oilfield Environments." Journal of Petroleum Technology (1977). p. 1483.

Kane, R.D. and S. M. Wilhelm, "Compatibility of Stainless and Nickel Base Alloys in Acidizing Environments", Corrosion/89, Paper No. 481, NACE (1989).

Kane, R.D. and W.K. Boyd. "Materials Technology for Oil and Gas Production." Alloys for the 80's. AMAX, 1980, p. 225.

King, J.A. and P.S.C. Badelek. "Performance of Valve Materials in Wet H_2S and CO_2 Contaminated Hydrocarbons." Corrosion/82, Houston, Texas: NACE, March 1982.

Kolts, J. "Temperature Limits for Stress Corrosion Cracking of Selected Stain less Steel and Nickel-Base Alloys in Chloride-Containing Environments." Corrosion/82, Houston, Texas: NACE, March 1982.

Krupowicz J.J., "Effect of Heat Treatment on Liquid Metal Induced Cracking of Austenitic Alloys", Slow Strain Rate Testing for the Evaluation of Environmentally Induced Cracking: Research and Engineering Applications, ASTM STP 1210 R.D. Kane, Ed., American Society for Testing and Materials, Philadelphia, 1993 pp.193-201

Krupowicz J.J.,"Slow Strain Rate Fracture Characteristics of Steel and Aluminum Alloys Tested in Mercury Environments", Journal of Engineering Materials and Technology, Vol 111 pp229-234, July 1989

Lund D.L., "Wyoming Operator Solves Mercury Exposure Problems", Oil and Gas Journal, May 13, 1996.

McIntyre D.R., English, J.J., and Kobrin G., "Mercury Attack of Ethylene Plant Alloys", Corrosion '89, New Orleans.

Mack, R., C. Williams, S. Lester and J. Casassa, "Stress Corrosion Cracking of a Cold Worked 22 Cr Duplex Stainless Steel Production Tubing in a High Density Clear Brine $CaCl_2$ Packer Fluid", Corrosion 2002, Paper No. 02067, NACE, 2002.

Mack, R. and A. Filippov, "The Effect of Cold Work and Strain Aging on the Sulfide Stress Cracking Resistance and Mechanical Properties of Expanded Tubular Steels", Corrosion 2003, Paper No. 03108, NACE, 2003.

Masamura, K., S. Hashizume, Y. Inohara and Y. Minami, "Estimation Models of Corrosion Rate of 13% Cr Alloys in CO_2 Environments", Corrosion 99, Paper No. 583, NACE, 1999.

Mehdizadeh, P. "Effect of Metallurgical Variables on Corrosion of Sucker Rods in Brine Containing CO_2 and H_2S." Materials Performance, 14 (1974), p. 13.

Metal Progress Databook. ASM. Mid-June 1981, p. 164.

Miyasaka, A. and H. Ogawa, "Corrosion Behavior of Corrosion Resistant Alloys in Acid Stimulation Environments", Corrosion/90, Paper No. 68, NACE (1990).

Moore, K.H. "Learn to Identify and Remedy Sucker Rod Failures." Oil and Gas JouRnal (April 9, 1973), p. 73.

Mowat, D.E., M.C. Edgerton and E.H.R. Wade, "Erskine Field HPHT Workover and Tubing Corrosion Failure Investigation", SPE/IADC Conf., Paper #67779, 2001.

National Association of Corrosion Engineers (NACE). "The Field Testing of 32 Alloys in the Flow Stream of Seven Condensate Wells." Publication No. 50-3. July 1950

National Association of Corrosion Engineers. Standards MR-01-75 and RP 04-75.

"CO$_2$ Corrosion Resistance of NK Cr13 and NK Cr9." Nippon Kokan (NKK) Technical Bulletin. Second Edition. February 1982.

Nippon, Kokan. Unpublished Research.

Peacock, D., Schutz R., Lunde, L., and Grauman, J., Titanium Information Group Data Sheet No. 9 "Titanium and Mercury", Issued 1st July 2000.

Seger, F.O. and 1. Maroofian. "Erosion, Cavitation and Abrasion Resistance of Choke Trim Materials," Paper No. 4710, 16th Annual OTC. Houston, TX (1984).

Snape, E. and D. Van Rooyen. "Corrosion of Sucker Rod Steels in a Simulated Sweet Oil Environment." Meeting of the Petroleum Division of ASME. Dallas, Texas, September 1968.

Silence, P., unpublished work.

Steward, W.B. "Sucker Rod Failures." Oil and Gas Journal (April 9, 1973), p. 56.

Sumitomo Metal Industries Ltd. Unpublished Research.

Thomas, P.D. "Steels for Oilwell Casing and Tubing."92nd AlME Annual Meeting. Dallas, Texas, 1963.

Traconis B., Mierez Y.D. and Kimenez A., "Mercury Removal System at Santa Barbara Extraction Plant", Proc. 75th Gas Processors Association Annual Convention 1996.

Treseder, R.S. and T. M. Swanson. "Factors in Sulfide Corrosion Cracking of High Strength Steels." Corrosion Journal, 24 (1968), p. 31.

Turissini R.L., Bruno T.V., Dahlberg E.P., and Setterlund R.B., "Mercury Liquid Metal Embrittlement Causes Aluminum Plate Heat Exchanger Failure", Materials Performance June 1998 pp 59-60.

Vaughn, G.A. and Hung-Erh Chaung. "Wireline Materials for Sour Service." Materials Performance, 21 (1982), p. 44.

Watkins, M. and J.B. Greer. "Corrosion Testing of Highly Alloyed Materials for Deep, Sour Gas Well Environments." Journal of Petroleum Technology (1976), p. 698.

Wilhelm S.M., "The Effect of Elemental Mercury on Engineering Materials Used in Ammonia Plants", Prepared for presentation at Ammonia Safety Symposium August 1990 Copyright AIChE, Unpublished.

Wongkasemjit, S. and Wasantakorn, A., "Laboratory Study of Corrosion Effect of Dimethyl Mercury on Natural Gas Processing Equipment", JCSE Vol 1 paper12, 2000.

5

METALLURGY FOR ENHANCED OIL RECOVERY

This chapter deals with metallurgy used in processes that extract oil from reservoirs after primary and secondary (waterflooding) production have essentially depleted the easy-to-remove reserve. Christmas tree metallurgy for waterflooding as well as downhole tubulars are usually conventional and are described in Chapter Four.

Tertiary recovery involves a number of different methods for recouping oil from a reservoir and can be divided into three principal types: thermal, chemical, and gas. These categories are further broken down as shown in Table 5-1. Steamflooding and CO_2 miscible floods are the most common forms of enhanced oil recovery (EOR). Moreover, there are many variations and combinations of these EOR methods. Some are used in small pilot studies and little information is available on them. Chemical EOR methods such as polymer flooding do not represent a unique challenge to existing metallurgy, so wells are completed with conventional carbon-steel equipment. Therefore, only two methods, thermal recovery and gas flooding, will be dealt with since they represent the greatest materials challenge and a larger literature base is available for them.

Although forms of enhanced oil recovery such as firefloods have been around for almost half a century, little information is available in the literature on the metallurgy utilized and the equipment problems encountered in tertiary recovery. Therefore, this chapter is a brief review of the more common forms of EOR and some of the metallurgy used in these processes.

Fireflooding (In Situ Combustion)

In fireflooding, air is injected into a well and ignition is started in the reservoir. As combustion progresses, the combustion zone moves away from the injection well where oxygen (air) is continually supplied to the production wells. During the burn, steam and other gases from combustion displace oil and connate water ahead of the combustion front.

Adjacent to and just ahead of the combustion front, the temperature reaches a plateau on the order of 200-350°F, while in the combustion zone, temperatures in the range of 600-1200°F can occur. The combination of combustion gases, steam, and temperature produce an exceptionally severe corrosion environment composed of oxygen, organic acids, carbon dioxide, sulfides, and chlorides. Examples of various products formed from combustion of different reservoir fluids are shown in Table 5-2. A typical gas composition arriving at a production well is shown in Table 5-3.

This aggregate of corrodents is transported to the producing wells throughout the fireflood and as such offers a serious materials problem. Results of both laboratory and field-testing of materials in fireflood environments are shown in Table 5-4 and from autoclave testing in Table 5-5 at various temperatures. It is readily

Table 5-1

Thermal methods:
  Steam
  Combustion in situ

Chemical methods:
  Micellular polymer
  Polymer
  Caustic
  Other chemical

Gas methods:
  CO_2 miscible
  Hydrocarbon miscible
  Other gases

(After Oil & Gas Journal, April 5. 1982)

Table 5-2 Analysis of Combustion-Tube Effluents from Various Reservoir Fluids.

| | | Reservoir | | | |
		AA	BB	CC	DD
Water	pH	4.0-7.0	3.8-7.2	3.7-7.4	4.5-7.3
	Cl⁻	65%	11%	7.2%	0.3%
	SO^-_4	0.22	0.16	0.44	0.3
	Acetic	<0.03	0.03-0.32	0.01-0.08	ND
	Formic	<0.03	ND	ND	<0.03
Oil	Acetic	<0.03	ND	<0.03	Tr
	Formic		ND	<0.03	ND<0.03
Gas	H2S	Tr	ND	ND	ND
	S-	1.5	1.1	7	3.7
		Corrosion Rates at 90°C (195°F), mpy			
	Carbon steel	34.7	–	57.6	87
	Incoloy 825	<0.1	–	1.6	–
	Inconel 625		–	1.1	–

ND = Not determined
Tr = Trace
(After Kohut et al.)

apparent that the commonly used oilfield material, carbon steel, is inappropriate for use in a fireflood and that even higher alloys such as 410 stainless steel (12% Cr) do not have adequate resistance to this severe environment. Furthermore, it is obvious that one alloy does not behave the same in all reservoirs since 12% Cr had a corrosion rate of 824 mpy and 14.9 mpy in the two different reservoirs described in Table 5-4.

The ignition well also presents a problem from the standpoint of a high temperature, highly oxygenated environment. Ignition in wells has been classified as either spontaneous or artificial. Some reservoirs are susceptible to spontaneous combustion when contacted with sufficient air. In these wells, combustion occurs a short distance from the wellbore and then burns back into the borehole. This can result in temperatures up to 1,700°F and has resulted in failure of pipe in the hole by creep or melting. Even stainless-steel liners have been reported to have melted following ignition.

The most widely used artificial means of ignition is electric or gas bottom-hole heaters. This method produces temperatures in excess of 1,200°F.

A review of firefloods by Chu described well completions for injectors and producers from various companies. A reorganized presentation of this work is shown in Table 5-6.

Table 5-3 Ambient Temperature Steady-State Composition of Gas at Production Well During Fireflooding.

Component	Concentration (%)
H_2	2.5
O_2	1.0
N_2	78.0
CO	5.0
CO_2	10.0
CH_4	2.5
H_2S	1.0

(After Johnson and Magnani)

Field experience has indicated that corrosion and erosion are the two most serious materials problems. Mild steel has been reported to have weight losses of 73% in 2 months. Stainless steel is also susceptible to rapid failure by chloride cracking, intergranular corrosion, and pitting attack. In some fields, 316 stainless steel and titanium have performed satisfactorily and are used for tubing and liners opposite the production interval. Corrosion and erosion failures of casing, tubing, chokes, valves, and fittings have been reported at producing wells.

A limited amount of work on valve-stem materials for producing wells has shown that 316 stainless steel is not resistant enough for this application and that measures such as metallic coatings are required (see Table 5-7).

Care must be taken in selecting oxygen injection equipment since each alloy has an oxygen threshold above which once ignited, combustion is sustained. Moreover, oxygen compatible pipe dope and elastomeric seals must be selected. An aid to selecting materials for oxygen service has been published by ASTM as Standard G63 (see references).

Table 5-4 Comparison of Corrosion Rates in Field and Laboratory Environments

Alloy	Reservoir AA (60°C)		Reservoir DD (90°C)	
	Field	Laboratory	Field	Laboratory
Carbon steel	Corroded away	2640 mpy	114mpy	87 mpy
12 Cr stainless	824 mpy	960	14.9	—
Incoloy 800	0.6	1.2	0.7	—
Incoloy 825	0.2	0.1	—	—
Inconel 600	477	334	—	—
Inconel 625	—	—	<0.1	<0.1

(After Kohut et al.)

Table 5-5 Autoclave Corrosion-Test Results in Simulated Fireflood Environment D

Test Temperatures, °C (°F)	140 (280)	175 (350)	205 (400)
Carbon steel	2,900-4,000 mpy	—	—
T 410 (12% Cr)	120-400	—	—
Incoloy 600	140-300	—	—
Incoloy 800	28	—	—
Inconel 825	0.4-1.1	22-46 mpy	—
Inconel 625	—	<0.1	0.9-6.4 mpy
Hastelloy C-276	—	2.6	0.8-1.4
MP 35 N	—	3.6-4.8	14.1
Hastelloy G	—	5.5	27.4
Ti 50 A	—	—	0.7-66.1

D = 100 psi carbon dioxide. produced brine. 0.1% acetic acid. 0.1% formic acid. 0.1% sulphur dioxide. 0.2% organic compounds.
(After Kohut et al.)

Steamflooding

There are two types of steam injection: continuous and cyclic. The first type involves continuous steam injection to the reservoir while the other involves intermittent injection—often referred to as huff 'n' puff—in which steam is injected for a short lime before the well is returned to production.

As in fireflooding, steam is injected into a number of wells and oil is produced from others. A steam-saturated zone forms around the injection well, while farther away is a zone containing condensed steam. Temperatures in the steam zone, which are equal to the steam temperature, decline over a distance from the injection well to a final temperature equal to the reservoir temperature. Steam temperatures can attain 500-700°F although lower-temperature steam has also been used successfully.

One of the major problem areas in steam injection wells is casing failure caused by compression, with most of the failures located at the connections. Telescoping and buckling are the most frequent forms of damage. It is believed that extensive thermal-linear expansion occurs during steam injection because the high temperatures cause excessive compressive stresses on the casing; during cooling, the stress reverses to tension and failure occurs.

Table 5-6   Fireflood Well Completions

| | Injectors | | | Producers | | |
Field	Casing	Tubing	Liner	Casing	Tubing	Liner
2	J-55				316 SS	316 SS
4			304 SS			304 SS
7	304 SS			304 SS		
	Shoe joint			on bottom		
10	K-55			K-55		
13		Incoloy				
		on bottom				
14	J-55	Inconel				
		on bottom				
17				J-55		
18	J -55			J-55	19	H-40
	H-40					
24		9 cr 1 Mo				

(After Chu, © 1981. SPE)

Unstressed casing elongates about 8 in. per 1,000 ft for every 100°F increase in temperature. If both ends of the casing are fixed such as in a conventional completion, the stress created by thermal expansion is:

$$S = \alpha\,(\Delta T)\,E$$

where:
   S = stress (psi)
   α = coefficient of thermal expansion (7.0×10^{-6} in./in./°F)
   T = increase in temperature over the average formation temperature (°F)
   E = modulus of elasticity (for steel: 30×10^{6} psi)
Since α and E are constants for steel, the following simple relationship for stress is:

$$S = 210(\Delta T)$$

As is immediately obvious from this formula, the stress is not a function of the length of the tubing or casing; rather it is solely a function of temperature change. Referring back to the earlier temperature regime of 500-700°F. using this formula, stresses on the order of 84,000-126,000 psi could be attained assuming an average reservoir temperature of 100°F. Comparing these values with the data in Table 5-8 on elevated temperature-tensile properties of seamless casing and tubing at 700°F, the yield strength would be exceeded on all grades.

Table 5-7 Operations to Failure for Letdown Valve Stems

Material	Operations
Type 316 stainless steel	30
Stellite No. 6	100
Composite W/TiB$_2$*	187**
Composite W/TiB$_2$*, set 2	450***

*Type 440C Stainless Steel shank with Kennametal K151A tip and with TiB$_2$ coating
**Failure occurred in threaded end of valve handle, not at tip.
***No failure after 450 operations; test continuing.
(After Johnson and Magnani)

Figures 5-1 and 5-2 present the yield and tensile data from Table 5-8 in graph form. From these curves, P-105 or P-110 have the most desirable properties for exposure to steam injection. These enhanced properties of P grades over the other grades are attributable to the chromium and molybdenum content of the steel, which helps develop good high-temperature properties such as creep and stress rupture resistance. Creep is the time-dependent increase in length of a metal subjected to a constant tensile load at elevated temperatures. Creep failure is usually defined as a specific amount of dimensional change occurring over a certain time increment. Stress rupture represents complete failure (fracture) of the material by creep.

The potential for failure of fixed casing can be reduced if the following temperature limits set by Gates are observed:

Grade Surface	Temp. Range, °F
H-40	270-330
J-55	350-410
N-80	470-580
P-1 1 0	620-730

This problem can be further decreased by using a thermal packer, which often will reduce the temperature by 120°F. More frequently, the wells are designed with expansion joints to permit vertical expansion of the tubing. Also, wellheads are available that allow for casing expansion through a stuffing box and for expansion of the tubing in a tubing hanger designed for thermal expansion. Many completions use no expansion joint but instead run gravel-pack liners that have a lead or brass hanger.

Another method that alleviates casing stress caused by temperature effects has been to prestress the casing during completion. This is based on the concept that, by placing the casing in tension before cementing, it will not exceed its yield

215

Table 5-8

Elevated Temperature-Tensile Properties of Various Grades of Seamless Casing and Tubing Tensile Properties*

Grade	Condition	Outside Diameter In.	Wall In.	Tensile Test Temp., °F	Yield Strength, psi	Tensile Strength, psi	Elastic Limit, psi	Modulus of Elasticity 1,000 psi	Percent Elongation, 2 in.	Percent Reduction of Area	Room Temp. Brinell Hardness
J55	Hot rolled	13-5/8	0.313	RT	59,320	107,950	52,530	25,750	21.5	45.0	207
				300	55,820	100,040	50,750	24,650	14.0	38.4	212
				500	57,870	122,125	42,050	23,800	18.75	19.1	229
				700	53,130	98,490	37,925	21,550	26.25	57.5	201
				900	44,445	68,030	28,000	24,000	24.9	55.1	201
N80	Normalized	13-5/8	0.500	RT	83,750	124,050	69,550	27,900	19.0	44.8	248
				300	80,150	120,675	65,950	25,400	14.0	40.6	248
				500	83,970	133,500	59,850	21,600	22.75	36.7	255
				700	74,415	116,775	51,900	16,300	24.0	61.0	248
				900	62,715	85,000	40,650	15,700	25.75	67.2	248
P105	N&T	3	0.375	RT	106,800	136,275	78,050	27,600	13.0	42.1	277
				300	102,100	131,600	73,500	26,500	11.0	46.2	269
				500	104,850	139,100	770,950	26,200	15.5	42.5	285
				700	95,900	129,100	67,500	25,200	18.25	59.7	269
				900	86,640	107,375	59,500	18,700	15.25	57.4	269
P110	Q&T	10-3/4	0.547	RT	128,825	145,500	120,200	27,900	14.5	44.5	302
				300	114,850	139,100	95,000	27,300	11.5	34.2	293
				500	110,025	146,050	87,750	25,500	18.0	38.6	285
				700	100,310	124,650	76,800	24,100	21.25	76.2	277
				900	78,545	92,145	51,400	19,200	21.5	77.3	277

* Average for two tests
RT = room temperature
(After Gates and Holmes)

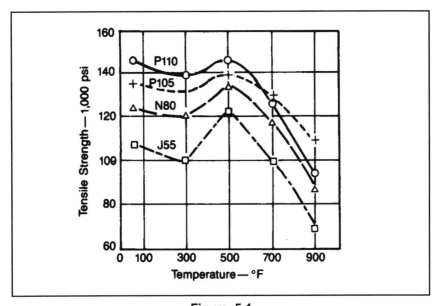

Figure 5-1
Tensile strength as a function of temperature for some common tubulars
(After Gates and Holmes).

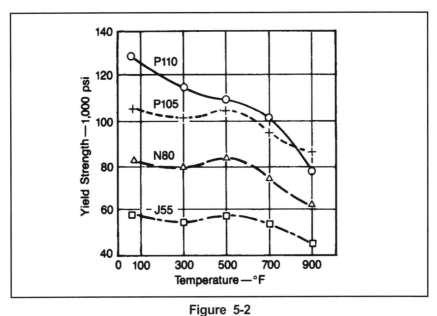

Figure 5-2
Yield strength as a function of temperature for the same alloys shown in
Figure 5-1 (After Gates and Holmes).

strength in compression when steam injection commences. Since the casing must pass from tension through a neutral point of no stress to begin compressive loading, prestressing the casing offers the capability to run lower grade pipe at higher temperatures yet remain below the compressive yield strength. Once the yield strength is exceeded in compression, on cooling the joint strength may not be sufficient and failure will occur by tensile overload.

Production wells are often completed the same way as injection wells, normally using H-40 or J-55 pipe. Also, The temperature in the producing wells is much lower, reducing the thermal expansion problem. Again, wellheads that allow expansion of the tubing and casing are frequently used, just as they are used in injection wells. Production wells are susceptible to increased abrasion because of the high sand production that accompanies steamflooding. Some of this erosion can be reduced by hardfacing critical areas in valves.

Carbon Dioxide (CO_2) Flooding

Carbon dioxide flooding is performed in one Or three ways: injection of pure liquid CO_2 followed by water or carbonated water; injection of carbonated water; and injection of carbon dioxide al sufficient pressure to produce miscibility with the reservoir oil.

Another method that is sometimes classed as secondary recovery is the injection of high-pressure carbon dioxide gas followed intermittently by water injection to enhance recovery. This latter method is often referred to as WAG (water alternating-gas). The most well-documented field (unit) in which this technique has been applied is the SACROC unit in the Kelly Snyder field in Texas.

The discussion of CO_2 flooding in this section will be primarily centered on the WAG method because it presents the greatest material problem and represents the most common method of CO_2 flooding. Also, once carbon dioxide mixes with connate water, production wells experience essentially the same problems regardless of injection technique. Furthermore, on the injection side, pure, dry carbon dioxide is noncorrosive to engineering alloys in the temperature regimes of flooding. This behavior of dry carbon dioxide and the effect of impurities are presented in Figure 5-3. Here, the effects of water content, oxygen content, and velocity are described. These data are presented as weight gain instead of weight loss, but they illustrate the same effects. It is evident that flow rate and moisture content have a large effect on corrosion rate.

Corrosion of injection wells and producing wells can be quite severe during CO_2 flooding, and various steps have been taken to reduce failures of equipment in both types of wells. Information accumulated from the literature is presented that describes the steps taken to mitigate corrosion in CO_2 flooding as well as some of the failures that led to these materials selections.

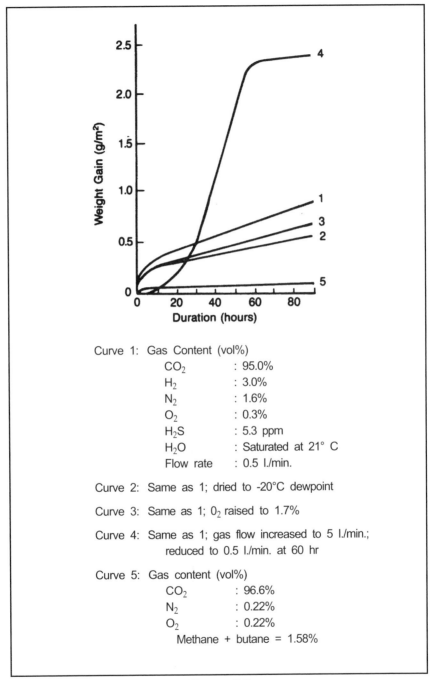

Curve 1: Gas Content (vol%)

CO_2	: 95.0%
H_2	: 3.0%
N_2	: 1.6%
O_2	: 0.3%
H_2S	: 5.3 ppm
H_2O	: Saturated at 21° C
Flow rate	: 0.5 l./min.

Curve 2: Same as 1; dried to -20°C dewpoint

Curve 3: Same as 1; O_2 raised to 1.7%

Curve 4: Same as 1; gas flow increased to 5 l./min.;
reduced to 0.5 l./min. at 60 hr

Curve 5: Gas content (vol%)

CO_2	: 96.6%
N_2	: 0.22%
O_2	: 0.22%
Methane + butane	= 1.58%

Figure 5-3
Weight gain of steel in flowing gas at 70°F (After Winkler and Nemeth).

Injection trees and wellheads originally constructed of carbon or low-alloy steel components that were either plastic coated or electroless-nickel plated have failed quickly under WAG conditions as a result of damage to the coating or plating, which presented areas for highly localized pitting and galvanic attack. These trees were replaced with 316 stainless-steel Christmas trees in which the gate valves had 316 stainless-steel gates or ceramic gates. Also, aluminum bronze valves with ceramic gates appear to be a successful alternative, according to Gill.

In other cases, 410 stainless-steel trees and valves were severely pitted under scales formed from the injection water but Type 316 replacement components showed no apparent problem. Even though 316 stainless steel is susceptible to chloride SCC, the temperatures of these wellheads is low enough (150°F) to avoid this type of failure. However, 316 stainless steel welded fittings have suffered intergranular corrosion in the weld and heat-affected zone. Stainless steels are also quite susceptible to crevice corrosion in areas such as flanges where gaskets can absorb moisture. This has been essentially solved using nonabsorbing gaskets.

Tubing hangers are usually made of 316 stainless steel, and tubing is restricted to J-55 grade steel coated with plastic. However, the coating is not always reliable and CRA tubing is sometimes used in WAG system. Of course, when no water is present, bare carbon steel will suffice.

Christmas tree valves on producing wells with electroless-nickel-plated gates have displayed numerous failures at coating breaks requiring application of 17-4 PH stainless steel gates. Full-length normalizing of J-55 is required to avoid ringworm corrosion. In some fields the most effective production tubing is 13 Cr.

Rod-pump wells have encountered serious corrosion of the rods. Pumps are run with Monel 400 for barrels, plungers, and all wetted parts and have performed without problems. Also, some pump barrels made of Monel 400 are spray metal coated with 316 stainless steel. Rod strings in some instances have only lasted one month, requiring replacement of the entire string. New steel rods plasma coated with 316 stainless steel, then coated with a baked-on epoxy, have performed satisfactorily.

Wells with submersible pumps have also experienced problems caused by corrosion. most failures were caused by attack of the pumps and motor housing. Pitting was the major form of corrosion aggravated by iron sulfide and mineral scales. Electroless-nickel coating of the pump and motor housing usually results in premature failure caused by mechanical damage of the coating. Again, the unfavorable galvanic situation of a large nickel cathode and small steel anode lead to rapid attack. Some success has been achieved by plasma spraying 316 stainless steel and Monel onto these parts followed by overcoating them with epoxy. However, because of the potential for corrosion at damaged areas of this coating, the consideration of manufacturing the pump and motor housings out of 300 series stainless steel is a better alternative. Pump internals made of Ni-resist cast iron have not had appreciable trouble.

Although stress-corrosion cracking strictly caused by carbon dioxide has not been reported from field data, it has been observed in the laboratory and should be considered in the design and application of equipment. N-80 tubing subjected to high partial pressures (300 psia) of carbon dioxide and deformation beyond the yield point was found to stress-corrosion crack at ambient temperature (see Table 5-9). One explanation by the investigators stated this stress-corrosion cracking was attributed to dissolution of the sulfide inclusions in the steel, which led to hydrogen sulfide evolution and eventually to sulfide stress cracking.

Much of the data developed for materials in CO_2 gas systems discussed in Chapter Four are also applicable to WAG systems. However, since the temperatures and partial pressure of CO_2 are not high other materials not acceptable in Chapter Four can be for WAG. Thus when H_2S is not present in quantities greater than 10 ppm copper base alloys can be quite effective.

Recently, corrosion testing has been carried out at high fugacities of CO_2. Since partial pressure is only valid for low concentrations and pressures of any gas, the fugacity must properly be considered as the pressures and concentrations increase, especially into the range used for CO_2 flooding and acid gas injection. Figure 5-4 shows that even as the CO_2 partial pressure and fugacity increases the corrosion rate actually declines contrary to the prediction of all of the CO_2 corrosion models. The current models for CO_2 corrosion of steels significantly over estimates the corrosion rate as the fugacity increases. There is presently no explanation for this behavior.

Table 5-9 Stress Corrosion Cracking Tests in CO_2 Solutions in Comparison with Other "Nonsulfide" Media

Environment	Material	Hardness	% Deformation	Failure Time
15 psia air[1]	N-80-2	35	105, 90, 70, 60, 40, 20	NF211 days[3]
315 psia CO_2[1]	N-80-1	38	130, 100, 80, 60, 40, 20	NF 695 days[3]
300 psia CO_2[1]	N-80-2	18	130	NF 520 days[3]
300psia CO_2[1]	N-80-2	25	130	NF 520 days[3]
300 psia CO_2[1]	N-80-2	34	110	326 days[3]
300 psia CO_2[1]	N-80-2	33	115	22 hours
300 psia CO_2[1]	N-80-2	33	115	NF 84 days[3]
300 psia CO_2[1]	N-80-2	33	100, 80	NF 112 days[3]
0.013 N HCl	N-80-2	34	110	5.8 hours
1.07 N HCl	N-80-2	34	110	0.35 hour
11.6 N HCl	N-80-1	36	100	0.03 hour
11.6 N HCl	N-80-1	36	80	0.25 hour
9.4 N H_2SO_4	N-80-1	39	100	0.18 hour

[1]Gases bubbled through 5% NaCl
[2]Triplicates
[3]Failure
(After Hudgins et al.)

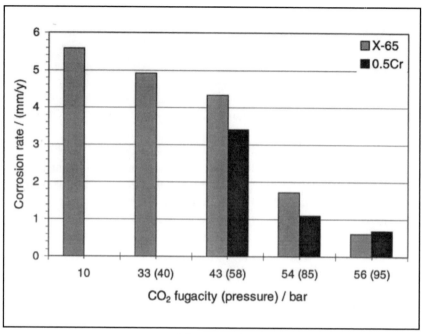

Figure 5-4

The average corrosion rate measured during 150-300 hours exposure at 40°C in water equilibrated with CO_2 at the given fugacity (pressure) (After Seiersten).

Inert Gas Injection

Inert gas injection, a form of miscible gas flooding, involves the injection of an inert gas, usually nitrogen, into the reservoir under high pressure. A typical method for procuring this inert gas is passing exhaust gas from compression engines over a catalyst bed. The composition of such a gas is shown in Table 5-10. This type of process is also commonly used for gas-pressure maintenance of reservoirs in which inert gas is injected into the gas cap to maintain the reservoir pressure, extending the life of the primary production.

At first glance, the gas composition does not look too aggressive, and one would expect only some CO_2 corrosion when water is present. However, field experience has shown that stress-corrosion cracking can occur in the presence of CO/CO_2 gas mixtures. Field failures of J-55 and N-80 tubing resulted when injection gas leaked through the tubing connection and contacted the packer fluid. Cracking frequently initiated at small pits on the outside surface of the tubing and progressed in a transgranular fashion. Although the mechanism for such cracking has not been determined, a laboratory study of this type of cracking led to the following conclusions by Kowaka and Nagata:

Table 5-10 Typical Inert Gas Composition

Component	Mole %
Hydrogen	2.3
Methane	0.067
Ethane	0.008
Water	0.001
Nitrogen	83.8
Oxygen	0.029
Argon	0.96
Carbon dioxide	9.4
Carbon Monoxide	3.4

(After Bowman et al.)

1. Stress-corrosion cracking did nol occur in water containing only carbon monoxide or carbon dioxide.
2. Cracking was transgranular and only occurred when water was present.
3. Cracking occurred over a wide range of CO/CO_2 ratios.
4. Susceptibility to cracking decreased with increasing temperature.
5. No cracking occurred in 18 Cr-10 Ni stainless steel.
6. Cracking was apparently caused by stress-corrosion cracking rather than hydrogen embrittlement.

The last conclusion is not completely in accord with the previous five conclusions since decreasing susceptibility with increasing temperature is more characteristic of hydrogen-stress cracking (HSC) than stress-corrosion cracking. In addition, carbon monoxide is also an effective hydrogen recombination poison and as such could promote the ingress of hydrogen into the steel. Thus, this form of cracking actually may be HSC but elucidation of the mechanism must await further research.

Figure 5-5 shows the reason for conclusion three and the need for a better understanding of this form of cracking since, in thermal recovery methods, as well as inert gas injection systems, various concentrations of carbon monoxide and carbon dioxide are developed and pose a potential cracking problem.

Describing the various problems associated with enhanced oil recovery presents a new challenge to the corrosion/materials engineer in the application of materials. Many of these environments are similar to basic petroleum production (e.g., hydrogen sulfide, carbon dioxide, chlorides, etc.), but some are not, such as significantly higher temperatures, oxidizing environments, increased sand production with associated erosion, and new cracking phenomena such as CO_2/CO

223

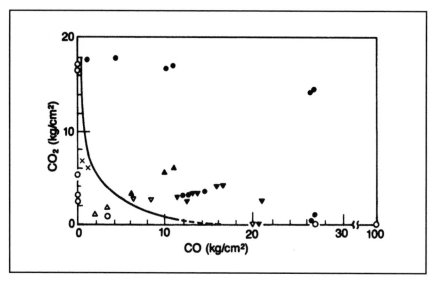

Figure 5-5
Effect of partial pressure of CO and CO_2 on stress-corrosion cracking of carbon
and manganese steels between 18-70°C for 168-1,000 Hours.
Closed symbols and X denote cracking and open symbols no cracking.
(After Kowaka and Nagata)

environments. All represent new areas of concern and challenge. Although there
are alloys currently available that circumvent many of these problems, using the
right combination to avoid other associated problems such as crevice corrosion,
SCC, and galvanic attack and the need for economic considerations make material decisions complex.

Experience with alloys in deep, aggressive wells should provide an information base that can be extended to the EOR realm and vice versa.

References

ASTM G63-80 "Standard Guide for Evaluating Materials for Oxygen Service"
(1980).

Bowman, R.W.; A.K. Dunlop; and J.P. Tralmer. "CO/CO_2 Cracking in Inert Gas-
Miscible Flooding." Materials Performance, 16 (1977), p. 28.

Chu, Chieh. "State-of-the-Art Review of Fireflood Field Projects." Second Joint
SPE/DOE Symposium on Enhanced Oil Recovery. Tulsa, Oklahoma, April 1981.

Clark, G.A.; R.G. Jones; W.L. Kinney; R.E. Schilson; H. Surkalo; and R.S. Wilson.
"The Fry in Situ Combustion Test—Field Operations." Journal of Petroleum
Technology (1965), p. 343.

Faroug, Ali, S.M., and R.F. Meldau. "Current Steamflood Technology." Journal of Petroleum Technology 31(1979), p. 1332.

Gates, C.F. and B.G. Holmes. "Thermal Well Completions and Operation." Proceedings of the Seventh World Petroleum Conference. Volume 3, Mexico, 1967, p. 419.

Gill, T.E. "Ten Years of Handling CO_2 for Sacroc Unit." Annual SPE of AIME meeting. New Orleans, September 1982.

Hudgins, C.M.; R.L. McGlasson; P. Mehdizadeh; and W.M. Rosborough. "Hydrogen Sulfide Cracking of Carbon and Alloy Steels." Corrosion 22 (1966), p. 238.

Johnson, D.R. and N.J. Magnani. "Materials Studies for Thermal, Enhanced Oil Recovery Processes." Proceedings of the Fourth Annual DOE Symposium on Enhanced Oil and Gas Recovery. Tulsa, Oklahoma, 1978.

Kohut, G.B.; J.R. Caldwell; and R.A. Morris. "Fireflooding—A Materials Challenge for the Eighties." Alloys for the 80's. Ann Arbor, Michigan: AMAX Conference, 1980.

Kowaka, M. and S. Nagata. "Stress Corrosion Cracking of Mild and Low Alloy Steels in CO-CO_2-H_2O Environments." Corrosion, 32 (1976), p. 395.

Moss, J.T. "Ignition Equipment and Procedures for Thermal Recovery Projects." Twelfth Annual Southwest Petroleum Short Course. Lubbock, Texas, 1965.

Patterson, K.W. "Downhole Corrosion Encountered in the CO_2 Flood at the SACROC Unit." Petroleum Engineer international, 51 (1979), p. 36.

Schremp, F.W. and G. R. Roberson. "Effect of Supercritical CO_2 on Materials of Construction." 48th Annual Fall Meeting of SPE. Paper 4667. Las Vegas, Nevada, 1973.

Secondary Tertiary Oil Recovery Process. Interstate Oil Compact Commission. Oklahoma City, OK, 1974.

Seierstein, M., "Materials Selection for Separation, Transportation and Disposal of CO_2." Corrosion 2001, NACE, Paper #01042, 2001.

Willhite, G.P. and W.K. Dietrich. "Design Criteria for Completion of Steam Injection Wells." Journal of Petroleum Technology (1967), p. 15.

Winkler, G. and M. Nemeth. "The Effect of Contaminations in Carbon Dioxide on the Corrosion Caused by the Gas." Corrosion Week, 41st Manifestation European Federation Of Corrosion, 1970, p. 788.

Zawlerucha, R., Drnevich, R.F., McIlroy, K. and Knecht, P. Material Compatibility and Systems Considerations in Thermal EOR Environments Containing High Pressure Oxygen." Journal of Petroleum Technology, p. 1477 (1988).

6

FACILITIES

In years past this area was referred to as surface facilities but with the large growth of subsurface equipment in deep water fields the term facilities is more complete. Surface and subsurface facilities represent a large group of equipment that is required for handling, separating, and transporting oil, gas, and water. In this chapter only those major components on the surface, downstream of the choke but upstream of a gas plant or refinery, are discussed. The major components are line pipe, vessels, tanks, rotating equipment (compressors and pumps), valves, and heat exchangers. Each of these components will be addressed in a general manner but it must be recognized that the conditions under which they operate can be quite broad.

Line pipe

Generally line pipe and piping are the same component except the former are longer sections and the latter are shorter pieces between for instance, vessels and pumps. The most common material for piping and line pipe is Grade B pipe made to either API 5L or ASTM A 106. For ease of discussion, this section will deal with API line pipe but many of the same attributes apply regardless of application. Pipe for flowlines, gathering lines and pipelines is commonly manufactured to API

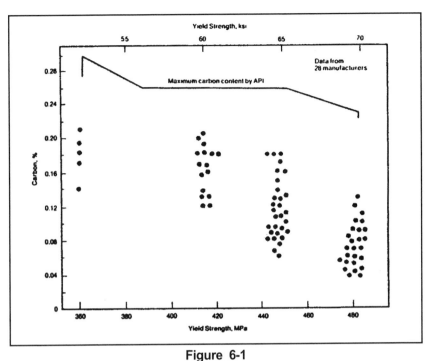

Figure 6-1

Trend in declining carbon content of linepipe steels with increasing strength since 1965 (courtesy American Welding Society).

Specification 5L (ISO 3183). The chemical composition and mechanical property requirements are presented in Tables 6-1 and 6-2. Similar to casing and tubing, API line pipe requirements are quite general and allow for considerable variation in chemistry and strength. Generally, the lower strength grades (X52 and lower) are C-Mn steels that are supplied in the as rolled or normalized condition. In the higher strength grades (X60 and higher), the carbon content is reduced considerably and small amounts of molybdenum, niobium, titanium, and vanadium may be added. These elements are added in such small quantities that this practice is referred to as microalloying. Through microalloying and control of the rolling practice, high strength line pipe steels can be manufactured with very low carbon content, Figure 6-1. These steels are either accelerated cooled during rolling or quenched and tempered. As will be discussed later, the lower carbon content increases weldability and fracture toughness. API 5L line pipe is supplied to one of two product specification levels (PSL). PSL1 is the more basic requirement with limited quality and inspection while PSL2 is the higher quality product. Coiled line pipe, similar to coiled tubing, is manufactured in accordance with API 5LCP, specification for Coiled Line Pipe. The use of CLP for flowline applications is growing and the benefits of such a product are obvious.

227

Table 6-1a PSL1 Chemical Requirements for Heat and Product Analysis by Percentage of Weight.

(1)	(2)	(3)	(4)		(5)	(6)
Grade & Class	Carbon, Maximum[a]	Manganese, Maximum[a]	Phosphorus		Sulfur, Maximum	Other
			Minimum	Maximum		
			Seamless			
A25, Cl I	0.21	0.60		0.030	0.030	
A25, Cl II	0.21	0.60	0.045	0.080	0.030	
A	0.22	0.90		0.030	0.030	
B	0.28	1.20		0.030	0.030	b, d
X42	0.28	1.30		0.030	0.030	c, d
X46, X52, X56	0.28	1.40		0.030	0.030	c, d
X60[e], X65[e], X70[e]	0.28	1.40		0.030	0.030	c, d
			Welded			
A25, Cl I	0.21	0.60		0.030	0.030	
A25, Cl II	0.21	0.60	0.045	0.080	0.030	
A	0.22	0.90		0.030	0.030	
B	0.26	1.20		0.030	0.030	b, d
X42	0.26	1.30		0.030	0.030	c, d
X46, X52, X56	0.26	1.40		0.030	0.030	c, d
X60[e]	0.26	1.40		0.030	0.030	c, d
X65[e]	0.26	1.45		0.030	0.030	c, d
X70[e]	0.26	1.65		0.030	0.030	c, d

Table 6-1b PSL 2 Chemical Requirements for Heat and Product Analysis by Percentage of Weight.

(1)	(2)	(3)	(4)	(5)	(6)
Grade	Carbon, Maximum[a]	Manganese, Maximum[a]	Phosphorus Maximum	Sulfur, Maximum	Other
		Seamless			
B	0.24	1.20	0.025	0.015	b, d
X42	0.24	1.30	0.025	0.015	c, d
X46, X52, X56	0.24	1.40	0.025	0.015	c, d
X60[e], X65[e], X70[e], X80[e]	0.24	1.40	0.025	0.015	c, d
		Welded			
B	0.22	1.20	0.025	0.015	b, d
X42	0.22	1.30	0.025	0.015	c, d
X46, X52, X56	0.22	1.40	0.025	0.015	c, d
X60[e]	0.22	1.40	0.025	0.015	c, d
X65[e]	0.22	1.45	0.025	0.015	c, d
X70[e]	0.22	1.65	0.025	0.015	c, d
X80[e]	0.22	1.85	0.025	0.015	c, d

Footnotes to Tables 6a and 6b:

[a] For each reduction of 0.01% below the specified maximum carbon content, an increase of 0.05% above the specified maximum manganese content is permissible, up to a maximum of 1.50% for Grades X42 through X52, up to a maximum of 1.65% for grades higher than X52 but less than X70, and up to 2.00% for Grades X70 and higher.

[b] Columbium [niobium], vanadium, titanium, or combinations thereof may be used by agreement between the purchaser and manufacturer.

[c] Columbium [niobium], vanadium, titanium, or combinations thereof may be used at the discretion of the manufacturer.

[d] The sum of the columbium [niobium], vanadium, and titanium contents shall not exceed 0.15%.

[e] Other chemical compositions may be furnished by agreement between purchaser and manufacturer, providing that the limits of Footnote d, and the tabular limits for phosphorus and sulfur are met.

Table 6-2a Tensile Requirements for PSL 1

(1)	(2)		(3)		(4)
	Ultimate Yield Strength, Minimum		Ultimate Tensile Tensile Strength, Minimum		Elongation, in 2 in. (50.80mm), Minimum,
Grade	psi	MPa	psi	MPa	Percent
A25	25,000	(172)	45,000	(310)	a
A	30,000	(207)	48,000	(331)	a
B	35,000	(241)	60,000	(414)	a
X42	42,000	(290)	60,000	(414)	a
X46	46,000	(317)	63,000	(434)	a
X52	52,000	(359)	66,000	(455)	a
X56	56,000	(386)	71,000	(490)	a
X60	60,000	(414)	75,000	(517)	a
X65	65,000	(448)	77,000	(531)	a
X70	70,000	(483)	82,000	(565)	a

Table 6-2b Tensile Requirements for PSL 2

(1)	(2)		(3)		(4)		(5)		(6)
	Yield Strength, Minimum		Yield Strength, Maximum[b]		Ultimate Tensile Strength, Minimum		Ultimate Tensile Strength, Maximum[c]		Elongation, in 2 in. (50.80mm), Minimum,
Grade	psi	MPa	psi	MPa	psi	MPa	psi	MPa	Percent
B	35,000	(241)	65,000[d]	(448)	60,000	(414)	110,000	(758)	a
X42	42,000	(290)	72,000	(496)	60,000	(414)	110,000	(758)	a
X46	46,000	(317)	76,000	(524)	63,000	(434)	110,000	(758)	a
X52	52,000	(359)	77,000	(531)	66,000	(455)	110,000	(758)	a
X56	56,000	(386)	79,000	(544)	71,000	(490)	110,000	(758)	a
X60	60,000	(414)	82,000	(565)	75,000	(517)	110,000	(758)	a
X65	65,000	(448)	87,000	(600)	77,000	(531)	110,000	(758)	a
X70	70,000	(483)	90,000	(621)	82,000	(565)	110,000	(758)	a
X80	80,000	(552)	100,000[e]	(690)	90,000	(621)	120,000	(827)	a

Manufacturing Processes of Line Pipe

Since the manufacturing of ERW and seamless pipe has already been discussed in Chapter Four only the manufacturing of submerged arc welded pipe will be presented here. Spiral weld pipe is another process but it is not as common as the other three processes and therefore is not described.

Submerged-Arc Welded Line Pipe

The manufacturing of double submerged-arc welded (DSAW) line pipe is usually restricted to diameters of 12-3/4-inch OD and above. Most DSAW pipe is manufactured from plate, although a few mills utilize strip or sheet product. Whether it is plate or strip, the first operation in the production sequence is the shearing and planing of the edges to ensure that each is parallel with the opposite side and square with the ends.

Crimping of the plate edges follows the planing operation and this is done to avoid a flat surface near the longitudinal weld seam. The crimped plate is "U"-ed by a large die with a 2,000-ton capacity or more. As the die moves down onto the plate, it forces it between sets of dies which assist in shaping the "U". The shaped plate is positioned in a bottom die, and a top die is operated by a hydraulic press which is forced down. The plate is deformed until it is almost a closed cylinder or "can".

The formed cylinder is welded longitudinally by a submerged-arc process using consumable electrodes and granular fusible flux. Usually a two- or three wire tandem electrode technique is used and the can is welded from the inside first. Specially designed welding heads deposit the flux along the weld groove and feed the consumable electrodes from a coil mounted on a reel. Both the coil and flux holder are mounted on a boom that travels through the pipe. which is held stationary by a set of clamps. A run-on lab is attached to both ends of the can to facilitate striking the arc and selling the welding parameters. After the inside weld bead is deposited, the weld is inspected and small weld repairs are made. External welding is then performed with a welding head similar to the internal unit. The weld is thoroughly inspected after the completion of the external welding and the loose flux is removed. Defects are usually repaired using a gas shielded medal-arc, a semi- automatic submerged-arc, or low hydrogen shielded metal-arc process.

The final diameter is obtained by cold expanding the pipe either hydraulically or mechanically. Hydraulic expansion uses a retaining die around the outside whereas an internal mandrel is employed to expand the pipe mechanically. Expansion by either method not only rounds out and straightens the pipe but also severely tests the weld and increases the yield strength of the base metal. Hydrostatic testing of the pipe generally follows the cold expansion process.

During the manufacturing of the pipe, the weld seam is nondestructively inspected by either radiography, ultrasonics or a combination of both.

Defects associated with DSAW pipe include cracks in the toe of the weld, lack of cross penetration between the external and internal weld passes, shrinkage cracks in the center of the weld, weld metal porosity, and external and internal undercut in the heat-affected zone.

Spiral welded pipe is also described in API5L but its applications are limited as a result of numerous failures and thus a reluctance by some operators to use this product.

Line pipe weldability

It has been found that lowering the carbon content of the steel and microalloying with elements like Mo, Ti, V and Nb, coupled with processing, can significantly increase strength while also enhancing fracture resistance. Moreover, lowering the carbon and manganese content significantly improves weldability.

Good weldability is important to the successful joining of line pipe and its long-term serviceability. There are several formulas used for weldability; however, one of the most common is the IIW (International Institute of Welding) carbon equivalent (CE):

$$CE = C + \frac{Mn}{6} + \frac{(Cr + Mo + V)}{5} + \frac{(Ni + Cu)}{15}$$

where the elements are in weight percent.

The CE is an indication of a steel's potential for cracking due to hydrogen underbead cracking. Hydrogen enters the weld from various sources such as the electrode coating, moisture, grease, etc. during welding. The lower the CE the less chance for cracking of the weldment. Generally the CE is considered a function of the hardenability of the steel and thus reflects the final hardness, which is also important for example in sour service.

Another method for evaluating cold (hydrogen) cracking potential of a steel is with the P_{cm} equation:

$$P_{cm} = C + \frac{Si}{30} + \frac{Mn + Cu + Cr}{20} + \frac{Ni}{60} + \frac{Mo}{15} + \frac{V}{10} + 5B$$

where the elements are in weight percent. Lower P_{cm} also increases toughness as shown in Figure 6-2. The P_{cm} is only strictly valid for low carbon steels and the CE for higher carbon steels. For improved weldability the typical limits for CE and P_{cm} are 0.40 and 0.18, respectively. Besides composition, the particular method of butt welding for field fabrication is also important to the final properties of the weld. The primary welding processes used for pipe welding are shielded metal-arc welding (stick electrode), gas metal-arc welding (GMAW or MIG), and gas tungsten-arc welding (GTAW or TIG). Welding high carbon-equivalent base metal can lead to extremely hard welds that are susceptible to fracture in H_2S. Besides the susceptibility of the base metal to corrosion and cracking in H_2S, the welds must also be considered. Pipeline steels may suffer damage from H_2S in four ways: corrosion which was discussed in previous chapters, hydrogen-induced stepwise cracking (HIC), stress oriented hydrogen induced cracking (SOHIC) and SSC. Since corrosion by H_2S has already been dealt with, it will not be covered again.

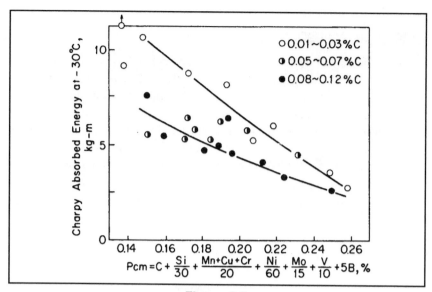

Figure 6-2

Charpy impact toughness of weld heat-affected zone as a function of the Pcm of the steel (courtesy Sumitomo Metal Industries).

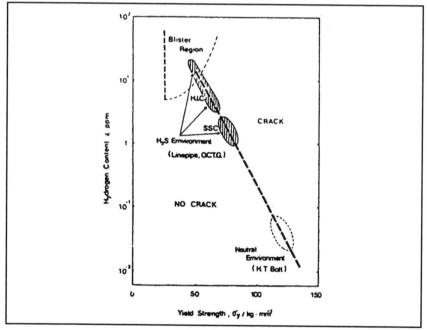

Figure 6-3

Transition in hydrogen cracking mechanisms as a function of hydrogen content and yield strength (courtesy T. Murata).

Table 6-3

Examples of Pipeline Failure Caused by Cracking Under H2S Environment

Year	Location	Plant	Material	Environment
1954	USA	Barkerdom Gathering Pipeline	X-52 SAW 24"Ø x 0.271"t	Natural Gas 15% CO_2, 1% H_2S
1961	FRG	Gas Pipeline	X-42 ERW Annealed	$H_2S \leq 0.95\%$ $CO_2 = 8.7\%$
1972	Arabian Gulf	Offshore Pipeline (Crude Oil)	X-65 SAW	Crude Oil + H_2S (with Sea Water)
1974	Arabia	Onland Pipeline (Sour Gas)	X-42 SAW (Spiral)	Natural GAs (CH_4) 3.4% H_2S, 8.8% CO_2

Generally, the lower strength pipeline steels, Grades X65 and lower, do not display SSC in the base metal because of their lower hardness, but the welds in these steels may fail by SSC. As higher strength grades have been developed, the tendency to SSC of the base metal as well as the welds has increased. Figure 6-3 illustrates the changes in hydrogen damage mechanism as a function of yield strength. As strength increases, lower hydrogen contents are necessary to cause cracking.

Even when the line pipe steel is low strength and the welds are made to provide a SSC resistant structure, another form of hydrogen damage may occur, referred to variously as hydrogen-induced cracking (HIC), stepwise cracking (SWC), blister cracking or any number of other terms. The commonly accepted term is hydrogen induced cracking (HIC). Table 6-3 shows examples of pipeline failures in H_2S caused by HIC. Unlike SSC, HIC typically occurs in the absence of stress and initiates at elongated nonmetallic inclusions (often MnS). Cracks linking the blisters formed at inclusions follow a stairstep pattern thus the term stepwise cracking. This feature is shown schematically in Figure 6-4 and compared to the crack path observed for SSC. For soft steels in which a high stress is applied, the fracture appears intermediate between HIC and SSC, (Figure 6-4) and is referred to as stress-oriented hydrogen-induced cracking (SOHIC). The mechanism of HIC is illustrated in Figure 6-5. HIC can occur in the base metal or the heat affected zone (HAZ) of welds in pipe as can SOHIC. The term HIC does not distinguish one mechanism of hydrogen damage from another, however, popular opinion has favored the term HIC. As Figure 6-5 illustrates, hydrogen ions in solution gain one electron (see the reaction in Chapter 2) to form atomic hydrogen on the surface of the steel. As a result of the large hydrogen gradient (concentration) at the surface, hydrogen atoms diffuse into the steel and accumulate

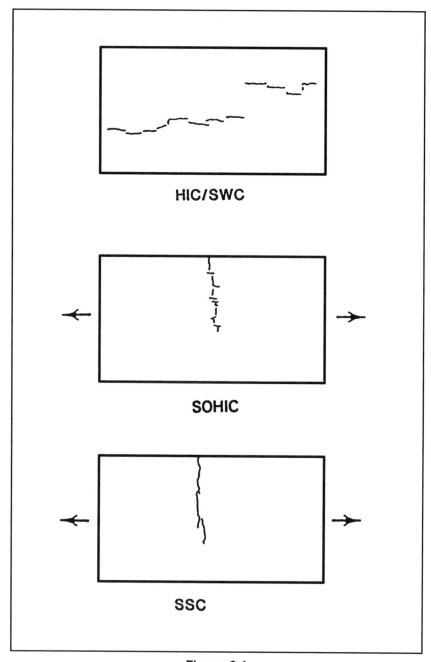

Figure 6-4
Crack morphology for HIC/SWC, SSC, and SOHIC.
The arrows indicate the direction of applied stress.

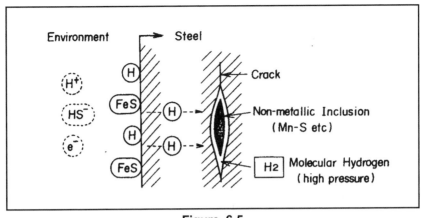

Figure 6-5

Schematic drawing for the mechanism as hydrogen-induced cracking (HIC)
(courtesy Sumitomo Metal Industries).

at nonmetallic inclusions where they recombine to form molecular hydrogen. The H_2 cannot diffuse out of the steel so the pressure increases until it exceeds the strength of the steel and a crack is generated.

As with SSC, there are a number of factors that affect HIC. The primary factors are:

- Solution pH
- Hydrogen content of steel
- Temperature
- Steel chemistry
- Processing/Microstructure

Figure 6-6 shows the degree of cracking as a function of hydrogen content. After a certain threshold is reached, C_{th}, cracking becomes significant. The concentration of hydrogen in a metal is a function of the solution pH and the partial pressure of H_2S. Figure 6-7 shows the partial pressure necessary for HIC and the dependence on composition of the steel. As the total system pressure increases and the H_2S content of the gas increases the tendency for HIC also increases and requires HIC resistant steels. Additions of Cu have been found to decrease both the corrosion rate in H_2S and the tendency to HIC.

Steel chemistry has been found to have a profound effect on HIC resistance. As might be expected, a reduction in sulfur content should increase resistance by reducing the number of nonmetallic inclusions from which HIC could initiate. This is observed to be the case in Figure 6-8. Furthermore, control of the sulfide shape using Ca treatment has also proven beneficial, Figure 6-9. It has been found that if the S content of the steel is reduced to 0.003 wt% or less there is no benefit from Ca additions and therefore, no need to include Ca in the steel.

235

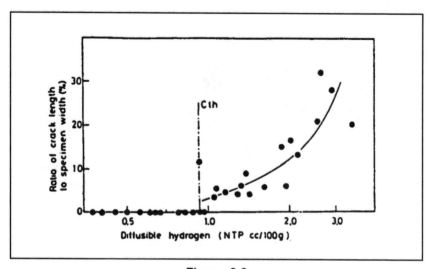

Figure 6-6

Relationship between HIC and the threshold hydrogen content (C_{th})
(courtesy Sumitomo Metal Industries).

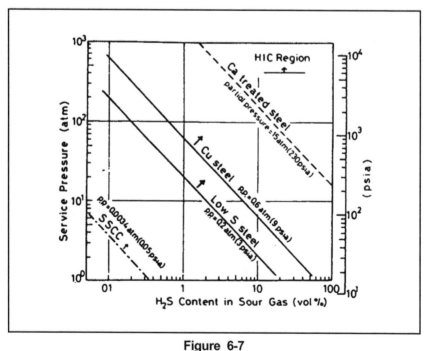

Figure 6-7

Critical H_2S partial pressure required to initiate HIC
(courtesy N. Totsuka and NACE).

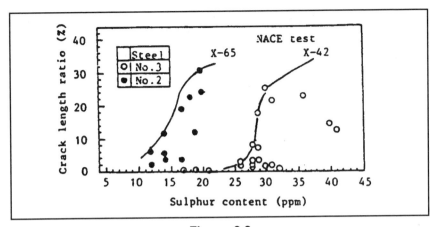

Figure 6-8
Influence of sulfur content in steel on HIC behavior measured as
crack length ratio (CLR) (courtesy ASM International).

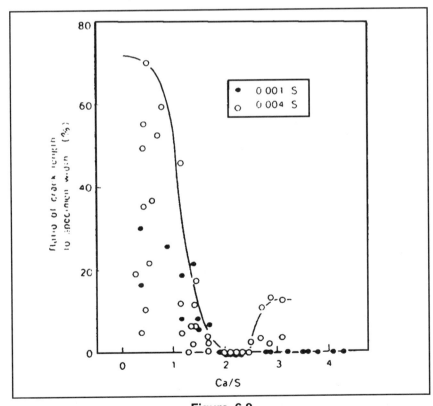

Figure 6-9
Effect of Ca/S ratio on HIC resistance in Ca treated steel
(courtesy A. Ikeda and NACE).

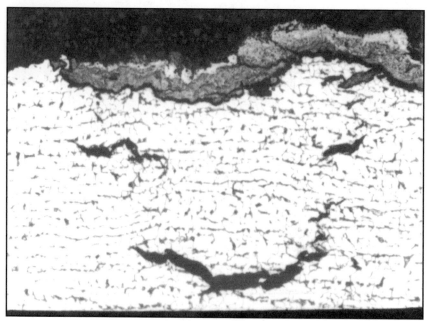

Figure 6-10
HIC below a scale filled pit in Grade B pipe.

Microstructure is also quite important in resisting HIC. A heavily banded (segregated) structure can reduce resistance to HIC even if all other precautions are taken. Since banding is dependent on Mn content, Mn levels are maintained as low as possible to reduce the incidence of banding. In a similar fashion for SSC, the temperature of greatest susceptibility for HIC appears to be about 30°C.

A standardized test procedure for susceptibility of pipe steels to SWC has been developed by NACE and designated TM-02-84. This procedure specifies the removal of test coupons from the pipe and the exposure of these coupons to either a seawater solution saturated with H_2S (Solution B) or a low pH solution that contains acetic acid (Solution A). The test is run for 96 hours after which the specimen is cleaned, sectioned and metallographically prepared. The extent of cracking is measured and the results are reported as crack length ratio (CLR), crack sensitivity ratio (CSR) and crack thickness ratio (CTR). However, this NACE test method does not provide accept/reject criteria, which must be selected by the user. A common requirement is to restrict the CLR to 10% maximum and the CTR to 1.5% maximum.

It is important when considering new construction of flowlines, gathering lines, and transmission lines that HIC be considered and pipe ordered that is resistant to this form of attack. Moreover, it has been found that seamless pipe does not generally display HIC because the inclusions are not elongated; there-

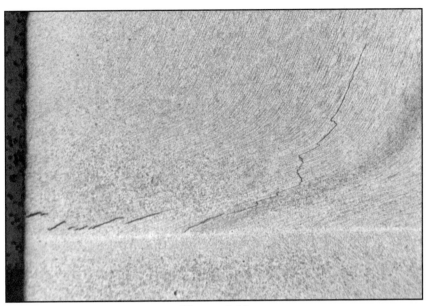

Figure 6-11
HIC in the area adjacent to the ERW (horizontal white line).

fore, ordering HIC-resistant seamless pipe is unnecessary. However, seamless pipe can fail from HIC under severe conditions. Figure 6-10 shows HIC that developed beneath a corrosion pit inside seamless Grade B pipe in a flowline carrying 15% H_2S. Methanol that was injected upstream of this location was not deoxygenated leading to reaction with H_2S to form $S°$ and the resulting failure. ERW and DSAW pipe may display HIC and precautions should be taken when ordering pipe to require HIC resistant pipe. Moreover, as shown in Figure 6-11 the ERW itself can be susceptible to HIC.

As pipeline steel strength increases to X80 and greater, the potential for SSC increases. The behavior of high strength pipeline steels to SSC is identical to other steels. Cracking in H_2S is also a function of the welding process and microstructure, Figure 6-12. The presence of increasing amounts of bainite and martensite in the weld increase the incidence of SSC. Figure 6-13 shows the relation between HAZ hardness and H_2S concentration to resist fracture. Although hard welds are expected to fail in H_2S from SSC, and they do, soft welds have also been observed to crack in sour environments. Thus SSC of welds is not solely a function of hardness. Fracture from SSC has been found in the base metal (BM), heal-affected zone (HAZ) and weld metal (WM) and not always associated with the hardest areas of the weldment. Above about HV260 there is a general correlation between SSC and hardness but below this fracture is less predictable. Generally below this hardness cracking manifests itself as SOHIC.

239

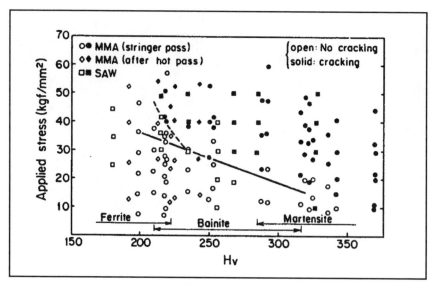

Figure 6-12

Relationship between the appliced stress, mircrostructure and the maximum
hardness for SSC of welds tested in the NACE solution
(courtesy Sumitomo Metal Industries).

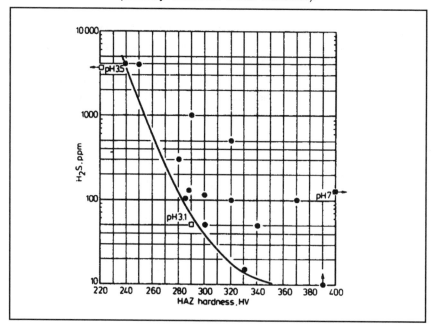

Figure 6-13

Maximum hardness of HAZ to avoid cracking in H_2S for pipeline welds
(courtesy The Welding Institute).

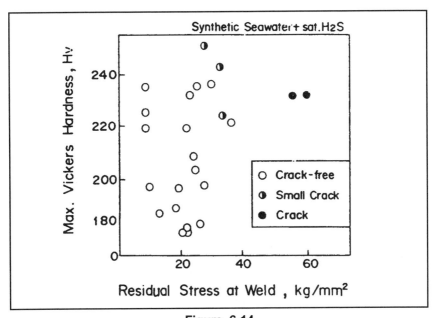

Figure 6-14

Influence of residual stress from welding and hardness on SSC
of welds in line pipe (courtesy Sumitomo Metal Industries).

Considerable work is being done in this area to better understand the SSC and SOHIC of welds in line pipe steels. However, at this time it is still considered good practice to stress relieve welds to reduce areas of high hardness and high residual stress, Figure 6-14. The cost of post-weld heat treatment (PWHT) on flowlines and pipelines can be prohibitive, so many companies use ASTM A 106 Grade B or API Spec 5L Grade B pipe with E6010 electrodes. The resulting hardness in the as-welded condition are sufficiently low that SSC has generally not been a problem. For high pressure piping, heavy wall Grade B pipe such as 1-in.-thick is commonly used, often with a preheat that helps reduce cracking. However, for long distance flowlines and sour gas pipelines, API5L Grade X60 has been used successfully when welded with properly qualified procedures using E6010 and E7010G electrodes. More information on HIC, SOHIC and SSC is available in ISO 15156.

One form of corrosion attack unique to ERW pipe is grooving corrosion. Grooving corrosion is the selective corrosion of the narrow weld line in ERW pipe that occurs as a result of the galvanic difference between the weld and the pipe body. Figure 6-15 shows the cross section of a corrosion groove on the inside of a section of line pipe. Once the corrosion has progressed to the stage where sufficient wall thickness does not remain to contain the pressure, rupture occurs. This

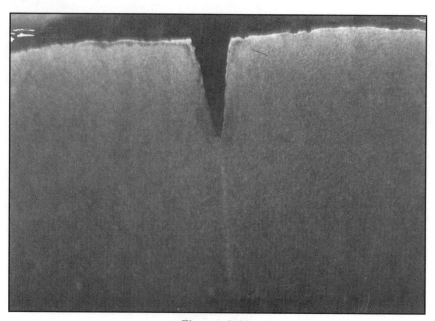

Figure 6-15
Grooving corrosion of the ERW in line pipe.
The top of the photograph is the inside surface of the pipe.

type of failure is frequently misinterpreted as the result of poor weld quality during manufacturing. Grooving corrosion is not dependent on grade or size and the susceptibility cannot be heat treated out or alloyed to correct the problem. Usually, lower carbon and sulfur content help reduce the susceptibility but cannot eliminate it altogether. Grooving corrosion almost always occurs in oxygenated high water cut systems, therefore, it predominates in surface piping, flowline, gathering lines, and water injection systems. Although grooving corrosion is most often observed internally, it has also been found on the external surfaces of line pipe. Since grooving is essentially a galvanic corrosion problem, the weld displays long narrow slits of corrosion along the weld while the remaining body of the pipe is often free of corrosion, Figure 6-16.

Another consideration in surface piping, flowlines, and gathering systems is corrosion from CO_2. Corrosion by wet CO_2 was discussed at length in Chapter Four, however, particular importance must be paid to surface piping because of the selective corrosion of girth welds from CO_2, Figure 6-17. Even though all surfaces of steel components are susceptible to corrosion in the presence of CO_2, the welds are generally attacked at a higher rate due to the turbulence created by the weld bead itself. This turbulence reduces the ability to form a protective or semi-protective iron carbonate film on the weld that often forms on the remainder of the pipe surface. Therefore, the corrosion is accelerated at welds both because of

Figure 6-16
View of inside of the pipe shown in Figure 6-15.
Note the distinct weldline attack in the center of the photograph (arrow).

the absence of a corrosion film and the turbulence created that also increases corrosion by erosion-corrosion or flow enhanced corrosion. Furthermore, there is also a galvanic couple created between the weld metal and the HAZ. In some cases the weld metal is anodic to the HAZ while in others the reverse is true. Attempts to solve this problem by small additions of Cu and Ni to the filler metal have only had limited success.

Of course, erosion-corrosion is not restricted to CO_2 systems, rather it can be a significant factor in any flowing system where corrosion is active. Erosion-corrosion is typically a greater problem in piping and line pipe compared to vessels because of the higher velocities. It is also of significant importance in tubing strings.

243

Figure 6-17

Selective weld line corrosion of a butt weld in pipe carrying fluids containing CO_2

The API has recognized that a critical velocity exists above which erosion corrosion can become a significant problem. API RP14E provides an equation to calculate critical velocity (Vc) for design purposes so these velocities can be avoided. The equation:

$$V_c = \frac{C}{\rho^{1/2}}$$

where V_c = velocity in ft/sec
ρ = fluid density in lb/cu.ft.
C = constant, 100-125

is strictly empirical and has been the source of much controversy as to its origin which has never been determined. Recently the API, unexplicably increased the C factor for CRAs to 200 with no explanation of how this value was arrived at nor what limits may be required since not every CRA an be expected to have the same C factor. Craig developed an equation of similar form based on two phase flow that better defines the constant C. In the equation:

$$V_c = \frac{C}{\rho^{3/7}}$$

the constant C is dependent on corrosion product composition such that for carbon and low-alloy steels C = 90 when the corrosion film is composed of $FeCO_3$, C = 95 when it is FeS and C = 150 when the corrosion product is Fe_3O_4. In the case

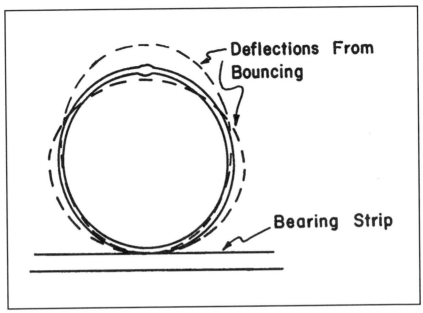

Figure 6-18

Deflection of pipe during transportation that results in fatigue loading
(courtesy Pipe Line Industry and Gulf Publishing).

of chromium containing steels ($\geq$13% Cr) the constant varies from 160 to 300 depending on the particular oxide that forms and the specific CRA being considered. At velocities below V_c corrosion from CO_2 can still be a problem; however, erosion is not typically involved. At velocities in excess of V_c chemical inhibition is often impossible because the inhibitor cannot remain on the pipe surface without being stripped off by the flowing fluid. The determination of the critical erosion corrosion velocity remains a significant problem and while attempts have been made to quantify this factor the results are not satisfactory. Moreover, when sand is present the above equations are invalid.

Serious problems can arise during the transportation of line pipe. Poor loading and shipping practices have led to numerous failures of pipe in transit. The cause of failure is fatigue and thus is referred to as transit fatigue. Transit fatigue results from gravitational and inertial forces that created cyclic stresses during transportation. An illustration of how these cyclic stresses arise is shown in Figure 6-18. The weight of the pipe provides a gravitational stress that fluctuates by bouncing and flexing as the pipe load moves up and down. As can be seen, the loads must be relatively high and there must be a large number of cycles to induce cracks, thus transit fatigue is not often observed when pipe is trucked. Most transit fatigue failures are associated with ship or rail transport where the pipe loads

245

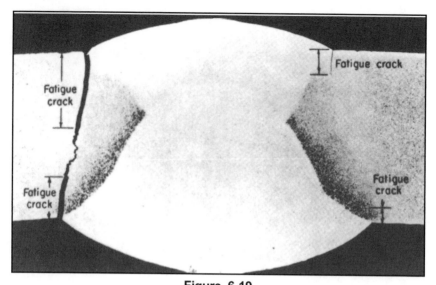

Figure 6-19

Fatigue cracks that initiated at the toe of the weld as a result of transit fatigue (courtesy Pipe Line Industry and Gulf Publishing).

are higher and the trip is longer (higher number of cycles). Some of the other variables that influence transit fatigue are size of the contact area, nature of the bearing surface, amount of surface damage, the ambient environment, and the diameter to thickness ratio. The latter variable is expected because of the greater flexing with greater D/t ratios.

Surface damage such as denting, abrasion, fretting, and corrosion pitting can lower the fatigue resistance.

Transit fatigue failures originating in the pipe body are almost always associated with surface damage, whereas fatigue of submerged-arc welded pipe frequently initiates at the weld toe because of the change in cross section from the weld to the pipe body, Figure 6-19.

Transit fatigue failures can be prevented by following good loading and shipping practices, for example those detailed in API RP5L1 and API RP5L5.

Solid and Clad CRA Line pipe

Two new methods of corrosion control using CRAs are: CRA clad line pipe and solid CRA line pipe. Clad line pipe is manufactured with carbon steel base metal and various CRA clad material such as 316 stainless steel, Alloy 825 and Alloy 625. There are several different methods of manufacturing clad pipe that fall into two basic categories: lined and metallurgically bonded. Both of these methods are described in API 5LD. The most common commercial methods for cladding pipe are: coextrusion, roll bonding, centrifugal casting, hydraulic shrink fit, and explosive bonding. The first three processes produce a metallurgical bond of the CRA material with the steel outer pipe. The latter two methods produce a lined product that results in an interference or mechanical fit but not a metallurgical bond at the interface.

In coextrusion, a piece of steel is initially extruded, then a block of CRA is introduced in this hollow and the two are extruded together so the CRA bonds to inside of the steel as the seamless tube is being made. Another variation on this method involves weld overlaying the ID of a steel billet with the CRA, then hot extruding the billet to length, resulting in a CRA clad layer on the inside. Roll bonding is typically for larger diameter pipes and is accomplished by rolling a thin sheet (~3mm) of CRA on a steel plate at elevated temperature. The plate is then formed similar to that described in the DSAW process and the pipe is long seam welded with CRA filler metal on the inside of the pipe and carbon steel on the outside. In centrifugal casting, the outer steel shell is rotated while the CRA powder is introduced inside and cast against the ID of the steel shell.

Mechanically lined pipe is made by a variety of similar steps. The hydraulic shrink fit method is performed several different ways, one is to introduce a CRA liner into a steel pipe that has already been heated to a moderate temperature (~800°F). The CRA liner is hydraulically expanded against the steel pipe as it cools, thereby providing a shrink fit. Another method uses the hydraulic expansion of the liner but without heating the steel outer pipe. There are other variations on these schemes for lining pipe. A unique method for lining pipe is to insert a CRA liner into a steel pipe and then set off an explosive charge inside the CRA liner to expand it against the steel. These methods of interference lining create a residual stress on the order of 15,000 psi or greater, thus preventing the liner from easily slipping out of the outer tube. The ends of lined pipe are often seal welded to ensure good weldability when the field butt weld is made. Figure 6-20 shows just such a butt weld in Alloy 825 lined, X65 pipe. Clad and lined pipe have been extensively used worldwide for flowline and pipeline projects, however, the welding rates of clad lines is slow compared to carbon steel pipeline welding and thus clad lines are typically only used in the most severe environments.

Solid alloy pipelines and flowlines have gained wider acceptance and as more lines are constructed, welding speeds are increasing. The lines laid to date have been weldable 13 Cr and duplex stainless steel for high CO_2 service and solid Hastelloy G-3 for gas containing appreciable H_2S. The selection of CRAs for solid or clad pipelines and piping follows the same methods as described in Chapter 4. In fact, Figures 4-39 to 4-45 can be used here as well as Figure 6-21.

Of course, there is one very important factor that must be considered in the selection of CRA line pipe that is not considered for downhole tubing. Besides CO_2, H_2S, and chloride content of the fluids, surface piping can contain oxygen so the environment is often more severe than downhole. Moreover, welds present another concern from a corrosion stand point. Materials such as duplex stainless

247

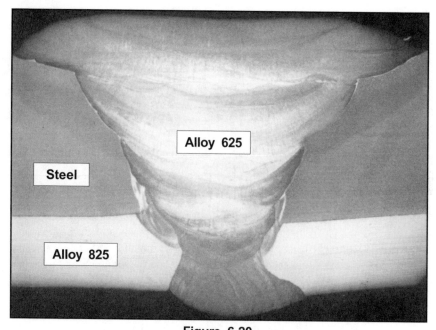

Figure 6-20
Macrograph of butt weld in mechanically lined steel pipe.
The liner is Alloy 825 and the filler metal is Alloy 625. Magnified 6X.

steels require special care to ensure the balance of ferrite and austenite is sufficient for maximum corrosion resistance. The increased use of Super 13 Cr pipelines (also referred to as weldable 13 Cr) has been brought into question recently as a result of several serious field failures in the welds.

Cracking in the long seam and butt welds of 13 Cr pipelines has been attributed to stress corrosion cracking in the sensitized heat affected zone. While sensitization of austenitic stainless steels is a well known phenomenon, as discussed in Chapter 2, martensitic stainless steels such as 13 Cr are generally considered immune to sensitization. However, during welding a portion of the HAZ is heated back into the delta ferrite region and with subsequent cooling of the weld some of the delta ferrite is retained. At the same time the carbon solubility is decreasing as the temperature drops so that chromium carbides precipitate at the delta ferrite grain boundaries producing a sensitized structure that is highly susceptible to SCC.

In addition to the above problems several subsea pipelines made from weldable 13 Cr have failed from hydrogen cracking as a result of the external cathodic protection system imposed on these lines.

The installation and operation of solid CRA pipelines is by no means a simple extension of steel pipelines. They must be properly engineered constructed and operated to avoid failure. Moreover, the CP requirements for each alloy are different and must be properly considered

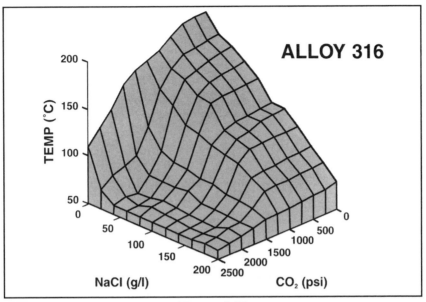

Figure 6-21

The corrosion resistance of Alloy 316 stainless steel in CO_2/NaCl
environments in the absence of oxygen and H_2S. Corrosion rates
of ≤0.05 mm/yr (2mpy) and no SSC or SCC.(Courtesy Nickel Institute)

Field Separators, Storage Tanks and Other Vessels

Separators, tanks and other vessels are designed and built to various codes and
standards depending on their intended use. For pressure containing vessels such as
separators the ASME Pressure Vessel Code is used for design requirements. For
storage tanks, API Standards 620 and 650 apply. Pressure vessels such as two and
three-phase separators are typically manufactured from ASTM (ASME) A 106 for
small diameter vessels that can be made from pipe, or A 516, Grade 60 or 70.
Likewise storage tanks are also constructed from these steels as well as ASTM A 36.

As with pipelines, several forms of hydrogen damage can occur in vessels and
tanks. Original fabrication welds used for construction of the vessel or attachment
of nozzles can produce hard welds that are susceptible to SSC. In addition, high
residual stresses from welding can lead to SOHIC in soft welds. The petroleum
refining industry recognized the problem of hard welds in the early 1970s.

The problem was most frequent when carbon steel vessels were submerged are
welded (SAW) using bonded (alloying) fluxes and put in wet H_2S service in the as-
welded condition. Transverse-weld cracking was found to occur at hardness levels
above and below the previously established HB 235 hardness (HRC 22) criteria.

249

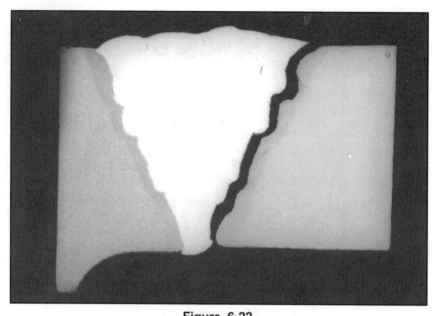

Figure 6-22
Cross section of dissimilar metal weld that failed by SSC.
The white weld metal is a stainless steel while the base metal is carbon steel.

API Recommended Practice 942 and NACE Recommended Practice RP-04-72 cover welds for carbon steel refinery equipment and contain discussions of the various factors affecting weld hardness and agree on a mandatory maximum weld hardness of HB 200. The API RP 942 places additional mandatory restrictions on weld medal chemistry. The limits for carbon, manganese, and silicon are based upon the P-1 chemistry limits of ASME Code Section IX, Table Q11.3, while the total content of chromium, nickel and molybdenum is set at 0.25%. It should be pointed out, however, that these two documents are by definition intended to cover carbon steel (P-1) material only and do not address steel such as Type SA 612 steel, which contains higher manganese and silicon than the more common SA 516 Grade 70 steel, but also allows additional small amounts of nickel and chromium for strengthening and grain refinement.

Failures in carbon steel vessels are often associated with high hardness and high manganese resulting from multipass welds using bonded fluxes. The additive effect of the alloying fluxes results in manganese contents often exceeding 2% and weld strengths, as measured by hardness, which are disproportionately high for unalloyed steel. When using bonded fluxes, it is not unusual to find weld deposits having over HB 225 hardness in a carbon steel Type SA 516-70 pressure vessel. High Mn content welds that are susceptible to SSC can also be obtained when E70S-6 electrodes are used.

All vessels and tanks intended for sour service should be post-weld heat treated to remove residual stresses from welding and reduce the hardness to BHN 200 or less.

One of the major problems in the petroleum industry is the narrow adherence by some (operators as well as manufacturers) to welding procedure qualification only as required by either ASME Section IX or API 1104 with no regard to the potential for SSC or SOHIC in service. Neither of these codes addresses the eventual service conditions of the welds that are made and thus some believe that as long as compliance with these welding codes meet the mechanical requirements as stated in the codes, there is no further obligation. This is dangerous and short sighted view point and should not be tolerated in the industry.

Another serious problem in corrosive service is the fabrication of dissimilar metal welds, especially between carbon or low-alloy steels and austenitic stain less steels or nickel-based alloys. Catastrophic failures have occurred in these welds by SSC and SCC. Figure 6-22 shows the cracking of a dissimilar metal weld between low alloy steel plate and the austenitic stainless steel filler metal from SSC. In these type of welds, chromium diffuses from the austenitic filler metal to the fusion line and carbon diffuses to the same region from the low-alloy steel side. The two elements (and other carbide formers if they are present, i.e., Ti, W, Mo, etc.) combine to form a hard, narrow, chromium-carbide-rich martensite phase approximately 0.002 in. wide adjacent to the fusion line, Figure 6-23. The hardness in this zone can exceed HRC 40. This hard zone _cannot_ be post-weld heat-treated (PWHT); in fact PWHT makes the situation worse by promoting additional diffusion of Cr from the stainless steel and carbon from the steel. Therefore, dissimilar metal welds are discouraged in very corrosive environments, especially if H_2S is present, because of the potential for catastrophic cracking failures. Numerous field failures of dissimilar welds have occurred yet this issue continues to be largely ignored.

Other forms of hydrogen damage such as blistering and HIC are often experienced by vessels in sour service. As discussed before, these forms of damage are not related to hardness but to the number and shape of inclusions, the H_2S content and pH of the water. HIC of production facility vessels especially slug catchers has become such an industry concern that many companies now require NACE TM-02-84 tests on plate material before construction of vessels. These tests are performed in either the TM-02-84 Solution A or the lower pH Solution B.

One system of particular interest is glycol dehydration, specifically within the contactor. Dehydration of gas is important from both a corrosion and operation standpoint. If water or moisture is removed from the gas stream to below the dew point at the lowest expected temperature of downstream operations, then corrosion should be eliminated. However, it has been found in practice that unless the gas is dehydrated to 3-4 pounds of water per million cubic feet it will still condense water and corrosion will occur.

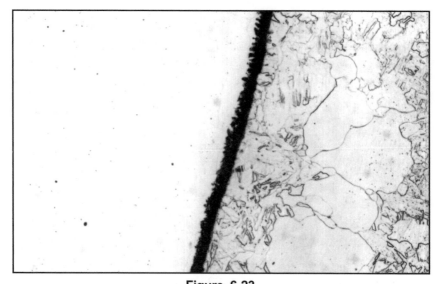

Figure 6-23

Magnified view (400X) of hard zone (black area) along the fusion line of the weld shown in Figure 6-22.

Wet gas enters the inlet scrubber where a pressure drop allows some water and condensate to drop out of the gas. The gas phase then enters the bottom of the absorber tower, which is filled with trays. As the gas rises in the absorber, it is contacted with lean glycol, which absorbs the water from the gas, becoming rich glycol. The dry gas then exits the top of the tower. The rich glycol comes off the bottom of the absorber tower and proceeds through a heat exchanger, then into the stripper (reboiler or regenerator). In the stripper, the glycol is heated so water is driven off to the top of the stripper and into the condenser and accumulator. The glycol moves out of the bottom of the stripper/reboiler as lean glycol for recycle of The process. Corrosion frequently occurs in the contactor because of the wet gas and the presence of CO_2 and H_2S. Contactors are often coated with a plastic coating or clad with a CRA when serious corrosion is expected.

During reboiling of a glycol, it must not be heated to its boiling point to remove water; otherwise, decomposition of the glycol may occur. These decomposition products are acidic organic compounds that are quite corrosive to steel. Even though the bulk temperature of the glycol may be below the decomposition limit, high metal skin temperatures can rapidly decompose glycol. To maintain low skin temperatures, proper control of heat flux by design and proper operation of reboilers is essential.

Degradation of glycols will lead to a lower pH of the solution and enhanced corrosion. The presence of oxygen can also lead to significant degradation of glycols again resulting in low ph solutions.

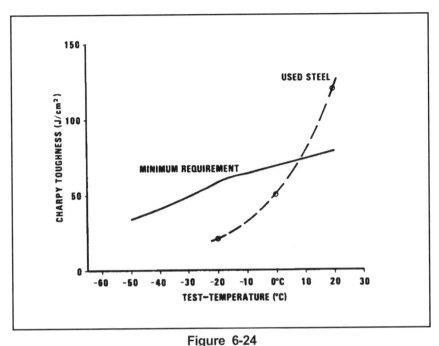

Figure 6-24

Degradation in impact properties of pressure vessel steel after sour gas service (courtesy G. Wilken and NACE).

The addition of H_2S and CO_2 aggravates this corrosive condition and/or creates additional problems. Corrosion from these acid gases will be greatest whenever water drops out of the gas, such as in the inlet scrubber or water knockout vessel. Also, regeneration of the rich glycol creates an environment of high temperature water or vapor that contains concentrated H_2S and CO_2. Thus reboiler/stripper vessels may experience severe corrosion in the hotter sections and in the event of high H_2S blistering or HIC of the vessel steel.

Inlet scrubbers or free water knockouts have been found to contain blisters after exposure to sour water. Blisters are frequently associated with nonmetallic inclusions (i.e., MnS, Al_2O_3) and predominate in banded steels. Blisters have been found to degrade the impact toughness of steels compared to their original properties, Figure 6-24.

As discussed before for pipelines, cladding can be used for corrosion control on the inside of vessels. Due to their low pressure and temperature tanks are more often coated with an organic coating or lining. Clad pressure vessels are manufactured from roll bonded or explosion bonded clad plate with the particular CRA selected according to the factors discussed previously in Chapter 4 and this chapter.

Table 6-4

Typical Centrifugal Pump Component Materials

		Service		
Component	Crude Oil (Low Water)[1]	Water[2]	Crude, Condensate Mildly Corrosive[3]	Crude, Condensate Very Corrosive[4]
Casing	CS	NiAlB, 410SS 316SS, DSS	CS, 316SS, DSS	316SS, DSS, Alloy C276
Impeller	CS, CI	NiAlB, 410SS 316SS, DSS	316SS, DSS	316SS, DSS, Alloy C276
Wear Rings	CI	HFSS	Cl, HFSS	HFSS, Monel Nitronic
Shaft	CS, 4140	4140	4140	316SS, Monel, Alloy 718
Shaft Sleeve	SS, HFSS	HFSS, Stell	HFSS, Stell	HFSS, Stell
"O" Rings	Teflon	Viton, Nitrile, Teflon	Teflon	Teflon

Footnotes 1 - For crude oil containing water less than about 30% by volume.

2 - Not containing significant amounts of H_2S or oxygen.

3 ,4 - The user must arrive at a definition for mildly and very corrosive. Moreover, if sufficient H2S is present in either case materials may also need to meet the requirements of NACE MR-01-75.

Materials - CS = Carbon Steel, (eg. 1045)

SS = Stainless Steel

DSS = Duplex Stainless Steel

HF = Hardfaced

Stell = Stellite

NiAlB = Nickel Aluminum Bronze

CI = Cast Iron

Compressors and Pumps

There are numerous types of compressors and pumps used in gas and liquid transport and processing. Common compressors are: centrifugal, axial, positive displacement, and reciprocating. Pumps also come in the same general configuration.

Typical material choices for different components of a centrifugal pump are shown in Table 6-4. In systems that are mildly corrosive, carbon steel, ductile iron or 316 stainless steel are satisfactory. However, as the severity of corrosion increases, those surfaces contacted by the process stream need to be more corro-

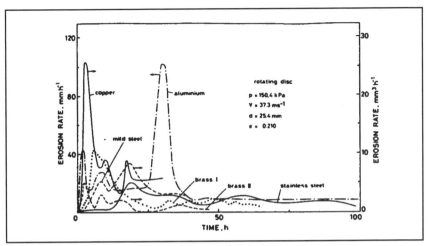

Figure 6-25

Erosion rate versus time for materials in a rotating disk test (courtesy ASM Int'l).

sion resistant, requiring the application of high alloy materials. These alloys often include duplex stainless steels, Monel 400, Hastelloy C, and Ti alloys. The need for this significant increase in alloying is not entirely due to corrosion but also to resist erosion damage, which may be quite severe in fluid and gas handling systems. Pumps are usually specified in accordance with the following API or ANSI Specifications:

> API 610, Centrifugal Pumps for General Refinery Service.

> ANSI/ASMR B73.1M—1984, Specification for Horizontal End Suction Centrifugal Pumps for Chemical Process.

> ANSI/ASME B73.2M—1984, Specification for Vertical In-line Centrifugal Pumps for Chemical Process.

In the same manner as pumps, compressors are subjected to corrosive gas streams often at high velocity so erosion-corrosion can be quite severe. However, compressors handling dry gas can be made of less corrosion-resistant alloys if the gas temperature exceeds the dew point during operation and water is not allowed to collect during shutdown.

For relatively benign environments, impellers are often manufactured from carbon steel or cast iron. However, where high strength is needed, 4320 or 4330 low-alloy steels are used. In the presence of H_2S, these impeller materials must be reduced in hardness to resist SSC and meet NACE MR-01-75/ISO 15156. This can be a problem since these components must have sufficient design strength to operate under high loads and resist erosion. As Figure 6-25 shows, erosion is best handled by the use of higher alloy materials such as stainless steel; however, it

255

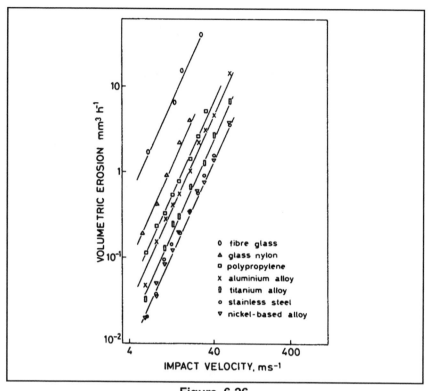

Figure 6-26
Influence of solid particle velocity on erosion rate of different materials
(courtesy ASM International).

must be determined whether solid particles are also involved since they exacerbate erosion, Figure 6-26; and if cavitation may occur, Figure 6-27. As evidence by these figures, stainless steels, nickel-base alloys and cobalt base alloys provide the best erosion/cavitation resistance. Likewise, corrosion resistance and resistance to both SCC and SSC are achieved through alloying. Intermediate alloys such as Ni-resist and 410 stainless steel are often successfully used in pumps and compressors in relatively mild service. Under no conditions are copper alloys (brasses, bronzes, etc.) acceptable for service in H_2S either for gas or liquid service. For the most severe service (hot H_2S, CO_2), Ti impellers, inducers, and diffusers have been found to perform excellently. In water injection and WAG service copper base alloys have been quite successful.

One other failure mode often observed on compressor impellers is fatigue and/or corrosion fatigue. The high alternating stresses imposed on the blades of the impeller provide easy development of fatigue cracks. As illustrated in Chapter Two the introduction of a corrosive environment will result in the loss of a fatigue threshold so that failure eventually results regardless of stress level.

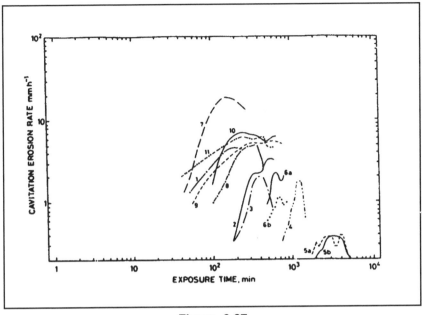

Figure 6-27

1) X15-5 CrVMo121	7) 41 CrMo S4
2) Hastelloy B-2	8) Gx-CrNiMo 18-10
3) Hastelloy C-4	9) X5 CrNiCuNb 17-4
4) Haynes alloy25	10) Gx-CrNiMoCu 25-6
5) Haynes alloy 6B	11) G-CuAl9NiFe
6) Mn steel	

(courtesy ASM International).

Valves

A variety of valves are used in facilities to regulate flow of gas, liquids, and combined fluids. Some of the more common valves are gate, ball, globe, plug, butterfly, needle, and check. The above names describe the type of internal feature that controls flow.

All valves have certain similarities and differences. However, in all cases the valve body must act as a pressure vessel and as such must be resistant to fracture under service conditions and leakage through the body where it has been intruded by the stem, fittings, etc. Valve bodies may be forged, cast, or machined from wrought material. The majority of valves are carbon or low-alloy steel. The low-alloy steels are most frequently used when increased fracture toughness at low temperature is required and as such are quenched and tempered. Increasing corrosion resistance is achieved by changing to stainless steels, bronzes, nickel base alloys, or titanium alloys. Also, CRA clad valve bodies are available for corrosive service.

Table 6-5
Typical Materials for Various Valves

Valve Type	Component	Service			
		Crude Oil (Low Water)[1]	Water[2]	Mildly Corrosive[3] Crude, Condensate, Gas	Very Corrosive[4] Crude, Condensate, Gas
Gate	Body & Bonnet	CS	CS, 13Cr	410SS, F6NM	DSS, Alloy 625 Clad
	Stem	CS	13Cr, 316SS Monel	316SS, Monel	Inconel 718 Inconel 725
	Gate	CS/13Cr	13Cr, 316SS, Stell	13Cr, HFSS 17-4PH	HF Inconel 718, 725
	Seat	CS/13Cr	CS, 13Cr, Stell	13Cr, Stell	Stell
	Packing	Teflon	Teflon Graphite Filled	Teflon	Aflas, Kalrez
Ball	Body & Bonnet	CS	CS, 316SS Monel	CS, 316SS	DSS, Alloy 625 Clad
	Stem/Trunnion	CSP, 316SS	316SS, Monel	CSP, 316SS	Alloy 718 or 725
	Ball	CSP, 316SS	CSP, 316SS, Monel	CSP, 316SS	Alloy 625
	Seat Holder	CSP	CSP, 316SS	316SS, Monel	Alloy 718
	Seat Insert	Teflon, Viton	Teflon, Viton	Peek, Teflon, Viton	Peek, TFE
	Seals	Teflon, Viton	Teflon, Viton	Teflon, Viton	Aflas, Kalrez
Plug	Body & Bonnet	CS	CS, 316SS, DSS	CS, 316SS, DSS	DSS, Alloy 625 Clad
	Stem	CS	316SS, 17-4PH	CSP, 316SS, DSS	718/725
	Plug	CS	316SS, 17-4PH	316SS, 17-4PH	625
	Seal	CS	CSP, 316SS	316SS, CSP	625
	Packing	Graphite Filled	Graphite Filled	Graphite Filled	Graphite Filled

258

Table 6-5 (cont'd)
Typical Materials for Various Valves

Valve Type	Component	Crude Oil (Low Water)[1]	Water[2]	Mildly Corrosive[3] Crude Condensate Gas	Very Corrosive[4] Crude Condensate Gas
Butterfly	Body	CS	CS, 316SS	CS, 316SS	(5)
	Stem	CSP, 17-4PH	17-4PH, Monel	17-4PH, Monel	
	Disc	CSP, 316SS	316SS, Monel	316SS, Monel	
	Seat	316SS	Reinforced Teflon, 316SS	Reinforced Teflon, 316SS	
	Packing	Teflon	Teflon Graphite Filled	Teflon Graphite Filled	
Check	Body & Bonnet	CS	CS, Brass	CS	316SS, DSS Alloy 625 Clad
	Clapper	CS, 3166SS	Brass, 3166SS	316SS	316SS, DSS Alloy 625 Clad
	Face Seal	Viton, Buna	Viton, Buna	Viton, Buna	Teflon
	Pin	13Cr, 316SS	316SS	316SS	Alloy 718
	Seat	CS, 316SS	316SS	316SS	Alloy 718 or 625
	Seals	Viton, Buna	Viton, Buna	Teflon	Teflon

Footnotes 1 - Crude oil with water cuts less than 30% by volume

2 - Not containing significant amounts of H_2S or oxygen.

3,4 - The user must arrive at definition for mildly and very corrosive.
Moreover, if suffcient H_2S is present in either case, materials may also need to meet The requirements of NACE MR-01-75.

5 - These valves are not typically used in very corrsive fluids, therefore resistant alloys are not available.

Materials = CS = Carbon steel

CSP = Carbon steel plated with hard chrome or electroless nickel

SS = Stainless steel

HFSS = Hardfaced SS

Gate valves are described by API Specification 6A and pipeline valves by API Specification 6D.

Besides the bodies, many valves have stems, springs, and seats in common. These internals, along with the gate, ball, plug, etc., are also manufactured from a variety of materials, depending on the service. Typical materials for the above components are presented in Table 6-5. While these do not represent all of the possible materials available they do illustrate some of the more common materials.

Care must be taken in the selection of materials for valves to ensure all components of the valve are suitable for the intended service. Moreover, valves are often a critical system component as they must be able to shut in the pressurized fluid without leaking.

Heat Exchangers

The three most common heat exchangers are shell and tube, air coolers, and plate. Shell and tube will be presented as representative of the other types although there are certain peculiarities for each type of exchanger. Heat exchangers are frequently constructed of carbon steel for most corrosion free or moderately corrosive environments. However, as the corrosivity of fluids on the shell side and/or tube side increases the need for alloying becomes greater. Besides the corrosivity of the fluid, design of the exchanger is critical to a long service life since hydrodynamics play an important role in corrosion and erosion. Thus the shell side will often have low flow and dead spot areas where corrosion may be typified more by static conditions rather than the dynamic conditions which are characteristic of tube sides.

As the corrosivity of the fluid increases, steps such as plastic coating or, for more severe environments, CRA cladding of exchanger shells may be required. The selection of specific alloys for the shell or cladding is dependent on the particular process stream, temperature, pressure etc. Shell material depends on the specific service conditions and may range from carbon steel, to clad CRAs on steel, to solid corrosion-resistant alloy shells. The decision between cladding and a shell constructed of solid CRA is determined primarily by the exchanger shell dimensions. Small vessels are more economically constructed of solid CRA compared to cladding or weld overlaying. Larger diameter vessels on the other hand are more suited to cladding and much more economical than solid alloy vessels.

In the event streams on the shell side will contain H_2S, the shell material and welds should be manufactured and specified in accordance with NACE MR-01-75. All welds should be stress relieved to reduce both hardness and residual welding stress. Likewise higher alloy material should be made in compliance with MR-01-75 when elevated concentrations of H_2S are expected. The same is true for the tube side but often the erosion-corrosion aspect is also important in selecting tube material. Tubes carrying seawater or chloride-containing water can often be handled successfully with stainless steels as long as the flow rate is high enough

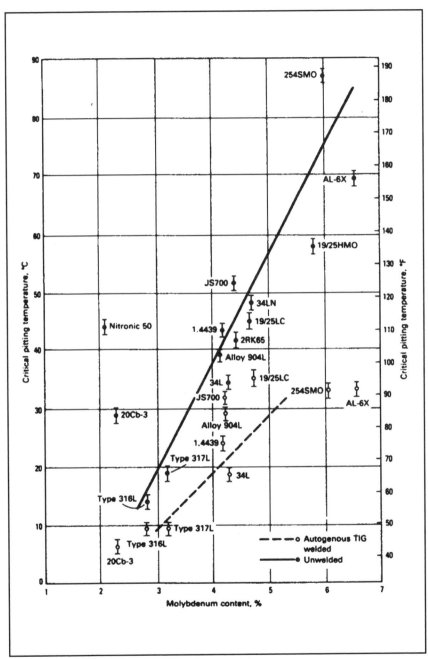

Figure 6-28

Critical pitting temperature versus molybdenum content of various welded and nonwelded austentitic stainless steels (courtesy ASM International).

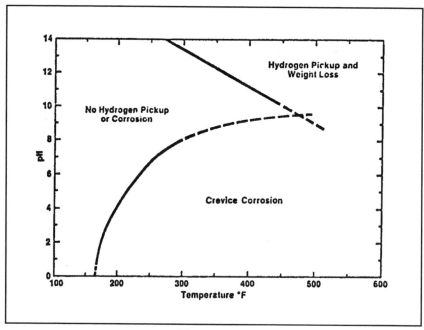

Figure 6-29

Effect of temperature and pH on crevice corrosion of unalloyed titanium
(ASTM Grade 2) in saturated brine (by permission of AIChe,© 1978;
After Covington, L.C., R.W. Schutz and I.A. Franson,
AIChe Meeting, New York, November 1977).

to avoid prolonged contact of the fluid with the tube wall. Moreover, it is necessary for exchanger tubes to be thin walled to permit maximum heat exchange, which limits the use of a corrosion allowance and requires corrosion resistant alloys. Duplex stainless steels have been successfully used for exchanger tubes where H_2S levels are relatively low. Since pitting resistance of stainless steel and nickel alloys from chlorides is a function of temperature, many alloys will be limited by temperature, Figure 6-28. This figure illustrates the benefit of increasing molybdenum content on pitting resistance and the detrimental effect of welding.

Pitting resistance of stainless steels can also be related to their chemical composition by the following regression equation:

$$PRE = (wt\% \ Cr) + 3.3 \ (wt\% \ Mo + 0.5 \ wt\% W) + (16 \ wt + \% \ N)$$

A comparison of the Pitting Resistance Equivalent (PRE) for different alloys is shown in Table 6-6. The strong effect of nitrogen in the above equation can be seen by comparing Alloy 2507 that contains 0.3%N to Alloy 2205 that contains essentially no N of course there is also the benefit of additional Cr and Mo. The real

Table 6-6

Pitting Resistance Equivalent of Some Common Stainless Steels and Nickel Based Alloys

ALLOY	PRE		ALLOY	PRE
Type 410	12		AL6X	42
Type 304	18		254 SM0	43
Type 316	24		2507 Duplex	43
Alloy 825	31		Alloy 625	52
2205 Duplex	34		Alloy C276	68
Alloy 28	39			

value of this equation is for comparison of the multitude of stainless steels of different chemical composition where no corrosion data are available. It does not predict the actual corrosion rate. This equation and others like it are often misapplied, they are strictly only applicable to oxygenated brines.

Increasing temperature, velocities, the presence of dissolved oxygen and H_2S can overwhelm stainless steel and nickel alloy tubes (e.g., 825, 800, etc.) so that titanium alloys are sometimes used for very aggressive streams at higher temperatures. Ti heat exchangers have been successfully used in the refinery and chemical process industry for many years and have been used for shell and tube seawater exchangers in the North Sea.

As with any alloy, there are some drawbacks to titanium. Titanium does have temperature limitations, becoming susceptible to crevice attack with increasing temperature, Figure 6-29. Hydriding of tubes and tube sheets has been reported when titanium is galvanically connected to less noble metals such as steel.

The selection of materials for heat exchangers is similar to that for all the other surface equipment and requires a specific knowledge of the process stream, temperature, pressure, etc., to make the correct choices.

References

API Specification 5L,. "Specification for Line Pipe." 1991.

Bruno, T. V. "How to Prevent Transit Fatigue of Tubular Goods." Pipeline Industry, (July 1988), p. 31.

Craig, B.D., "Critical Velocity Examined for Effects of Erosion-Corrosion", Oil and Gas J., p. 99, 1985.

Craig, B.D., "Equation Clarifies Critical Velocity Calculation", Pet Eng. Int., p. 42, 1990.

Couper, A. S., and A. Dravnieks. Corrosion, 18 (1962), p. 291t .

Garner, A. "How Stainless Steel Welds Corrode," Metals Progress, 27, (April 1985) p. 32.

Gas Engineers Handbook, 51 (1968) p. 8.

Glenny, R. J. E., J. E. Northwood and A. Burwood-Smith. International Metals Review 193, 20 (1975), p. 1.

Gooch, T. G. The Welding Institute Research Bulletin, (Aug. 1982), p. 241.

Gray, M. and A. B. Rothwell, "How Welding Affects Pipeline Steels." AWS Conference, Houston,TX (Feb. 1980).

Ikeda, A., T. Kaneko and F. Terasaki. Paper No. Eight. Corrosion/80, National Association of Corrosion Engineers (1980).

Ikeda, A., et al. Sumitomo Search, No. 26 (1981), p. 91.

Kaneko, T., M. Takeyama, M. Nakanishi, Y. Sumitomo, and A. Ikeda. "Improve ment of Hydrogen Sulfide Cracking Susceptibility in Line Pipes for Sour Gas Services." Middle East Corrosion Conference, National Association of Corrosion Engineers (1979).

Karimi, A., and J.1,. MarLin. International Metals Review, 31 (1986), p. 1.

Nakai, Y., il. Kurahashi, N. Totsuka and Y. Wesugi. "Effect of Corrosive Environment on Hydrogen-induced Cracking." Corrosion/82, National Association of Corrosion Engineers, Houston, TX (1982).

Sato, E.. M. Hashimoto, R. Matsuhashi, and T. Murata. "Corrosion of Steels in a Wet H_2S and CO_2 Environment," Second Asian-Pacific Corrosion Control Conference, Kuala Lumpur. (1981).

Smith, L.S. and M. Celant, "Practical Handbook of Cladding Technology", Second Edition, CASTI, 2000.

Tanaka, T., Y. Ito, M. Nakanishi, T. Kaneko and Y. Komizo, Sumitomo Search, 23 (May 1980) p. 27.

Wilken, G. Paper No. 158. Corrosion/83, National Association of Corrosion Engineers (1983).

Yamada, K., et al. Paper No. 8306-032. 1983 ASM Metal Congress, Philadelphia, PA (1983).

7

FAILURE ANALYSIS

This chapter deals with failure analysis. The analysis of failures is important for several reasons. First and foremost, understanding the cause of a failure of a component can often lead to correction of the problem and prevention of a recurrence of the failure. Other advantages of a failure analysis are: a better understanding of the actual operation of a piece of equipment versus its intended use or design operation; recognition of upset conditions in the system that were not anticipated: evaluation of the performance of maintenance programs; and corrosion control program and legal liability.

The important stages of a failure investigation will be presented and discussed; however, failure analysis is a complex field, quite often involving an interdisciplinary approach that may include metallurgy, analytical chemistry, surface science, stress analysis, fracture mechanics and a host of other disciplines. Therefore, the discussion that follows is but a brief introduction to the subject.

The primary stages of a failure analysis are as follows: however, the sequence may vary depending on the particular investigation and may not involve every step.

1. Retrieval and security of as many pieces of the failed component as possible.
2. Preliminary visual examination and identification of all pieces of the failed component.
3. Cataloging of all the components.
4. Background data collection.
5. Planning of tests to be performed and samples to be selected.
6. Removal of samples for chemical analysis (e.g., corrosion products, deposits, coatings, etc.) that may be affected by further work.
7. Nondestructive evaluation (NDE).
8. Macroscopic examination.
9. Removal of samples for destructive testing and preservation of all remaining pieces.
10. Mechanical testing.
11. Microscopic examination, including metallography, electron microscopy.
12. Chemical analysis of bulk components (alloys and surface analysis of components (scale. corrosion films, etc.).
13. Stress and fracture mechanics analysis.
14. Review of all the data and formulation of a scenario for cause(s) of failure.
15. Re-confirmation that the scenario and mechanisms for failure are consistent with the data.
16. Report and recommendations to prevent the failure in the future.

Retrieval of Failed Components

The retrieval of all or as many of the failed pieces of equipment is of the utmost importance in ascertaining the cause of a failure. Every effort should be made to obtain the original failure and not just similar components for analysis. In the event a sample is to be forwarded to a laboratory for analysis, the engineer performing the analysis should be contacted to inquire as to the desired pieces for analysis and how they should be shipped and handled.

Preliminary Visual Examination
and Cataloging Components

Before performing any work, a preliminary visual examination of all the pieces of the failure should be carried out. Moreover, all pieces should be identified for future reference. Frequently, this stage is best suited to macrophotography to provide a photographic record of the condition of the failure and the pieces received for examination. At this time dimensional analysis is also performed to obtain data that may be necessary later on in the investigation for reconstruction of the failure.

When photography is not acceptable, such as in a very large catastrophic failure, or the conditions do not allow for photography, then a schematic or sketch should bc made with critical dimensions included.

In cases where numerous places of a failure exist, it is often necessary to produce a detailed list and description of all components of the failure to ensure they are accounted for at every stage of the investigation. Furthermore, in cases of litigation, handling by countless people and years of legal action may ensue before issues are resolved. This accountability of all components is a major responsibility during any failure analysis.

Background Data Collection

Collection of background data is a very important part of a failure evaluation. This includes information regarding the manufacturing of the components, the standards it was designed and built in accordance with, the way it was actually operated in service, the nature of the service environment, and any upsets in the normal operations. Many failures occur as a result of upset conditions that were not anticipated when the equipment was designed or selected. Any and all of this information is of value in determining the cause of a failure. Contrary to the thinking of some unfamiliar with failure analysis, the cause of a failure often cannot be solely determined from the failure itself, especially when competing mechanisms may be equally possible. Operational history can often sway the final determination of the cause simply because failure by another mechanism could not occur under those operational conditions.

Planning of Tests and Sample Selections

Before any destructive work is performed, planning the tests to be accomplished can save time and money as well as reduce the risk of damaging necessary evidence that may not be readily apparent. Time spent in planning and sample selection is time well spent in the investigation but most often is the stage that is carelessly undertaken or eliminated because of pressure to perform a quick analysis.

In the case of fractures, samples must be selected such that a minimum of damage occurs during sample removal so that if additional samples are necessary later in the investigation there are undamaged surfaces available. This is even more important in the next stage.

Samples for Chemical Analysis

Before any sample cutting or nondestructive testing is performed, it is important that corrosion products, paint, coating samples, deposits, or representative surfaces with in situ films be removed for further examination. If a corrosion product film is not removed before further testing then the fluids from NDE (dye, ultrasonic couplant, etc.) or heat from cutting the sample may interfere with or change the composition. This also holds true for many paints and coatings.

Nondestructive Evaluation (NDE)

This is a large field unto itself and many texts are available to aid in deciding which NDE method is appropriate for a failure analysis. The most common testing methods are liquid (dye) penetrant, magnetic particle, electromagnetic, radiographic, and ultrasonic. All of these methods have advantages and disadvantages over the others and it is often necessary to use more than one method to fully characterize defects and imperfections in a component. However, it is often advisable to use NDE prior to destructive testing of components to ensure a complete picture of the failure is obtained prior to cutting samples for additional analysis. Moreover, it gives the failure analyst the opportunity to select the best samples for further analysis.

Macroscopic Examination

Macroscopic examination, which includes the use of hand lenses and low power (~25X) microscopes, can provide a significant amount of information, yet is often bypassed in favor of high magnification microscopic techniques. In fact, macroscopic and microscopic examination are complementary and both are necessary. For example, the determination of the fracture origin in a long running brittle fracture of a pipeline can easily be traced by following the chevron pattern on the fracture surface back to the origin. Figure 7-1 is an illustration of how chevrons on the fracture point back to the origin. This can save significant time in examining only the origin for the cause of failure rather than the large amount of crack propagation surfaces that are actually secondary to the failure. Figure 2-9 in Chapter Two is a good example of macroscopic examination. The fracture origin in fatigue of a sucker rod is near the flat portion of the failure while the final tensile overload shows a 45° shear lip. Figure 7-2 is an example of environmental cracking of an S-125 coupling. The fan-shaped pattern emanates from a single point; the origin of the fracture. Thus, the failure analyst can concentrate the analysis on the fracture initiation area and not other areas of the fracture that were not pertinent to the cause.

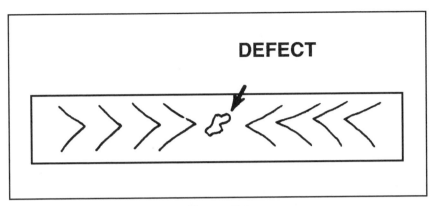

Figure 7-1
Illustration of the chevron pattern formed during crack propagation
and the location of the crack origin.

If the macroscopic features of the fracture display necking, then the failure was probably ductile and further testing will often take a different course than if the features are more brittle in appearance. Brittle fractures are usually flat in appearance. However, care must be taken in using generalities. For example, Figure 7-3 shows a schematic of ductile and brittle macroscopic fracture appearance under tensile loading and the reversal of this pattern under torsional loading. Thus it is important to know the stress history as well.

Sample Removal and Preservation

After all visual and macroscopic work has been completed, samples for mechanical testing, chemical analysis, metallography, and electron microscopy can be removed. All remaining pieces should be carefully preserved and stored for future work. Frequently in failure analysis, after results of the above mentioned destructive results are obtained, either further confirmation testing is necessary or the results send the investigation into another direction that may require additional, albeit different, tests to confirm different mechanisms.

Mechanical Testing

Mechanical testing can be as simple as a standard tensile test or hardness test or may involve sophisticated fracture mechanics testing. Depending on the original specifications for manufacturing or operation, impact testing, creep testing, etc., may be necessary to evaluate the failed part in comparison to the original requirements.

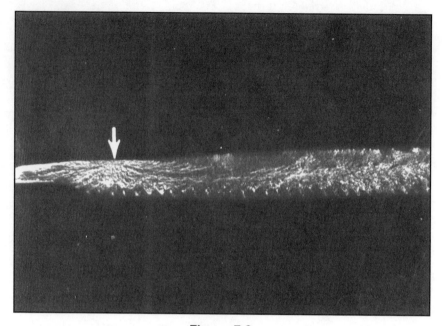

Figure 7-2

Crack origin (arrow) and fan-shaped pattern emanating from it on an S-125 coupling that failed from environmental cracking. Shown at original size.

Mechanical testing for failure analysis is probably misapplied as often as it is correctly applied. For instance, tensile testing a component that has failed from hydrogen damage several weeks after the failure may show no effect of hydrogen because the hydrogen has had sufficient time to diffuse back out, returning the alloy to its original ductile condition. Similarly, high strain-rate impact testing (Charpy V-notch) is not sensitive to hydrogen damaged steels, unless irreversible damage has occurred. Thus it is crucial that the analyst utilize the correct tests to evaluate certain properties, otherwise the data and the analysis will be misleading.

Microscopic Examination

Both metallography and electron microscopy have been included in this section. While scanning electron microscopy (SEM) and transmission electron microscopy (TEM) can both be valuable tools in failure analysis, the latter is infrequently used since it primarily views the internal structure of metals while the former is for surface examination.

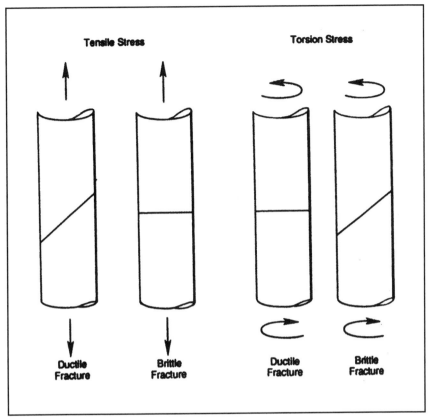

Figure 7-3

Macroscopic difference in fracture appearance for a ductile fracture and a brittle fracture under a tensile load and the same appearance under a torsional load.

Metallography has been extensively used in this book to provide examples of materials and failures in the oil and gas industry. It is a valuable and indispensable tool to evaluate the microstructure of the material and investigate various types of failures.

Microscopic examination using SEM has been less often presented in this book but also is extensively used in failure analysis. At low magnification, 15-50X, it can be useful for determining the fracture origin or examining the morphology of cracks and corrosion pits. At higher magnification, SEM provides a key to the nature of a cracking process and if changes occurred from initiation to propagation. There are several standard fracture morphologies or modes that are frequently observed and are useful to the failure analyst.

271

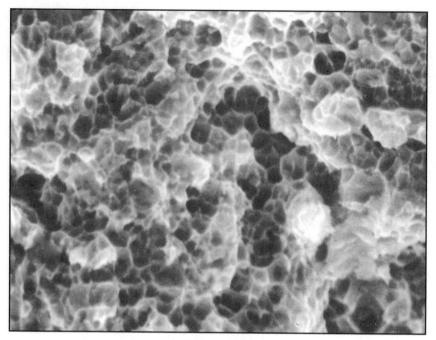

Figure 7-4

Electron micrograph of ductile dimple rupture, also referred to as microvoid coalescence.

Figure 7-4 to 7-7 show examples of some of these modes. Dimple rupture, also referred to as microvoid coalescence, which is a ductile failure mode is shown in Figure 7-4. Transgranular tearing, another ductile fracture mode is not shown but appears feathery. Quasi-cleavage, which is a brittle transgranular fracture mode, is illustrated in Figure 7-5. Cleavage that is also a brittle transgranular fracture mode but follows more crystallographic planes than quasi-cleavage is shown in Figure 7-6. Intergranular brittle fracture is shown in Figure 7-7.

These various fracture modes and combinations of each aid in determining the cause of a failure.

Chemical Analysis

During this stage, bulk chemical analysis of the components can provide information on the composition of the alloys and whether they meet the original requirements. Moreover, coatings and paints can be tested for composition.

In combination with SEM work, the surface can be analyzed by either wavelength or energy dispersive spectroscopy (WDS or EDS) for the presence of different elements both in the alloy and on the surface. Generally, only a semiquan-

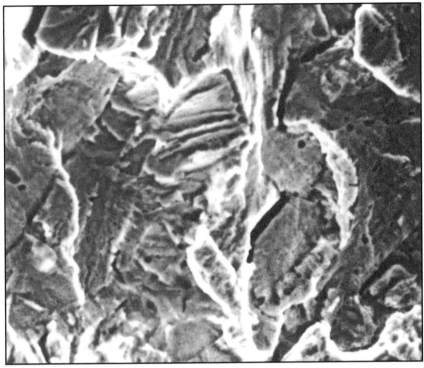

Figure 7-5
Electron micrograph of a quasi-cleavage fracture in steel.

titative analysis can be performed and the composition of compounds cannot be determined. Thus compounds must be inferred by this analysis.

Newer surface science techniques can be used to gain a better understanding of surface composition than can be obtained by WDS or EDS. Moreover, they are much more sensitive to low concentrations than WDS and EDS. Two of the most useful are Auger Electron Spectroscopy (AES) and X-ray Photoelectron Spectroscopy (XPS) or as it is also known, Electron Spectroscopy for Chemical Analysis (ESCA). Both of these surface analysis techniques can measure elemental composition as low as one atom layer thick on the sample and can detect all elements except hydrogen. XPS can also provide information on the bonding states of different elements so that compounds can be described. There are numerous other surface science techniques, but these two have already proven to be quite useful in failure analysis in the oil and gas industry.

Bulk crystallized compounds removed from the surface of a sample can be analyzed by X-Ray diffraction (XRD) for compound composition, and those compounds not well-crystallized can be analyzed for elemental composition by X-ray fluorescence (XRF).

273

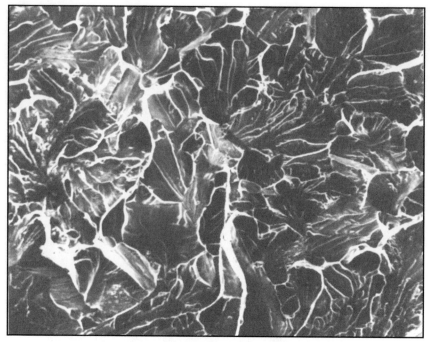

Figure 7-6
Electron micrograph of cleavage fracture.

Stress and Fracture Mechanics Analysis

In some cases it is necessary or desirable to perform a stress analysis of the component and/or analyze the fracture mechanics involved. This may take the form of simple calculations or the requirements of detailed computer analysis using finite element techniques. At this time, more mechanical testing may be required to augment the mathematical analysis. A word of caution is pertinent here, there are currently no valid methods or equations to relate SSC or SCC to fracture mechanics parameters

Review of Data, Formulation of Failure Scenario Report

Once the data are accumulated and analyzed, the number of possible causes for a failure are considerably reduced, sometimes to just one reasonable cause but at other times to several possible causes. Often more evaluation and investigation is necessary, either through additional testing or review of the technical literature to eliminate those possibilities for failure that are least likely and maintain the one

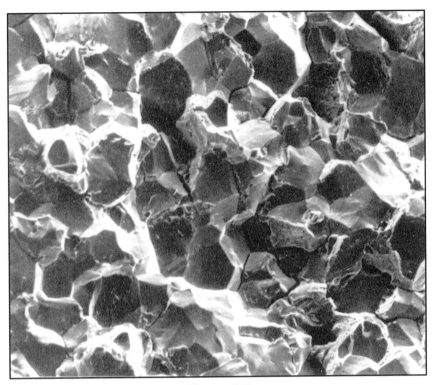

Figure 7-7
Electron micrograph of intergranular fracture.

or two that are the most reasonable in light of the evidence. In many failure analysis, the cause of failure is finally determined through deductive rather than inductive reasoning. It is at this stage that many potentially good and correct failure analysis fall short by reaching an incorrect conclusion. During this stage, the conclusions and purported cause of failure must be substantiated by the data and not merely reflect the wishes or bias of parties involved in the investigation.

Once the analysis is complete, it is prudent to produce a written report for the benefit of those parties involved in the particular failure but also to provide a record for the future that can be an aid in eliminating or reducing such failures or improving the design and operation of a component.

References

ASM International, Metal Handbook, Failure Analysis and Prevention, Vol. 11, (2002).

ASNT, Nondestructive Testing Handbook, Second Edition, Vol. 1-5, (1975 1987).

F

G

H

I

impingement: 68
Incoloy: 48
Inconel: 48
Industry Recommended Practices (IRP): 92
Inert gas injection: 222
Intergranular corrosion: 62
internal upset: 99
International Standards Organization (ISO): 92
interstitial solid solution: 4
ISO 15156: 147

L

Laves phase: 153
line pipe: 226, 230
liquid metal embrittlement: 197
lower critical temperature: 30

M

malleable iron: 38
martensite: 25
mercury: 197
Metallic coatings: 80
metallography: 4, 270
microalloying: 227
microhardness: 13
microvoid coalescence: 272
Miu: 99
modulus of elasticity: 9
MR-01-75: 147
mu phase: 153

N

neutral point: 94
Ni containing steels: 146
nickel based alloys: 141
Nonmagnetic drill collars: 90
Normalizing: 33
NORSOK Standards: 92
notch fatigue: 99

P

packer fluids: 187
Pcm: 231
pearlite: 24
pipeline valves: 260
Pitting attack: 59
pitting resistance equivalent (PRE): 182, 262
post-weld heat treatment: 241
precipitation hardening stainless steels: 41
pumps: 254
pure fatigue: 99

Q

Quasi-cleavage: 272
Quench cracking: 127

R

ram preventers: 85-86
reduction in area: 9
ringworm corrosion: 118, 135
Rockwell hardness: 12
rotary expansion: 161

S

S-N curve: 17
Sacrificial anodes: 81
seamless welded: 118
Separators: 249
shielded metal-arc welding: 231
sigma phases: 153
solid CRA line pipe: 246
spherical preventer: 86
stabilizers: 90
steam injection: 213
Steamflooding: 209
Steel: 20
stepwise cracking: 233
stress oriented hydrogen induced cracking: 231
stress-corrosion cracking: 69, 131, 154
subs: 89-90
subsea bolting: 181
Subsea Christmas trees: 180